Data Analysis Techniques

	Response Variable is a Measurement	Response Variable is a Count	Response Variable is a Category
Data Collected Under One Condition	Chapter Five	Chapter Nine & Chapter Ten	Chapter Eleven
Data Collected Under Two Conditions	Chapter Six	Chapter Nine & Chapter Ten	Chapter Eleven
Data Collected Under Three or More Conditions	Chapter Seven	Chapter Nine & Chapter Ten	Chapter Eleven
Data Collected At 3 or More Values of a Single Variable	Chapter Eight	Chapter Nine & Chapter Ten	Get Professional Help

The Six Sigma Practitioner's

Guide
to
Data
Analysis

Other books by Donald J. Wheeler:

Understanding Variation–the Key to Managing Chaos

Understanding Statistical Process Control

Advanced Topics in Statistical Process Control

Evaluating the Measurement Process

Making Sense of Data

Understanding Industrial Experimentation

Tables of Screening Designs

The Process Evaluation Handbook

Beyond Capability Confusion

Normality and the Process Behavior Chart

Short Run SPC

The Six Sigma Practitioner's

Guide to Data Analysis

Donald J. Wheeler

Fellow American Statistical Association
Fellow American Society for Quality

SPC Press
Knoxville, Tennessee

SPC Press
5908 Toole Drive, Suite C
Knoxville, Tennessee 37919
(865) 584–5005
Fax (865) 588–9440
www.spcpress.com

ISBN 0–945320–62–0
410 + *xiv* pages
178 figures
41 data tables
24 reference tables
index

1 2 3 4 5 6 7 8 9 0

Contents

About the Author

Donald J. Wheeler is a consulting statistician who had the good fortune to work with Dr. W. Edwards Deming and David S. Chambers. Dr. Wheeler graduated from the University of Texas, Austin, with a Bachelor's degree in Physics and Mathematics, and holds M.S. and Ph.D. Degrees in Statistics from Southern Methodist University. From 1970 to 1982 he taught in the Statistics Department at the University of Tennessee, Knoxville, where he was Associate Professor. Between 1981 and 1993 he periodically assisted Dr. Deming with his four-day seminars. He is a Fellow of the American Statistical Association and a Fellow of the American Society for Quality. He has conducted over 900 seminars in sixteen countries on five continents. He is author or co-author of 25 books and over 140 articles. Through these seminars and books Dr. Wheeler has had a profound impact on companies and organizations around the world.

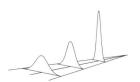

Acknowledgments

The author gratefully acknowledges the many suggestions and clarifications provided by those who read various versions of the manuscript. Among those who read early versions are Jose Rameriez, Denton Bramwell, Bill Scherkenbach, and Ed Zunich. Those who reviewed later versions were Rip Stauffer, Ray Phillips, Bruce White, Stephanie Allison, and Al Pfadt.

Their comments have been instrumental in creating a better book. Their experience in practice has helped to keep this book focused on its intended audience: those who are involved in various forms of process improvement and who, therefore, need to use statistical techniques effectively.

Introduction

This is not a book that will tell you how to do Six Sigma. It is instead a book that will tell you how to do Six Sigma more effectively.

At its core, Six Sigma is a process improvement paradigm. As such, like all other data-based improvement strategies, it has to deal with processes that are inherently dynamic rather than static. Success in dealing with dynamic processes will require techniques and ways of thinking that differ from those used for static populations and enumerations. These differences are the reason that a laundry list of statistical tools and techniques appropriate for static situations will not be sufficient to guarantee success. In order to gain the greatest insight with the least complexity practitioners will also need to understand and use the thinking and tools that are appropriate for analytic studies.

While there are many books that claim to be complete references and guides for Six Sigma, most of these books turn out to have weaknesses of one sort or another. Some that are good on the organizational side of things tend to be weak, or even wrong, on the statistical side of things; while others are merely a traditional statistics textbook in disguise, with an extra chapter or two on the organizational aspects of Six Sigma included. Rather than going down either of these two roads, this book is intended to provide practitioners with a useful guide that is at once both comprehensible and theoretically sound. As such, this is not a book on probability theory or statistical inference. It is rather a practitioner's guide to data analysis—how to understand, interpret, and communicate the message contained within your data as a prelude to taking appropriate actions on the underlying process.

"So Knights are mythical,"
the younger dragons cried.
"We always thought so."

"At least they are getting rare."
thought the older and wiser worms,
"Far and few and no longer to be feared."

J. R. R. Tolkein

PART ONE

THE FOUNDATIONS
OF
DATA ANALYSIS

Part One provides an overview of those topics and ideas that are essential in the analysis of collections of data. Many of these topics are covered in elementary courses and textbooks on statistics, however they are rarely considered from the perspective of data analysis. The next four chapters are provided to help the reader make those fundamental distinctions that will provide a sound basis for carrying out insightful data analysis. They are essential reading for both beginners and advanced students of statistics.

Chapter One

Four Statistical Problems

It is always best to begin by avoiding unnecessary confusion. Unfortunately, confusion seems to be an inherent part of instruction in statistics. In most textbooks, and in most statistics courses, there is more than enough confusion to cover the students, and sometimes the instructor as well. Perhaps this is why, at one university, the drop rate for statistics was exceeded only by the drop rates for freshman chemistry and courses in German. In fact this is completely appropriate since, to most students, statistics is a foreign language.

One of the major causes of all this confusion is a failure to make a distinction between four different aspects of statistics. These four aspects are outlined here as four different problems and the questions they address. By giving an overview of these four different problems this chapter seeks to provide the reader with the perspective needed to make sense of what is usually thought of as a jumbled and chaotic mess.

By way of attribution, I was taught these four aspects by my mentor, David S. Chambers, who evidently got them from an article by E. B. Ferrell which appeared in *Industrial Quality Control* in 1953.

1.1 Descriptive Statistics

> *Given a collection of numbers, is there some meaningful way to summarize the information contained in that collection using one or two summary values?*

The objective is to capture those aspects of the data that are of interest. Intuitive summaries such as totals, averages, and proportions need little explanation. Other summaries that are less commonly used may require some explanation, and even some justification, before they make sense. However, in the end, in order for a descriptive statistic to be effective it has to make sense—it has to distill some essential characteristic of the data into a value that is both appropriate and understandable.

Table 1.1: The Wire Length Data

108.5	108.9	107.4	103.8	105.0	108.7	109.8	112.5	113.5	110.3
102.8	109.7	113.4	108.4	112.4	112.1	109.3	110.1	106.8	111.1
111.2	113.5	104.9	108.9	116.4	110.1	104.8	109.1	112.0	114.8
115.2	105.9	110.4	104.1	110.5	113.5	105.5	107.4	110.4	110.9
107.4	110.6	109.0	110.0	104.1	108.3	106.3	111.2	111.9	107.6
109.5	108.2	110.2	108.4	110.3	106.4	107.8	111.6	108.4	110.6
114.1	111.3	108.9	107.1	108.8	109.0	109.6	106.1	113.1	110.1
110.2	107.9	107.5	108.8	109.3	103.2	110.8	114.0	110.3	107.6
105.4	111.2	108.9	108.5	108.0	110.1	104.5	107.0	105.7	110.6
107.0	106.7	108.6	107.9	107.7	115.5	113.4	105.0	111.6	106.5

Table 1.1 shows the lengths of 100 pieces of wire. Two summaries of location are the average and the median. Here the average length of 109.19 is essentially the same as the median value of 109.0. Two summaries of dispersion are the range and the standard deviation statistic. Here the range is 13.6 and the standard deviation statistic is $s = 2.823$. While the interpretation of the last statistic is not always clear, these are the descriptive statistics that are commonly used for a set of measurements. Having said this, we still have not defined a framework that will allow us to use these statistics as the basis for taking action.

Descriptive statistics are the language we use to frame our problems. While various descriptive statistics will be discussed in greater detail later, for now it is sufficient to note that every summary statistic is the result of an arithmetic operation:

Data + Arithmetic = Statistic

As soon as we have said this, it becomes apparent that the justification for computing any given statistic must come from the nature of the data themselves—it cannot come from the arithmetic, nor can it come from the statistic. If the data are a meaningless collection of values then the summary statistics will also be meaningless—no arithmetic operation can magically create meaning out of nonsense. Therefore, the meaning of any statistic has to come from the data, while the appropriateness will depend upon the use we intend to make of that statistic.

This means that before we compute the simplest average, range, or proportion, *it has to make sense to do so.* Thus we have to know the context for any collection of values before we can select appropriate summary statistics.

Once we have learned to summarize collections of data with descriptive statistics, we will eventually turn our attention to describing the *processes that generated those data.* When this happens we will need to know something about the relationship between the origins of the data and the behavior of the descriptive statistics. And this is the second problem.

1.2   Probability Theory

> *Given a known universe, what can we say about samples drawn from this universe?*

Here we enter the world of deductive logic, the enumeration of possible outcomes, and mathematical models. For simplicity we usually begin with a universe that consists of an urn filled with known numbers of black and white beads. We then consider the properties of various samples of a given size that might be drawn from this urn. This is illustrated in Figure 1.1.

When we reason from a general situation, which is known, to descriptions of specific outcomes, which are presently unknown, we have an argument that is said to be deductive in nature. Deductive logic proceeds from generalities to specifics and always has a correct answer. It is a process of reasoning in which a conclusion follows necessarily from the premises presented.

When we begin with simple universes, such as beads in an urn, we can often list all of the possible outcomes. From these enumerations it is then possible to characterize the likelihoods of different events.

Since enumeration of outcomes quickly becomes tedious, shortcuts are sought. By developing mathematical models we can skip the enumeration step and jump directly from the known universe to the likelihoods of different possible outcomes.

As the mathematical models became increasingly sophisticated, and as the methods of computing and approximating the probabilities progressed, the models could be used to characterize more complex problems—problems that could never be handled by the enumeration approach.

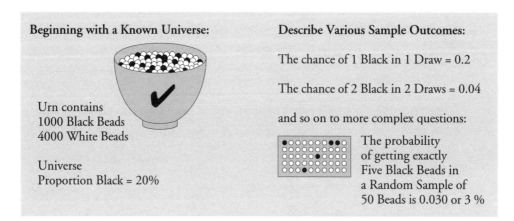

Figure 1.1: The Problem Addressed by Probability Theory

Thus, in probability theory we are, in effect, playing a game so we can learn how things behave in order to use this knowledge later. In introductory classes we restrict ourselves to playing this game with homogeneous and fixed universes.

Obviously, before students can make much headway in probability theory they will need to be comfortable with deductive logic and mathematical models—two more elements of the foreign language of statistics. While probability theory is a necessary step in the *development* of modern statistical techniques, it is not a step that has to be mastered in order to analyze data effectively. (So if you found yourself hyperventilating as you read the previous paragraphs you can relax. There will be no exam on probability theory at the end of this book.)

1.3 Statistical Inference

> *Given an unknown universe, and given a sample that is known to have been drawn from that unknown universe, and given that we know everything about the sample, what can we say about the unknown universe?*

This is usually thought of as the inverse of the problem addressed by probability theory. Here, it is the sample that is known and the universe that is unknown. Now the argument proceeds from the specific to the general, which makes it inductive in nature.

Unfortunately, all inductive inference is fraught with uncertainty.

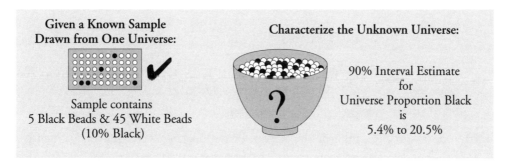

Figure 1.2: The Problem Addressed by Statistical Inference

A sample result of 5 black beads and 45 white beads corresponds to a 90% Interval Estimate for the universe proportion black of 5.4% to 20.5%. The middle ninety percent of the plausible proportions fall in this interval. Thus, with inductive logic there is not a single right answer, but many plausible answers. Any percentage from 5.4% to 20.5% is plausible, given this sample result.

(In contrast to this, the deductive logic of probability theory has a single right answer. For example, for the urn shown in Figure 1.1, which has 20 percent black beads, a random sample of 50 beads will have 5 black beads and 45 white beads three percent of the time.)

Statistical inference is the realm of tests of hypotheses, confidence intervals, and regression. These techniques allow us to estimate and evaluate the parameters of the unknown universe—proportions, means, and standard deviations. Of course such estimates make sense only when our outcomes are all obtained from a single universe. This assumption of a single universe is equivalent to the assumption that the behavior of these outcomes is described by one probability model. Once we have made this assumption, it is possible to use the probability model in reverse—given this outcome, these are the parameter values that are most consistent with the outcome.

While the mathematics of using the probability model in reverse makes everything seem to be rigorous and scientific, you should note that the whole argument begins with an assumption and ends with an indefinite statement. The assumption is that all of the outcomes came from the same universe, and the indefinite statement is couched in terms of interval estimates. With inductive inference there is not one right answer, but many plausible answers.

1.4   The Homogeneity Question

Given a collection of observations, is it reasonable to assume that they came from one universe, or do they show evidence of having come from multiple universes?

To understand the fundamental nature of the homogeneity question, consider what happens if the collection of values does not come from one universe.

Descriptive statistics are built on the assumption that we can use a single value to characterize a single property for a single universe. If the data come from different sources, how can any single value be used to describe what is, in effect, not one property but many? In Figure 1.3 the sample has 10 percent black. But if the 50 beads are the result of three separate draws from the three bowls at the bottom of Figure 1.3, which bowl is characterized by the sample result?

Probability theory is focused on what happens to samples drawn from a known universe. If the data happen to come from different sources, then there are multiple universes with different probability models. If you cannot answer the homogeneity question, then you will not know if you have one probability model or many.

Statistical inference assumes that you have a sample that is known to have come from one universe. If the data come from different sources, what does your interval

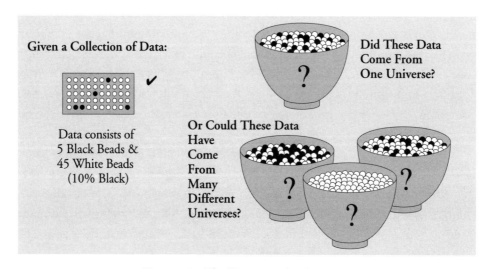

Figure 1.3: The Homogeneity Question

estimate represent? Which of the multiple universes does it characterize?

Therefore, before you can use the structure and techniques developed to answer the first three problems, you will need to examine your data for evidence of that homogeneity which is implicitly assumed by both the problems and their solutions.

We cannot learn anything from descriptive statistics when we find evidence of a changing universe in a situation where there should be one universe. When the universe is changing we cannot gain from statistical inference, nor can we make predictions using probability theory. Any nonhomogeneity in our collection of values completely undermines all of these statistical techniques. The lack of homogeneity is a signal that unknown things are happening, and until we discover and remove the causes of these unknown happenings we will continue to suffer the consequences. Computation cannot remedy the problem of a lack of homogeneity; action is required.

How can we answer the homogeneity question? We can either *assume* that our data possess the appropriate homogeneity, or we can *examine* them for signs of nonhomogeneity. Since anomalous things happen in even the most carefully controlled experiments, prudence demands that we use the approach of examining our data for possible nonhomogeneity.

To do this we begin with the tentative assumption that the data are homogeneous and then look for evidence that is inconsistent with this assumption. When we reject the assumption of homogeneity we will have strong evidence which will justify taking action to remedy the situation. When we fail to reject the assumption of homogeneity we will know that any nonhomogeneity present is below the level of detection. While this is a weak result, we will at least have a reasonable basis for proceeding with estimation and prediction.

1.5 Two Perspectives on These Problems

Historically we had to tackle these four problems in the order given here. Descriptive statistics were needed to express and formulate the problems. Probability theory was needed to describe the relationship between a universe and samples drawn from that universe. The rigorous development of probability models made it possible to obtain a consensus about which situations were covered by the various models and how to proceed to use the models to make predictions about future outcomes.

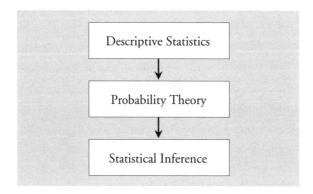

Figure 1.4: The Textbook Approach

Once we had some useful probability models the next logical step was to use them to answer the question of statistical inference. While various approaches have been used with the problem of statistical inference, the inherent uncertainty of inductive inference has made it impossible to agree on a single, unified approach. For this reason, statistical inference is often seen by students as a grab bag of different techniques having no unifying theme or overall structure. (The details of the various probability models and the different approaches to inference generally suffice to overwhelm those students that have not yet dropped out.)

Since the historical development makes sense from the perspective of mathematics, and since most statisticians are mathematicians by training and inclination, the pedagogy of statistics has followed the path outlined above: Descriptive Statistics followed by Probability Theory followed by Statistical Inference followed by Confusion. Since any analysis may have to be defended, people tend to avoid analysis techniques that they do not understand. As a result, the pedagogy based on this historical development has resulted in a whole string of presidents of statistical societies asking "Where are the clients?"

This historical, developmental, and pedagogical perspective could be called the *Textbook Approach*. In this traditional sequence the question of homogeneity is commonly ignored. The data are *assumed* to possess the appropriate homogeneity, any needed distributional conditions are verified, and the techniques of statistical inference are immediately applied to draw conclusions from the data.

In contrast, practitioners must approach these problems differently than the mathematicians. While they also use the language of descriptive statistics to frame the problem, they have to begin at the other end. For the practitioner, the first question should always be the question of homogeneity: Given a collection of data, did they come from one universe? In fact, is it reasonable to assume that there is a universe? Only after this fundamental question has been addressed does the practitioner know how to proceed. If the assumption of a universe is reasonable, then the techniques of statistical inference may be used to characterize that universe, and then, with reasonable estimates of the parameters, probability models may be used to make predictions. But if the assumption of a universe is not justified, the practitioner needs to find out why.

This latter approach could be called the *Data Analysis Approach*. It can be summarized as shown in Figure 1.5. There the loop on the right commonly results in process improvements while the loop on the left allows us to make process characterizations.

Most statisticians, including those who teach the Textbook Approach, use the Data Analysis Approach in practice. The homogeneity question is commonly dealt with by a careful consideration of how the data are to be collected and an informal, intuitive, or graphic check for possible nonhomogeneity, before proceeding to the estimation and prediction questions. This shift from the Textbook Approach to the Data Analysis Approach usually occurs following years of study and one or more

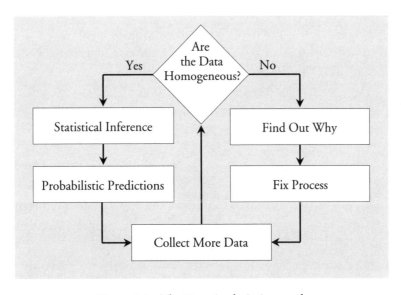

Figure 1.5: The Data Analysis Approach

blunders in practice. (Suddenly we all recall our professors telling us to always begin with a plot of the data!)

But what happens to those who do not have the luxury of the in-depth training that comes with degrees in statistics? For the first twelve years of my career I taught classes using the Textbook Approach. Most of these students were majoring in areas other than statistics or mathematics. During that time I had very few students who ever tried to use what I had taught them. The transfer from the classroom to practice was very low, and when attempted was not always correctly done.

For over twenty years now I have taught my classes using the Data Analysis Approach. Beginning with the very first of these classes I saw a much higher degree of utilization. Not only were more of the students applying what they had learned in class, but they were also using data analysis successfully to *improve* their products and processes.

The increasing use (and misuse) of the traditional statistical techniques that are part of the various programs collectively referred to under the heading of "Six Sigma" has made it apparent that a book incorporating both the Data Analysis Approach and the techniques statistical inference is needed.

1.6 Axioms of Data Analysis

Since data analysis is different from mathematical statistics, and since moving back and forth between the different perspectives represented by the four problems listed earlier can be confusing, it is helpful to have some axioms of data analysis laid out as fundamentals. These axioms fit into three categories:

> What Numbers to Compute (Axiom 1);
> The Origins of Data (Axioms 2, 3, 4, & 5); and
> Guides for Interpretation (Axioms 6, 7, & 8).

WHAT NUMBERS TO COMPUTE

Axiom 1:

No statistic has any meaning

apart from the context for the original data.

Axiom 1 was discussed earlier in Section 1.1. While the appropriateness of a descriptive statistic depends upon the way in which it is to be used, the *meaning* of any statistic has to come from the context for the data. In particular, the data will have to display a reasonable degree of homogeneity before summary statistics can be used to extrapolate beyond the data to characterize the underlying process that generated the data.

THE ORIGINS OF DATA

Axiom 2:
Probability models do not generate your data.

Axiom 2 should be self evident. However, current usage suggests that it has apparently escaped the attention of many practitioners. Probability models are mathematical descriptions of the behavior of random variables. They live on the plane of mathematical theory where measurements are frequently continuous and observations are independently and identically distributed, and usually assumed to be normally distributed as well, often with known mean and known variance.

While such assumptions allow you to work out answers for the questions of probability theory, it is important to always remember that probability models are merely approximations for reality. They do not generate your data.

Axiom 3:
Every histogram has finite tails.

Axiom 3 is a reminder that data sets are finite in size and extent and invariably display some level of chunkiness in the measurements. This is just one more way that real data differs from probability models which commonly involve continuous variables and often have infinite tails.

Axiom 4:
No histogram can be said
to follow a particular probability model.

Axiom 4 is actually a corollary of Axioms 2 and 3. It focuses on the fact that a probability model is, at best, a limiting characteristic of an infinite sequence of data. Therefore, it cannot be a property of any finite portion of that sequence. For this reason it is impossible to say that any finite data set is distributed according to a particular probability model.

But what about the tests of fit? Tests of fit may allow you to say that a particular data set is *inconsistent* with a particular probability model, but they can never be used to make a positive statement of the form "these data are normally distributed." Such statements are impossible—inductive inference will allow us to eliminate some possibilities, but it will not allow only one unique answer.

Moreover, since histograms will always have finite tails, and since many probability models have infinite tails, it is inevitable that with enough data you will always reject any probability model you may choose. Hence G. E. P. Box's statement that "All models are wrong. Some models are more useful than others."

Axiom 5:
Your data are generated by a process or system which, like everything in this world, is subject to change.

Axiom 5 is a reminder that data have a context. They are the result of some operation or process. Since the process that generates our data can change, we cannot blithely assume that our data are independently and identically distributed, nor can we define a unique probability model for our data. Even if we choose a probability model to use, and estimate the mean or the variance for that model, the fact that processes change will make both our model and the estimated parameter values inappropriate at some point.

GUIDES FOR INTERPRETATION

Axiom 6:
All outliers are *prima facie* evidence of nonhomogeneity.

While the procedures of statistical inference can be "sharpened up" by deleting any outliers contained in the data, the very existence of the outliers is evidence of a lack of homogeneity. So while deleting the outliers may help us to characterize the hypothetical potential of our process, it does not actually help us to achieve that potential. Processes that operate up to their full potential will be characterized by a homogeneous data stream.

Axiom 7:
Every data set contains noise.
Some data sets also contain signals.
Before you can detect the signals within your data
you must filter out the noise.

Axiom 7 is an expression of the fact that variation comes in two flavors—routine variation and exceptional variation. Until you know how to separate the exceptional from the routine you will be hopelessly confused in any attempt at analysis.

Axiom 8:
You must *detect* a difference
before you can legitimately *estimate* that difference,
and only then can you
assess *the practical importance* of that difference.

When the noise of routine variation obscures a difference it is a mistake to try to estimate that difference. With statistical techniques a detectable difference is one that is commonly referred to as "significant." Statistical significance has nothing to do with the practical importance of a difference, but merely with whether or not it is detectable. If it is detectable, then you can obtain a reliable estimate of that difference. If a difference is not detectable and you attempt to estimate it anyway, you will be lucky to end up with the right sign, much less any correct digits. When the routine variation obscures a difference, it cannot be estimated from the data with any reliability. Finally, only after detecting and estimating a difference, can you assess whether or not that difference is of any practical importance. Try it in any other order and you are likely to be interpreting noise.

As a result of all this we can say that statistical techniques will provide approximate, yet reliable, ways of separating potential signals from probable noise. This is the unifying theme of all techniques for statistical analysis. Analysis is ultimately concerned with filtering out the noise of routine variation in a systematic manner that will stand up to the scrutiny of skeptics. This filtration does not have to be perfect. It just needs to be good enough to let us identify the potential signals within our data.

At the same time, using the theoretical relationships developed by means of probability theory will result in inference techniques that are reasonable and that will allow the appropriate level of filtration to occur. While statistical techniques may only be approximate, they are more reliable, more precise, and more reproducible than the alternative of *ad hoc*, experience-based interpretations of the data.

1.7 Summary

Everything you do under the heading of data analysis should be governed by the preceding axioms. Otherwise you risk the hazards of missing signals and being misled by noise.

Probability theory is necessary to develop statistical techniques that will provide reasonable ways to analyze data. By using such techniques we can avoid *ad hoc* analyses that are inappropriate and misleading. At the same time we have to realize that, in practice, all statistical techniques are approximate. They are merely guides to use in separating the *potential signals* from the *probable noise*. However, they are guides that operate in accordance with the laws of probability theory and which avoid the pitfalls of subjective interpretations.

All the techniques mentioned here have a fine ancestry of high-brow statistical theorems. In addition, these techniques have all been found to work in practice. Since this is a guide for data analysis, not a theoretical text, the theorems will not be included. Instead, this book will focus on when and how to use the various techniques.

The remainder of Part One will continue to lay the foundations of data analysis. Chapter Two will review descriptive statistics and the question of homogeneity in greater detail. Chapter Three will provide an overview of the use of process behavior charts. Chapter Four will make the distinction between statistics and parameters and will provide a simplified approach to statistical inference.

Part Two focuses on the techniques of data analysis. Chapter Five will look at analysis techniques appropriate for data collected under one condition. Chapters Six and Seven will consider analysis techniques suitable for data collected under two and three conditions. Chapter Eight will look at issues related to the use of simple linear regression. Chapters Nine and Ten will consider count-based data while Chapter Eleven will look at counts for three or more categories.

Part Three presents the keys to effective data analysis. Chapter Twelve outlines a new definition of trouble that is fundamental to any improvement effort. Chapter

Thirteen integrates capability and performance indexes with the new definition of trouble.

Chapter Fourteen introduces the concept and use of the Effective Cost of Production, while Chapter Fifteen explains the basis for the Effective Cost of Production. Chapter Sixteen then uses this concept to provide the first rigorous explanation of why you need to operate in the Six Sigma Zone.

Chapter Seventeen deals with some problematic concepts that have created more confusion than clarity. Chapter Eighteen presents an especially effective improvement model.

This book is not intended to be an introductory statistics textbook. Instead, it is intended to help those who have been "introduced to statistics" to figure out what to do and when to do it. The emphasis throughout is how to analyze data appropriately with as little time and effort as possible. The guiding principle throughout has been that the best analysis is the simplest analysis that gives the needed insight.

Chapter Two

Descriptive Statistics and Homogeneity

Since the question of homogeneity is the first question of data analysis, we shall begin with the problem of using descriptive statistics to examine a data set for homogeneity.

2.1 What Does the Standard Deviation Statistic Do?

Given a collection of values $\{ X_1, X_2, X_3, \ldots, X_n \}$ the two basic statistics used to summarize the location of these values are the average and the median:

the arithmetic average will be denoted by $\bar{X}$

the median will be denoted by $\tilde{X}$

These two statistics for location are fairly intuitive and easy to describe—the average is interpreted as the balance point for the data while the median is the fiftieth percentile of the data.

The simplest measure of dispersion is the range of the data. The range is simply the difference between the maximum value and the minimum value and will be denoted by the symbol R.

Other common measures of dispersion are the standard deviation statistic, s, defined as:

$$s = \sqrt{\frac{\Sigma (X_i - \bar{X})^2}{n - 1}}$$

and the root mean square deviation, s_n, defined as:

$$s_n = \sqrt{\frac{\Sigma (X_i - \bar{X})^2}{n}}$$

To anyone other than a mathematician or a physicist these last two measures are neither intuitive nor comprehensible. Nevertheless, for good and sufficient reasons

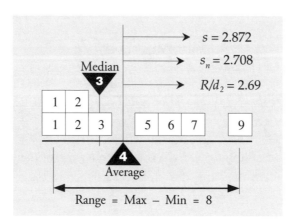

Figure 2.1: Summary Statistics for Data Set Two

they are routinely used. In fact, these values are so commonly used that we will occasionally want to convert the range statistic into a value that will be comparable to these other two measures of dispersion. This is done by dividing the range by the appropriate value of the bias correction factor d_2. Throughout this book this value will be referred to as the *adjusted range*, R/d_2. The values of d_2 are given in Table A.1 of the Appendix.

We shall refer to the nine values { 5, 3, 6, 2, 2, 1, 9, 7, 1 } shown in Figure 2.1 as Data Set Two. The six summary statistics defined above are shown in Figure 2.1. The Average of 4.0 is the balance point for the histogram, the Median of 3 is the fiftieth percentile for the data, and the Range of 8 is the span of the histogram. The Standard Deviation Statistic of $s = 2.872$ does not have any obvious relationship with the histogram above. Neither does the Root Mean Square Deviation of 2.708 or the Adjusted Range value of 2.69. This lack of a clear and obvious meaning for these measures of dispersion is a huge obstacle for most students of statistics. For those who are interested, Figure 2.2, shows how the standard deviation statistic does provide a summary of the dispersion of the histogram. Unfortunately, this mathematical explanation does not provide a clear and simple interpretation of the standard deviation statistic.

So what does the standard deviation statistic tell us about the data? How can we use it to characterize the data? To see how to answer these questions we use a set of nested intervals centered on the average with radii equal to multiples of the standard deviation statistic.

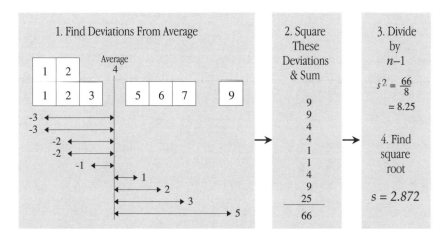

Figure 2.2: The Standard Deviation Statistic for Data Set Two

For Data Set Two the first of these intervals is:

$$\bar{X} \pm s = 4.0 \pm 2.9 = 1.1 \text{ to } 6.9$$

This interval contains five of the nine values in Data Set Two. As we shall see in subsequent examples, this basic interval will generally contain the bulk of the data.

Next we compute the interval: [Average ± twice the standard deviation statistic]. For Data Set Two this interval is:

$$\bar{X} \pm 2s = 4.0 \pm 2(2.9) = -1.8 \text{ to } 9.8$$

This interval contains all of the values in Data Set Two. With small data sets this is typical. With large data sets this interval will generally contain at least 90 percent of the data.

Thus, the standard deviation statistic defines a radius to use in creating intervals that will contain certain proportions of the data. This idea will be further illustrated and developed with the following data sets.

Table 2.1 shows the lengths of 100 pieces of wire. The average length is 109.19, the median is 109.0, the range is 13.6, and the standard deviation statistic is $s = 2.823$. (For comparison, the d_2 value for $n = 100$ data is 5.015, giving an adjusted range value of 2.71, which is quite similar to the s value.)

Table 2.1: The Wire Length Data

108.5	108.9	107.4	103.8	105.0	108.7	109.8	112.5	113.5	110.3
102.8	109.7	113.4	108.4	112.4	112.1	109.3	110.1	106.8	111.1
111.2	113.5	104.9	108.9	116.4	110.1	104.8	109.1	112.0	114.8
115.2	105.9	110.4	104.1	110.5	113.5	105.5	107.4	110.4	110.9
107.4	110.6	109.0	110.0	104.1	108.3	106.3	111.2	111.9	107.6
109.5	108.2	110.2	108.4	110.3	106.4	107.8	111.6	108.4	110.6
114.1	111.3	108.9	107.1	108.8	109.0	109.6	106.1	113.1	110.1
110.2	107.9	107.5	108.8	109.3	103.2	110.8	114.0	110.3	107.6
105.4	111.2	108.9	108.5	108.0	110.1	104.5	107.0	105.7	110.6
107.0	106.7	108.6	107.9	107.7	115.5	113.4	105.0	111.6	106.5

- The interval 109.19 ± 2.82 = 106.37 to 112.01 contains 69 of the 100 values.

- The interval 109.19 ± 2 (2.82) = 103.55 to 114.83 contains 95 values.

- The interval 109.19 ± 3 (2.82) = 100.73 to 117.65 contains all of the values.

These nested intervals and their corresponding percentages are shown in Figure 2.3.

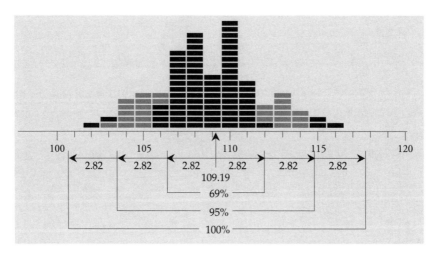

Figure 2.3: Characterizing the Wire Length Data

Table 2.2: The Data from Bead Board No. 7

9	14	9	12	10	11	7	9	12	13	14	11	10	14	12	11
11	10	13	9	14	17	17	13	13	12	14	16	15	18	12	14
17	12	11	13	15	16	14	13	5	10	9	7	6	6	9	9
10	11	14	14	12	10	13	12	8	9	13	11	16	15	15	15
16	18	18	17	15	17	15	12	16	17	14	12	12	12	18	14
6	9	8	7	5	6	7	3	8	7	15	13	10	10	9	15
14	15	10	13	21	16	16	18	14	14	17	15	18	18	16	16
15	12	16	17	13	14	15	14	9	11	8	7	13	11	10	8
9	9	14	15	13	16	12	15	13	13	16	16	17	19	18	17
19	17	23	19	21	18	16	11	12	12	14	13	15	13	14	15
6	11	12	12	11	11	10	12	9	13	15	12	10	11	12	13
11	13	11	12	16	14	16	17	12	17	14	19	12	17	11	14
14	9	8	17	12	9	9	12								

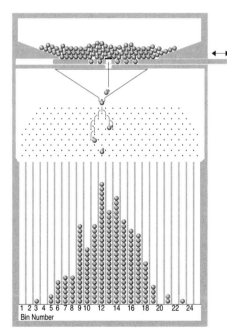

Figure 2.4: Bead Board No. 7

The Data from Bead Board No. 7 in Table 2.2 and pictured in Figure 2.5 consists of 200 values produced by the bead board pictured in Figure 2.4. When a bead falls in a given bin, the number of that bin is recorded as the observation.

The average for these 200 values is 12.855, the median is 13, the range is 20, the standard deviation statistic is:

$$s = 3.462$$

and the root mean square deviation is:

$$s_n = 3.453$$

- As shown in Figure 2.5, the interval $12.86 \pm 3.46 = 9.40$ to 16.32 contains 132 of these 200 values which is 66% of the total.

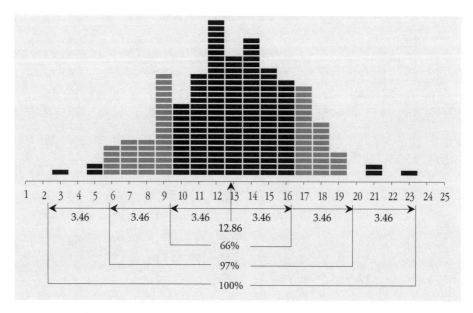

Figure 2.5: Characterizing the Data from Bead Board No. 7

- The interval 12.86 ± 2 (3.46) = 5.94 to 19.78 contains 194 of the 200 values which is 97% of the total in Figure 2.5

- The interval 12.86 ± 3 (3.46) = 2.48 to 23.24 contains all of the values in Figure 2.5.

The Batch Weight Data given in Table 2.3 and shown in Figure 2.6 consist of 259 observations collected from one process over the course of one week. They are the weights in kilograms of the batches as they are dropped from the blender. These 259 observations have an average of 937.0 kilograms and a standard deviation statistic of $s = 61.3$ kilograms.

- The interval 937.0 ± 61.3 = 875.7 to 998.3 contains 182 of the 259 values which is 70.3% of the data.

- The interval 937.0 ± 2 (61.3) = 814.4 to 1059.6 contains 245 of the 259 values which is 94.6% of the data.

- The interval 937.0 ± 3 (61.3) = 753.1 to 1120.9 contains 256 of the 259 values which is 98.8% of the data.

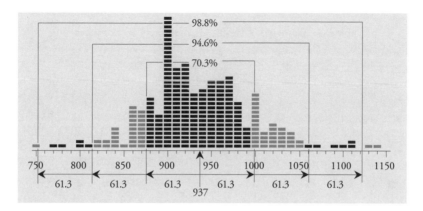

Figure 2.6: Characterizing the Batch Weight Data

Table 2.3: Batch Weight Data

Batches	Batch Weights (kilograms of product exiting blender)									
1-10	905	930	865	895	905	885	890	930	915	910
11-20	920	915	925	860	905	925	925	905	915	930
21-30	890	940	860	875	985	970	940	975	1000	1035
31-40	1020	985	960	945	965	940	900	920	980	950
41-50	955	970	970	1035	1040	1000	1000	990	1000	950
51-60	940	965	920	920	925	900	905	900	925	885
61-70	1005	1005	950	920	875	865	880	960	925	925
71-80	875	900	905	990	970	910	980	900	970	900
81-90	895	885	925	870	875	910	915	900	950	880
91-100	910	965	910	880	900	920	940	985	965	925
101-110	925	975	905	890	950	975	935	940	900	915
111-120	980	880	905	915	960	900	915	920	865	980
121-130	935	840	900	965	890	875	1020	780	900	900
131-140	800	960	845	820	910	885	940	930	925	850
141-150	965	1010	1030	980	1010	950	940	1005	880	930
151-160	845	935	905	965	975	985	975	950	905	965
161-170	905	950	905	995	900	840	1050	935	940	920
171-180	985	970	915	935	950	1030	875	880	955	910
181-190	1050	890	1005	915	1070	970	1040	770	940	950
191-200	1040	1035	1110	845	900	905	910	860	1045	820
201-210	900	860	875	1005	880	750	900	835	930	860
211-220	960	950	1020	975	950	960	950	880	1000	1005
221-230	990	1020	980	1020	920	960	1000	1000	860	1130
231-240	830	965	930	950	945	900	990	865	945	970
241-250	915	975	940	870	890	915	935	1060	1015	1100
251-259	810	1010	1140	805	1020	1110	975	970	1090	

Table 2.4: Camshaft Bearing Diameters (1.37xx inches)

Camshaft	1	2	3	4	5	6	7	8	9	10	11	12	13
Bearing 1	49	51	51	52	56	52	51	52	50	49.5	51	52	53
Bearing 2	50	50	52	49	52	49	49	50	48	48	49	48	50
Bearing 3	50	46	52	51	42	50	50.5	44	48	49	43	49.5	50

Camshaft	14	15	16	17	18	19	20	21	22	23	24	25	26
Bearing 1	52	51	51	55	51	50.5	49	51	51	52.5	50	50	50
Bearing 2	49	49	51	51	52	50	50	48	49	50	50	48	50
Bearing 3	46	49	43	42	45	42	43	43	45	42	46	47	45

Camshaft	27	28	29	30	31	32	33	34	35	36	37	38	39
Bearing 1	53	52	50	53	52	52	51.5	51	49.5	52	51	51.5	51
Bearing 2	47	48	49	48	52	52	53	53	51	51	51.5	49	54.5
Bearing 3	42	49	49	52	46	50	51	50	51	50	52	52	54

Camshaft	40	41	42	43	44	45	46	47	48	49	50		
Bearing 1	51	50	50.5	51	51	51	56	50	50	52.5	57		
Bearing 2	50	48	50	47	49	49	48	50	52	48	48		
Bearing 3	52.5	54	51	51	51	49.5	52	49	49	50	50		

The 150 observations in the Camshaft Bearing Diameter Data have an average of 49.81 and a standard deviation statistic of $s = 2.78$.

- The interval $49.81 \pm 2.78 = 47.03$ to 52.59 contains 118 of the 150 values which is 78.7% of the data.

- The interval $49.81 \pm 2\,(2.78) = 44.25$ to 55.37 contains 137 of the 150 values which is 91.3% of the data.

- The interval $49.81 \pm 3\,(2.78) = 41.47$ to 58.15 contains all of the values.

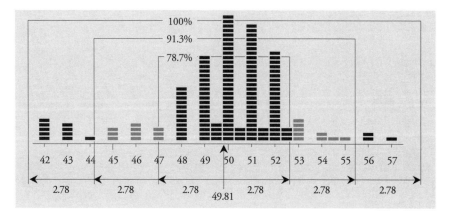

Figure 2.7: Characterizing the Camshaft Bearing Diameter Data

Table 2.5: Hot Metal Delivery Times in Minutes

40	45	125	100	40	40	100	65	55	40	125	65	40	45	95
105	45	110	40	50	120	45	65	105	35	70	55	25	50	55
50	40	40	45	55	50	45	125	55	100	40	70	40	40	110
55	50	30	50	105	45	45	55	50	25	65	60	60	55	70
55	45	100	60	45	145	45	50	65	180	60	45	35	35	55
55	55	50	120	35	45	35	45	55	50	70	45	75	60	45
60	40	60	40	50	60	65	95	65	60	50	25	25	100	50
60	45	35	40	30	180	50	30	30	30	65	130	80	20	45
65	65	45	40	50	25	120	30	115	50	85	40	35	40	40
55	50	25	75	55	50									

The 141 observations in the Hot Metal Delivery Time Data have an average of 59.92 and a standard deviation statistic of $s = 29.69$.

- The interval $59.9 \pm 29.7 = 30.2$ to 89.6 contains 105 of the 141 values which is 74.5% of the data.

- The interval $59.9 \pm 2\,(29.7) = 0.5$ to 119.3 contains 131 of the 141 values which is 92.9% of the data.

- The interval $59.9 \pm 3\,(29.7) = -29.2$ to 149.0 contains 139 of the 141 values which is 98.6% of the data.

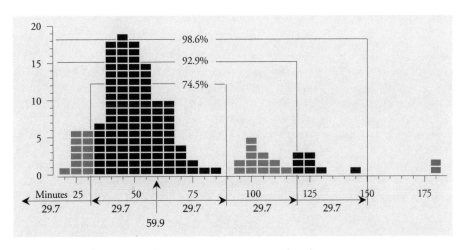

Figure 2.8: Characterizing the Hot Metal Delivery Time Data

Table 2.6: Creel Yield Data

Date	Yields				
8/1	3534	3542	3532	3537	3532
8/2	3533	3524	3524	3525	3527
8/3	3531	3526	3529	3524	3527
8/4	3525	3522	3521	—	—
8/5	3521	3521	3521	3521	3515
8/6	3498	3498	3506	3513	3536
8/7	3526	3529	3524	3525	3520
8/8	3517	3517	3519	3516	3517
8/9	3453	3445	3451	3445	3452
8/10	3445	3449	3454	3447	3446
8/11	3440	3423	3416	3419	3415
8/12	3458	3457	3457	3452	3446
8/13	3448	3451	3453	3453	3455
8/14	3475	3475	3474	3486	3490

The Creel Yield Data in Table 2.6 are the computed yield values for a 14 strand roving of fiberglass. They characterize the amount of fiberglass per unit length of roving. These 68 observations have an average of 3492.1 and a standard deviation statistic of $s = 38.3$.

- The interval $3492.1 \pm 38.3 = 3453.8$ to 3530.4 contains 40 of the 68 values which is 59% of the data.

- The interval $3492.1 \pm 2\,(38.3) = 3415.5$ to 3568.7 contains 67 of the 68 values which is 98% of the data.

- The interval $3492.1 \pm 3\,(38.3) = 3377.2$ to 3607.0 contains all the values.

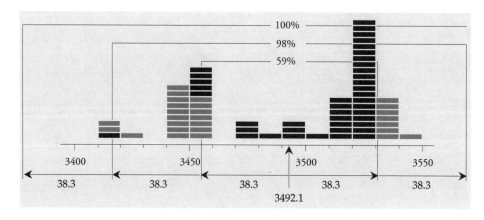

Figure 2.9: Characterizing the Creel Yield Data

These seven data sets serve to illustrate how the average and standard deviation statistic characterize a data set. The average defines a midpoint and the standard deviation statistic defines a radius to use in creating a set of nested intervals that will contain increasing proportions of the data. The proportions found in the preceding examples are summarized in Table 2.7.

Table 2.7: Coverage of Nested Intervals Centered on the Average

	Coverage *Avg ± s*	Coverage *Avg ± 2 s*	Coverage *Avg ± 3 s*
Data Set Two	55%	100%	100%
Wire Length Data	69%	95%	100%
Bead Board No. 7 Data	66%	97%	100%
Batch Weight Data	70.3%	94.6%	98.8%
Bearing Diameter Data	78.7%	91.3%	100%
Hot Metal Delivery Data	74.5%	92.9%	98.6%
Creel Yield Data	59%	98%	100%

- An interval centered on the average with a radius equal to the standard deviation statistic will generally contain the bulk of the data.

- An interval centered on the average with a radius equal to twice the standard deviation statistic will generally contain at least 90% of the data.

- An interval centered on the average with a radius equal to three times the standard deviation statistic will contain virtually all of the data.

These generalizations hold for all but the most unusual data sets. They work with skewed data. They even work when the data contain multiple clusters. It is through these nested intervals and their associated coverages that the standard deviation statistic can be said to describe the dispersion of the data.

2.2 What Descriptive Statistics Do Not Do

Hopefully the previous section has provided a more intuitive feeling for how descriptive statistics can be used to characterize a collection of values. While this understanding is important, it is equally important to understand the limitations on the use of descriptive statistics.

As the name suggests, descriptive statistics merely report what they find. They do not editorialize. They do not speculate. They do not analyze or interpret. *They characterize the various aspects of a collection of values without any consideration of whether or not that collection of values makes sense.*

Table 2.7 summarizes how the descriptive statistics characterize each of the seven data sets in Section 2.1. Each of the seven data sets had the appropriate proportions within the nested intervals. Yet some of these data sets are not homogeneous. Thus we come to the problem with descriptive statistics: while they *describe* the data, they do not provide any leverage for *analyzing* those data. The failure to understand this one point created an obstacle to effective data analysis that persisted for over thirty years in the middle of the Nineteenth Century (for more on this see Section 2.5 of *Normality and the Process Behavior Chart* by this author).

This problem with descriptive statistics raises its head any time that we wish to go beyond the data. Whenever we want to know about the process that generated the data or the universe from which the data were obtained, we are asking questions that only make sense when there is exactly one universe. Thus we come back to the homogeneity question.

Some of the data sets shown in the previous section are homogeneous— others are not. *The consistency of the coverage in Table 2.7 shows that none of the descriptive measures of dispersion computed up to this point can provide an answer to the homogeneity question.* So what can we do? We need to have an alternative method of measuring dispersion that will allow us to check for homogeneity.

2.3   Local Measures of Dispersion

The measures of dispersion computed in the previous section have one thing in common: each was computed using *all* of the data. That is, each of the traditional measures of dispersion is computed *globally*. For example, with Data Set Two the adjusted range of 2.69, the standard deviation statistic of 2.872, and the root mean square deviation of 2.708 were each computed using all nine values simultaneously. Therefore we could say that all three of these statistics are *global measures of dispersion*.

If a collection of values is indeed homogeneous, then that homogeneity should guarantee that *local* measures of dispersion, computed in various ways within the data set itself, should be reasonably similar to the global measures of dispersion computed using all of the data.

On the other hand, if a collection of values comes from two or more universes the global measures of dispersion will be inflated by the differences between the universes while local measures of dispersion will not be inflated by these differences to the same extent or in the same way.

Thus, the homogeneity question can be addressed by using this differential effect that multiple universes have upon global and local measures of dispersion.

The simplest local measure of dispersion is the *two-point moving range*. When the data have a known time-order sequence, the two-point moving ranges will consist of the differences between successive values when the data are arranged in their time order. For Data Set Two the time order is given by the order of the values themselves:

$$\{\, 5, 3, 6, 2, 2, 1, 9, 7, 1 \,\}$$

These nine values can be used to form eight successive pairs of values:

$$\{\, 5, 3\,\} , \{\, 3, 6\,\} , \{\, 6, 2\,\} , \{\, 2, 2\,\} , \{\, 2, 1\,\} , \{\, 1, 9\,\} , \{\, 9, 7\,\} , \{\, 7, 1\,\}$$

which result in the eight two-point *moving ranges*:

$$\textit{Local Two-Point Moving Ranges:} \ \{\, 2, 3, 4, 0, 1, 8, 2, 6 \,\}$$

The average, $\overline{mR}$ (or sometimes the median, $\widetilde{mR}$) of this set of localized ranges is divided by the appropriate bias correction factor (either d_2 or d_4 for $n = 2$) and the result is a local measure of dispersion, *Sigma(X)*:

$$Sigma(X) \ = \ \frac{\overline{mR}}{1.128} \ \text{ or } \ \frac{\widetilde{mR}}{0.954}$$

For Data Set Two the Average Moving Range is 3.25, giving a value of *Sigma(X)* of 2.88. This value is almost identical to the global standard deviation statistic of 2.87 which was computed earlier.

To help to distinguish between local and global measures of dispersion the *Sigma(X)* notation will be reserved for local measures of dispersion throughout this book.

When the global and local measures of dispersion are similar, as is the case in Figure 2.10, it is likely that the data are reasonably homogeneous. When the global measure is distinctly larger than the local measure, it is likely that the data are not homogeneous. However, since there are many different local and global measures of

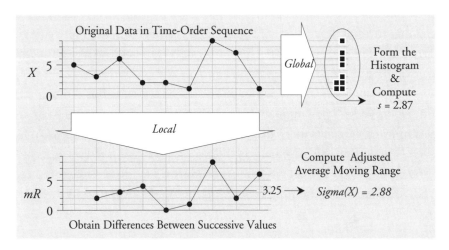

Figure 2.10: Global and Local Measures of Dispersion

dispersion, and since these different measures operate with different efficiencies, it is difficult to compare them directly. Instead we shall compare them indirectly in the manner outlined in the next section.

WHY DID WE USE THE RANGE?

Could we use the standard deviation statistic with each of the eight pairs of values above? Yes, but there is no point in doing so. For the eight pairs above we might compute the local standard deviation statistics:

{ 1.414, 2.121, 2.828, 0.000, 0.707, 5.657, 1.414, 4.243 }

Thus the average local s statistic would be 2.298. When this value is divided by the appropriate bias correction factor of $c_4 = 0.7979$ we get:

$$Sigma(X) = \frac{\overline{s}}{c_4} = \frac{2.298}{0.7979} = 2.88$$

This is exactly the same value we found using the Average Moving Range. This will always happen. Since we end up with the same value, why work harder to get there?

The local, two-point moving standard deviation statistics are completely equivalent to the local, two-point moving ranges, only harder to compute, harder to use, and harder to explain to others.

2.4   Are the Data Homogeneous?

- In Section 2.1 we found that a symmetric interval of the form:

  Average ± 3 [Global Measure of Dispersion]

  will contain virtually all of the values in any data set. The universality of this result prevents us from using global measures of dispersion to separate homogeneous data sets from nonhomogeneous collections of data.

- The previous section introduced the idea of a localized measure of dispersion, *Sigma(X)*. Two formulas for *Sigma(X)* were given, and it was shown that for homogeneous data sets the global and local measures of dispersion will be reasonably similar.

- Finally, it was suggested that when a collection of values is not homogeneous a local measure of dispersion will be distinctly smaller than a global measure of dispersion.

The combination of these three observations suggests a simple test for homogeneity. Compute the local three-sigma interval:

  Average ± 3 [Local Measure of Dispersion]

and see if any observed values fall outside these *Natural Process Limits*.

If the data are homogeneous the local and global measures should be similar, and the local interval above should contain virtually all of the data. However, if the data are not homogeneous the disparity between the local and global measures will be sufficient to result in several of the values falling outside the local interval.

To illustrate this approach we will revisit the data sets of Section 2.1. For each we will compare the global and local measures of dispersion and will compute Natural Process Limits:

  Average ± 3 Sigma(X)

These *Natural Process Limits* will be superimposed on a running record of the data and a judgment about the homogeneity of those data will be rendered.

◆ ◆ ◆

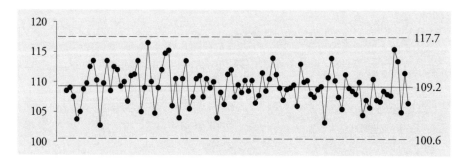

Figure 2.11: The *X* Chart for the Wire Length Data

The Wire Length Data has an Average of 109.19. The Average Moving Range is 3.234, giving a local measure of dispersion of *Sigma(X)* = 2.87. The Natural Process Limits are:

$$Natural\ Process\ Limits\ =\ 109.19 \pm 3\ [\ 2.87\ ]\ =\ 100.6\ to\ 117.7$$

All 100 values fall within these limits, as seen in Figure 2.11. There are no points outside the limits. Neither are there any obvious trends, shifts, cycles, or upsets. Thus it would appear that these data show no evidence of a lack of homogeneity. The graph in Figure 2.11 is a type of process behavior chart known as an *X* Chart or a Chart for Individual Values.

◆ ◆ ◆

The *X* Chart for the Data from Bead Board No. 7 is shown in Figure 2.12. The Average is 12.86. The Average Moving Range is 2.42, giving a *Sigma(X)* value of 2.14. The Natural Process Limits are:

$$Natural\ Process\ Limits\ =\ 12.86 \pm 3\ [\ 2.14\ ]\ =\ 6.4\ to\ 19.3$$

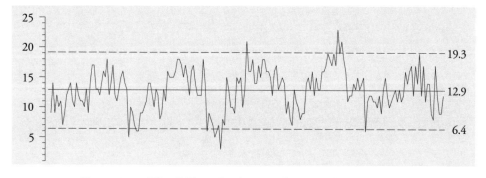

Figure 2.12: The *X* Chart for the Data from Bead Board No. 7

The global *s* statistic for Figure 2.12 is 3.46. Thus the global measure is 61 percent larger than the local measure of $Sigma(X)$ = 2.14. This discrepancy suggests that the homogeneity of these data is suspect. The *X* Chart agrees, showing 11 of the 200 values outside the limits. In addition, Figure 2.12 shows several places where long sequences of points all fall on the same side of the central line. (Generally whenever 8, 9, or 10 successive values fall on the same side of the central line it is taken as evidence of a lack of homogeneity in the data.)

◆ ◆ ◆

The Batch Weight Data have an Average of 937.0 kg. The first sixty values give an Average Moving Range of 25.8 kg which results in a $Sigma(X)$ value of 22.9 kg and Natural Process Limits of:

$$Natural\ Process\ Limits\ =\ 937.0 \pm 3\,[\,22.9\,]\ =\ 868.3\ kg\ to\ 1005.7\ kg$$

The global *s* statistic is 61.3 kg, which is almost three times $Sigma(X)$. This discrepancy and the *X* Chart in Figure 2.13 both suggest that the process was changing while these data were being collected. Of the 259 values a total of 56 are outside the limits. These data are not homogeneous.

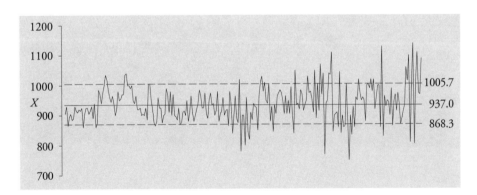

Figure 2.13: The *X* Chart for the Batch Weight Data

◆ ◆ ◆

The 150 Camshaft Bearing Diameters were arranged in time order for each bearing, as shown in Figure 2.14. The overall Average is 49.81 and the Average Moving Range is 1.91, giving the limits of 44.7 to 54.9 shown. Even though each of the three

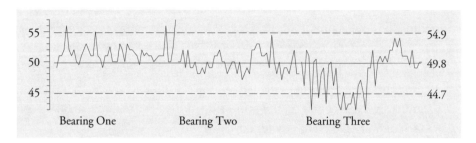

Figure 2.14: An *X* Chart for the Camshaft Bearing Diameters

bearing surfaces are supposed to be identical, the *X* Chart makes it clear that they are not. Different averages and different amounts of variation are seen in the three separate bearings. These data are not homogeneous.

If we compare the global *s* statistic of 2.78 with our *Sigma(X)* value of 1.69 we find the global *s* statistic to be 64 percent larger.

The Hot Metal Delivery Times have an Average of 59.92 and a Median Moving Range of 20. Thus *Sigma(X)* is 20.96 and the Natural Process Limits are 59.9 ± 3 (20.96) = −2.98 to 122.8. Since delivery times cannot be negative the lower limit is replaced by the boundary value of zero in Figure 2.15.

Seven of the 141 times are above the upper limit, which is more than we would expect from a homogeneous data set. The global *s* statistic is 29.7 minutes, which is 42 percent larger than *Sigma(X)*.

Here we also see a running record with many spikes suggesting the presence of different processes. As the Transportation Department Foreman said when he saw

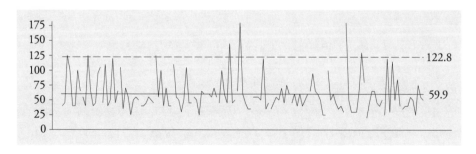

Figure 2.15: The *X* Chart for the Hot Metal Delivery Times

these data, "The only way they can take 100 minutes to go one mile is to unhook and go do another job." Of course this is exactly what was happening, but it took a graph to bring out this aspect of these data.

◆ ◆ ◆

The Creel Yield Data have an Average of 3492.1 and a Median Moving Range of 4.0. This results in a *Sigma(X)* value of 4.2 and Natural Process Limits of 3479.5 to 3504.7. Only 4 of the 68 values fall within these limits, confirming the impression given by the running record that these data are not homogeneous. The global *s* statistic for the Creel Yield Data is 38.3 which is essentially ten times larger than the *Sigma(X)* value of 4.2.

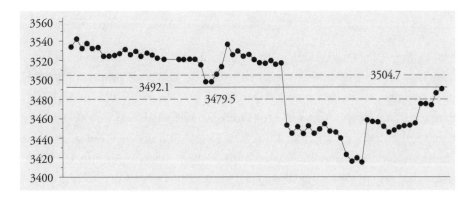

Figure 2.16: The *X* Chart for the Creel Yield Data

◆ ◆ ◆

Data Set Two and the Wire Length Data are homogeneous. The five remaining data sets all displayed evidence of nonhomogeneity. Using a local measure of dispersion to compute **three-sigma limits** will generally allow you to detect a lack of homogeneity when it occurs. Using a global measure of dispersion to compute **three standard deviation limits** will not allow you to differentiate between homogeneous data sets and nonhomogeneous collections of values.

On the next page Table 2.8 shows the proportions of the data found outside both the three standard deviation limits and the three-sigma limits for the seven data sets considered here. Inspection of this table should convince you of the necessity of using local measures of dispersion when analyzing data.

Table 2.8 **Number of Points Outside Global and Local Limits**

	Global Measures: Three Standard Deviation Limits Average ± 3 s		Local Measures: Three-sigma limits: (Natural Process Limits) Average ± 3 Sigma(X)	
Homogeneous Data Sets				
Data Set Two	0 of 9	0%	0 of 9	0%
Wire Length Data	0 of 100	0%	0 of 100	0%
Nonhomogeneous Data Sets				
Bead Board Data	0 of 200	0%	11 of 200	5.5%
Batch Weight Data	3 of 259	1.2%	56 of 259	21.6%
Bearing Diameter Data	0 of 150	0%	14 of 150	9.3%
Hot Metal Delivery Data	2 of 141	1.4%	7 of 141	5.0%
Creel Yield Data	0 of 68	0%	64 of 68	94.1%

Because *three standard deviation limits* do not allow us to distinguish between homogeneous and nonhomogeneous data sets we do not compute such limits. Neither do we directly compare a global measure of dispersion with a local measure of dispersion. We simply compute the *three-sigma limits* and look for individual values that fall outside these Natural Process Limits. When we have points outside these limits we can be reasonably sure that the data are not homogeneous, therefore the process that is generating our data is changing and we need to find out why.

2.5 The Difference Between Global and Local

Descriptive statistics merely characterize a collection of values. Nested intervals centered on the average will capture certain percentages of the *data*. The problem of using global measures of dispersion is not with our statements about the data, but rather with our ability to generalize from the data to the underlying process or universe from which those data came.

Global measures of dispersion *assume* **that the data were all obtained from one universe.** When this is true, these measures provide an appropriate characterization of both the data and the underlying process. But when this assumption is not true, the global measures of dispersion do not provide any useful information about the underlying process. Therefore, we need to have some way of examining this assumption of homogeneity for the data. Since global measures of dispersion do not provide any way of doing this we have to turn to local measures of dispersion.

Modern statistical analysis is built on the foundation of the difference in the local and global measures of dispersion. While the details change, this comparison between local and global remains at the heart of all analysis techniques. And it is the local measures of dispersion that are the standard in all of these comparisons.

So what does this mean with regard to computing descriptive statistics? The traditional descriptive global measures of dispersion are appropriate when you only wish to summarize the *data* or when you *know* that the data were obtained from one universe. Outside of these two very narrow situations their use is based upon wishful thinking. Thus, global measures of dispersion are, in general, gullible with respect to the assumption of homogeneity, while local measures of dispersion are skeptical with regard to the assumption of homogeneity. Knowing the difference is fundamental to performing any kind of data analysis.

Chapter Three

Process Behavior Charts

As was noted in the previous chapter, there is a fundamental difference between summarizing data and characterizing the underlying system that generated those data. In the quest to understand this underlying system our greatest clue is the homogeneity, or the lack of homogeneity, of the data themselves. And the simplest tool for detecting a lack of homogeneity within the data is the process behavior chart.

3.1 The Chart for Individual Values

The simplest of the process behavior charts is the *Chart for Individual Values and Moving Ranges*, the *XmR Chart*. The previous chapter contained several *X* Charts. There, in the interest of simplicity, the companion charts for the moving range values were not included. In practice, however, it is generally best to present both charts together.

As the names suggests, the *XmR* Chart makes use of the localized measures of dispersion known as moving ranges. Either the *Average Moving Range* or the *Median Moving Range* is used to obtain a *Sigma(X)* value, and then this value is used to compute *Three-Sigma Limits,* centered on the Average, for the original data.

If the original data fall within these three-sigma limits, then there is no overt evidence that the data came from multiple universes. However, if one or more of the original data fall outside the three-sigma limits, or if a moving range falls above its upper three-sigma limit, you have strong evidence of nonhomogeneity.

This simple procedure produces limits that can be applied both to the original data and to future observations as well. This is helpful when dealing with an ongoing process. The three-sigma limits are limits that define the routine, localized variation present in the data. If your collection of values is indeed homogeneous, and remains so, then virtually all of the observations should fall within the three-sigma limits.

To illustrate the *XmR* Chart and the two alternatives for computing limits for these charts we shall use Data Set Two with the formulas and constants in Table A.2.

LIMITS BASED ON THE AVERAGE MOVING RANGE

When the Natural Process Limits and the Upper Range Limit are computed from the Average Moving Range the formulas look like:

$$\textit{Natural Process Limits} = \textit{Average} \pm 3\ \textit{Sigma(X)}$$

$$= \bar{X} \pm 3\ \frac{\overline{mR}}{1.128}$$

$$= \bar{X} \pm 2.660\ \overline{mR}$$

and

$$\textit{Upper Range Limit} = \textit{Average(R)} + 3\ \textit{Sigma(R)}$$

$$= d_2\ \textit{Sigma(X)} + 3\ d_3\ \textit{Sigma(X)}$$

$$= 1.128\ \textit{Sigma(X)} + 3\ (0.8525)\ \textit{Sigma(X)}$$

$$= [\ 1.128 + 3\ (0.8525)\ ]\frac{\overline{mR}}{1.128}$$

$$= 3.268\ \overline{mR}$$

The scaling factors of 2.660 and 3.268 are merely convenience factors that reduce the arithmetic down to the minimum.

When used with Data Set Two, which has an Average of 4.0 and an Average Moving Range of 3.25, these formulas result in the limits shown in Figure 3.1. With no points outside the limits on either part of the chart, there is no evidence of a lack of homogeneity in these data.

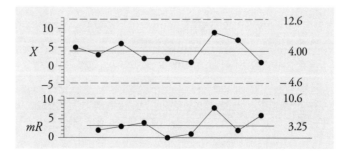

Figure 3.1: An *XmR* Chart for Data Set Two

LIMITS BASED ON THE MEDIAN MOVING RANGE

When the Natural Process Limits and the Upper Range Limit are computed from the Median Moving Range the formulas look like:

$$\textit{Natural Process Limits} = \textit{Average} \pm 3\ \textit{Sigma(X)}$$

$$= \bar{X} \pm 3\ \frac{\widetilde{mR}}{0.954}$$

$$= \bar{X} \pm 3.145\ \widetilde{mR}$$

and

$$\textit{Upper Range Limit} = \textit{Average(R)} + 3\ \textit{Sigma(R)}$$

$$= d_2\ \textit{Sigma(X)} + 3\ d_3\ \textit{Sigma(X)}$$

$$= [\,1.128 + 3\,(.8525)\,]\,\frac{\widetilde{mR}}{0.954}$$

$$= 3.865\ \widetilde{mR}$$

As before, the scaling factors of 3.145 and 3.865 are merely convenience factors that reduce the arithmetic down to the minimum. When used with Data Set Two which has an Average of 4.0 and an Median Moving Range of 2.5 these formulas result in the limits shown in Figure 3.2. While the numbers change slightly from those in Figure 3.1, the story remains the same.

While I will occasionally show the *X* Chart by itself, as I did in the previous chapter, I cannot agree to the suppression of the *mR* Chart as a general practice.

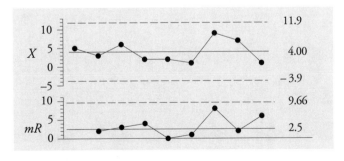

Figure 3.2: Another *XmR* Chart for Data Set Two

While it is true that the *X* Chart tells the story, and that we will undoubtedly find the *X* Chart to be the most interesting part of the *XmR* Chart, there are times when the *mR* Chart can clarify and extend what we see on the *X* Chart.

3.2   What Do We Gain from the *mR* Chart?

It has been suggested that the Moving Range Chart adds so little to the Chart for Individual Values that you should not bother to show it—"Simply show the *X* Chart and forget the *mR* Chart." The basis for this recommendation seems to be the documented fact that the combined *XmR* Chart does not have any appreciably greater ability to detect signals than does the *X* Chart alone.

However, this mathematical analysis overlooks the interpretative benefits to be gained by including the *mR* Chart. Consider the *XmR* Chart for the Data from Bead Board No. 7 in Figure 3.3. The six moving ranges that exceed their upper limit identify six points where the funnel of the bead board was moved. Two of these six shifts do not correspond to points outside the limits on the *X* Chart. Thus, this Moving Range Chart provides additional information and reinforces the message of the *X* Chart.

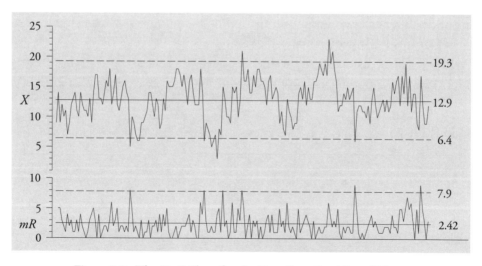

Figure 3.3: The *XmR* Chart for the Data from Bead Board No. 7

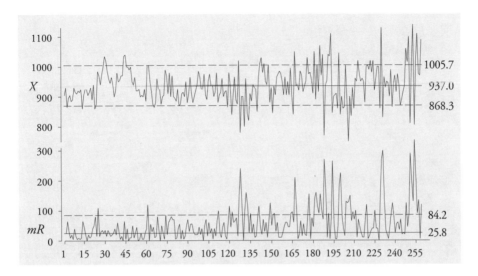

Figure 3.4: The *XmR* Chart for the Batch Weight Data

When computing the limits for the Batch Weight Data, I only used the first 60 moving ranges to compute the Average Moving Range. Inspection of the *mR* Chart in Figure 3.4 will show why I did this—there is an increase in the process variation after the first sixty values. Since the objective is to compute limits that characterize what the process is capable of doing, the first 60 moving ranges do this better than the rest.

The *XmR* Chart in Figure 3.5 has limits based on the Median Moving Range. The six spikes on the *mR* Chart allow us to break the original data into seven segments and use a separate central line for each segment, resulting in an X Chart that shows the changes in level and also reveals the presence of other types of nonhomogeneity. Thus, while the *mR* Chart may not add much to the likelihood of detecting a change, it can be very helpful in interpreting changes that occur.

The second reason that I cannot agree to the suppression of the *mR* Chart is that there are many people and many software packages that actually compute *three standard deviation limits* rather than *three-sigma limits*. If you are shown a naked X Chart you will have no way of knowing if the limits have been computed correctly. However, if you are shown an *XmR* Chart, you will immediately have a higher level of confidence that the limits have been computed correctly. Moreover, by using the central line of the *mR* Chart, you can quickly check to see if the limits are indeed cor-

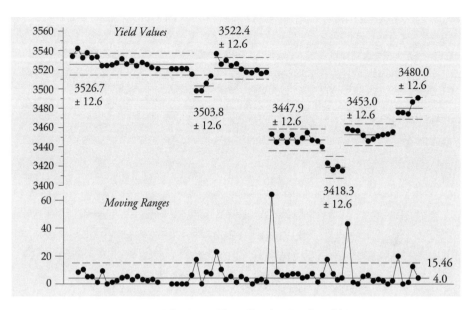

Figure 3.5: The *XmR* Chart for the Creel Yield Data

rectly computed. Thus, the *mR* Chart is the secret handshake of those who know the correct way of computing limits for an *X* Chart. Omit it and your readers cannot be sure that you are a member of the club.

Finally, the *mR* Chart allows you and your audience to check for a problem that will be explained in Section 3.7, the problem of chunky data.

Thus, while there may be little mathematical justification for showing the *mR* Chart, there are three practical reasons to do so, any one of which is sufficient to justify the inclusion of the *mR* Chart with your *X* Chart.

3.3 What Makes the *XmR* Chart Work?

There are two basic ideas or principles that need to be respected when creating an *XmR* Chart. The first is that successive values need to be logically comparable. The second is that the moving ranges need to isolate and capture the local, short-term, routine variation that is inherent in the data.

While the use of the time-order sequence of the data will usually be sufficient to satisfy these two requirements of the *XmR Chart*, there are times when a careful consideration of the structure in the data will require a different organization. As a case in point consider the Camshaft Bearing Diameters shown in Table 2.4. The strict time-order for these data is:

Camshaft No. 1; Bearing 1, Bearing 2, Bearing 3,
Camshaft No. 2; Bearing 1, Bearing 2, Bearing 3, etc.

When the data are arranged in this order the Average Moving Range is 3.10. With an Average of 49.81 we obtain Natural Process Limits of 41.6 to 58.1. These limits are shown in Figure 3.6.

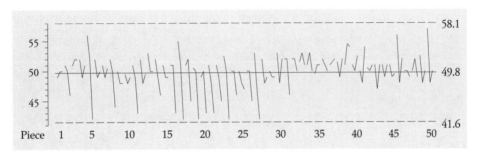

Figure 3.6: An *X* Chart for the Camshaft Bearing Diameter Data in Time-Order

With this arrangement the moving ranges represent the differences between the three bearings. Since the three bearings were produced by three separate parallel processes there could be systematic differences between the three bearings that have nothing to do with routine variation. Even though the three bearings are supposed to be the same, the fact that they are produced by parallel operations makes it a bit naive to assume that they are indeed the same.

The idea of checking your data for homogeneity is based on a skeptical view of homogeneity, not a gullible one. Therefore, rather than using the strict time order shown in Figure 3.6, a more rational approach is to organize these data according to bearing number, and then within each bearing to use the time order to create moving ranges. When this is done the moving ranges will represent the natural, short-term, routine variation within each production process rather than the differences, if any, between the three processes. Now the Average Moving range is 1.91, giving the limits of 44.7 to 54.9 shown in Figure 3.7. This running record and these limits allow us to see the differences between the bearings with greater clarity.

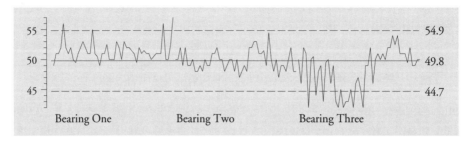

Figure 3.7: The Second *X* Chart for the Camshaft Bearing Diameter Data

Thus, when there is a structure within your data, it is imperative that you consider that structure when organizing the data for an *XmR* Chart. If there are logical partitions or subsets in your data, isolate those subsets from each other so that successive values will be logically comparable and the moving ranges can characterize the routine variation rather than the differences between the subsets.

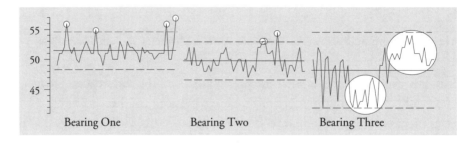

Figure 3.8: The Third *X* Chart for the Camshaft Bearing Diameter Data

In fact, for the Camshaft Bearing Diameters we could take the next step and compute a separate set of limits for each bearing. This *X* Chart is in Figure 3.8. Not only are the three bearings different, but each bearing shows evidence of nonhomogeneity in the production processes.

◆ ◆ ◆

With the Hot Metal Delivery Times the changes occur so often that it is virtually impossible to obtain an Average Moving Range that will characterize the routine variation. In cases like this it is customary to shift to using the Median Moving Range. Since median values are less severely inflated by extreme values than averages, the use of the Median Moving Range allows us to extract an estimate of routine variation even in the face of an abundance of signals of change. Here the Median Moving Range is 20, giving the limits shown in Figure 3.9.

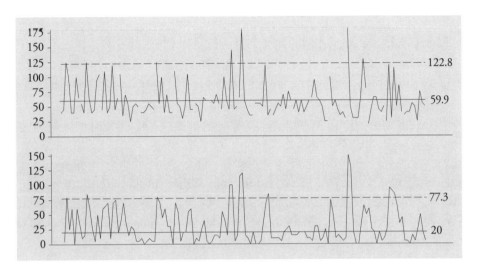

Figure 3.9: The *XmR* Chart for the Hot Metal Delivery Times

No Lower Natural Process Limit is shown in Figure 3.9 because the computed value was less than zero while the delivery times cannot be less than zero. Whenever a boundary or barrier value falls within the computed Natural Process Limits, that boundary value will take precedence over the computed limit, and you end up with a one-sided chart.

While the Median Moving Range provided tighter limits and a more sensitive chart in Figure 3.9, you could argue that the Median Moving Range and the limits have still been inflated by the sheer multiplicity of large ranges. While this may be true, it is useful to recall that *we are not trying to estimate the parameters of a probability model, but we are instead examining the data for evidence of nonhomogeneity.* Having found this evidence, we know that these data did not come from one universe, but from several, so the whole question of estimation is moot. The limits are good enough to do their job. We need to discover why the process is operating with multiple personalities, and do something about this problem. Estimation will not help here; action is required.

Once you have organized the data in a rational manner, there are many ways to use the limits to tell the story that is contained within the data. The objective is understanding and insight rather than computing a particular value. There is an element of judgment involved in using a process behavior chart, and this element cannot be removed. It is essential to an effective analysis.

3.4 How Many Values Do I Need?

When examining a finite data set for homogeneity you should have at least six values before you place the data on a process behavior chart.

When computing limits for an ongoing sequence of values you should have at least four values in the baseline used to compute limits.

However, with four values it is impossible to have one of the baseline values fall outside the limits. With five or six values it is highly unlikely that you will get a baseline value outside the limits. So while we may compute limits with small amounts of data, the process behavior chart will be fairly insensitive when used with less than 10 values.

So what can you do if you have a small amount of data and one value seems to be different from the rest? You might exclude that one value from the computation of the limits. If that suspect value is then outside the limits computed from the remainder of the data it can be said to be detectably different from the rest of the values.

Limits are soft when they are computed from the Average Moving Range using less than 10 values or a Median Moving Range using less than 20 values. This means that uncertainty in the limits will make points close to the limits hard to call. However, when a point falls comfortably outside such limits you can be reasonably sure that the data are nonhomogeneous.

Limits begin to gel when they are based on 10 to 20 values with an Average Moving Range or on 20 to 40 values with a Median Moving Range. While a point that is just outside the limits may or may not be a signal, points comfortably outside the limits are definite signals of nonhomogeneity.

Limits based on more than 20 values with an Average Moving Range, or more than 40 values with a Median Moving Range, will have solidified to the extent that any point outside the limits should be considered to be a signal of nonhomogeneity.

Limits obtained from an Average Moving Range that is based on more than 50 values will have solidified. Using additional data to compute the limits will not substantially improve the limits. (The same happens when limits are obtained from a

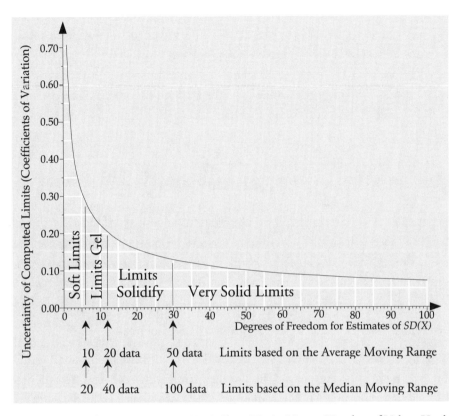

Figure 3.10: The Uncertainty in *XmR* Chart Limits Versus Number of Values Used

Median Moving Range based on more than 100 values.)

So, while it is nice to have 15 to 20 values, and even better to have 50, you can compute and use limits based on as few as a half-dozen values.

The basis for these statements is the curve shown in Figure 3.10. The limits will be soft when fewer than 6 degrees of freedom are used. The limits will have begun to gel when 6 to 12 degrees of freedom are used, and they will have gelled when more than 12 degrees of freedom are used. The larger numbers of original data needed with a Median Moving Range reflect the lower efficiency of the median. This lower efficiency is why I consider the Median Moving Range as an alternative computation, only to be used when it appears that the Average Moving Range will be inflated.

What is the penalty for computing limits with only a few values? If you find a signal, it is almost certainly a real signal. If you do not find a signal, at least you will have looked for one, which is still better than merely assuming the data are homogeneous. The objective is not to compute the best limits, but to compute limits that will allow you to characterize the homogeneity of the data.

When hundreds of values are placed on a chart there will be occasional false alarms. These points tend to be isolated points that fall on or just beyond one of the limits. While false alarms do occur, they do not occur very often with three-sigma limits.

3.5 Rules for Detecting Nonhomogeneity

Process behavior charts may be interpreted using several detection rules. In addition to the default rule of a point outside the limits, there are three "run tests" that are commonly used. Collectively, the following four rules are known as the Western Electric Zone Tests.

> **Detection Rule One:** (a point outside the limits) A single point outside the limits is interpreted as a potential signal of nonhomogeneity.

Since the likelihood of a point falling outside the limits is very small when the data are homogeneous, any points outside the limits deserve to be investigated as potential signals of dramatic process changes. The Assignable Cause of such changes

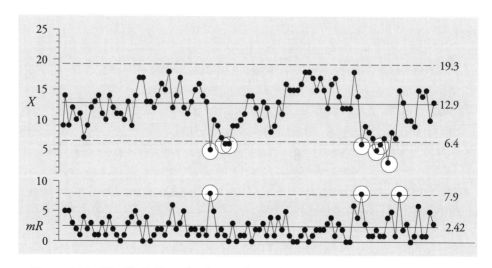

Figure 3.11: The *XmR* Chart for the Bead Board No. 7 Data with Rule One Signals

should be sought out, and if possible, you should seek to keep this Assignable Cause from affecting your process in the future.

This detection rule applies to both the *X* Chart and the *mR* Chart. Using the first 100 values from the Bead Board No. 7 Data we find 10 points outside the limits in Figure 3.11. This is more than enough to justify an investigation.

> **Detection Rule Two:** (a run beyond two sigma) Whenever at least two out of three successive points are both on the same side of the average, and are more than two-sigma units away from the average, you have a run beyond two sigma. Such a run is interpreted as a signal of a *sustained shift in location*.

Using Detection Rule Two with the first 100 of the Bead Board No. 7 Data results in three signals. One of these is not part of a run containing a point outside the limits. While this is a new signal, did we need more signals?

In the presence of points outside the limits we do not usually need to dig deeper using the additional detection rules. We already have enough signals to investigate, especially when we remember that points outside the limits represent the stronger signals.

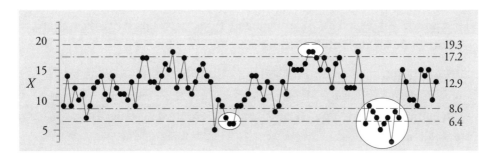

Figure 3.12: The *X* Chart for the Bead Board No. 7 Data with Rule Two Signals

Detection Rule Two cannot be used with the *mR* Chart. Moreover, this rule can only be used where the notion of sequence makes sense. If the data are ordered in their natural time-order sequence, then this rule may be used. If the data have been arranged in an arbitrary ordering, then this rule should not be used. This rule does require the computation of two-sigma lines, but most computer programs allow for the use of this rule.

Detection Rule Three: (a run beyond one sigma) Whenever at least four out of five successive values are on the same side of the average, and are more than one-sigma unit away from the average, you have a run beyond one sigma. Such a run is interpreted as a signal of a *sustained shift in location.*

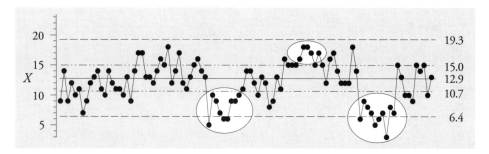

Figure 3.13: The *X* Chart for the Bead Board No. 7 Data with Rule Three Signals

In Figure 3.13 we see that Detection Rule Three identifies the same three excursions found by Detection Rule Two.

Detection Rule Three cannot be used with the *mR* Chart. This rule can only be used when the notion of sequence for the original data makes sense. This rule requires the computation of one-sigma lines. Since the signals detected here are smaller than those detected by Rules One and Two, they will be of lesser interest in the presence of Rule One or Rule Two signals.

Detection Rule Four: (a run about the central line) Whenever eight or more successive values are all on the same side of the central line you have a run about the central line. Such a run is interpreted as a signal of a *sustained shift in location.*

As with Rules Two and Three, this rule cannot be used with the *mR* Chart and only makes sense when the notion of sequence for the original data makes sense. Since the signals detected by Rule Four are smaller than those detected by the other rules, they are of lesser interest in the presence of Rule One, Rule Two, or Rule Three signals.

Once again, the three runs about the central line redundantly identify excursions already detected. However, in Figure 3.8, Detection Rule Four was the only way to detect the nonhomogeneity in Camshaft Bearing Three.

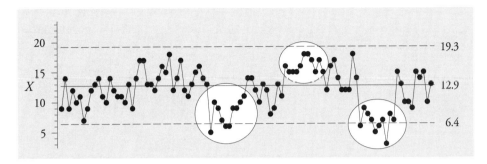

Figure 3.14: The *X* Chart for the Bead Board Data with Rule Four Signals

The fact that the different detection rules are looking for different types of signals is what makes them interesting. While stronger signals are more easily detected, smaller signals are harder to detect against the background noise of the routine variation. Which is why, in practice, many people use Detection Rules One and Four together. When the charts are done by hand these two rules do not require the computation of additional lines, yet they check for large changes and smaller, sustained shifts.

When all four rules are used together the process behavior chart will have essentially the same power as any comparable statistical technique. This combination of power and simplicity is what makes process behavior charts so useful in practice. On the down side, since these four rules boost the power of the charts to the limit of what can be achieved, the use of additional detection rules can only increase the false alarm rate. Since this is undesirable the routine use of additional detection rules is discouraged.

Since using all four detection rules can create so much clutter that the actual data get lost I tend to turn off Detection Rules Two, Three, and Four, and focus on Detection Rule One signals. When a point goes outside the limits I consider not only that one point, but also all the adjacent points that are on the same side of the central line. By including adjacent points I am more likely to discover the cause of the change than would be the case if I focused on the single point outside the limits. When this approach is used with all 200 values of the Bead Board No. 7 Data we get Figure 3.15. There the *mR* Chart identifies six breaks in these data while the *X* Chart shows seven excursions.

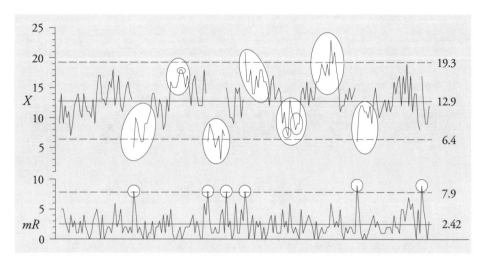

Figure 3.15: The Interpreted *XmR* Chart for the Bead Board No. 7 Data

Use only as many detection rules as you need to tell the story of your data. Using all four detection rules with all 200 Bead Board Data results in 36 distinct signals. Thirty of these signals identify seven or eight excursions on the *X* Chart, while six are spikes on the *mR* Chart. Of these latter six, five of the abrupt changes are associated with the excursions already identified on the *X* Chart, thus eight or nine changes result in 36 signals. So use Rules Two, Three, and Four to complement Rule One, rather than firing the whole battery at once and obliterating the target.

Finally, when a running record shows a recurring pattern you have a right to be suspicious. Therefore, as a simple aid to investigation I use the following pattern detection guideline.

> **The Pattern Detection Guideline:** Whenever a pattern consisting of two or more points repeats itself eight times in a row you should look for some systematic explanation.

Figure 3.16 is a repeat of Figure 3.6. There Camshafts 16 to 27 show the same pattern. In and of itself, twelve repetitions of this pattern is enough to make you suspect that the bearings are different and to reorganize the data so that you can obtain a more powerful analysis.

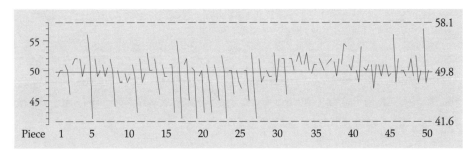

Figure 3.16: The First *X* Chart for the Camshaft Bearing Diameter Data

3.6 Average and Range Charts

A second type of process behavior chart is the Average and Range Chart. Rather than working with the individual values this chart arranges the data into *k* subgroups of size *n* and plots the *k* Subgroup Averages and Subgroup Ranges. The original data are broken up into these subgroups based on judgments regarding the conditions under which the values were obtained—*when two values may be judged to have been collected under essentially the same conditions they may be placed in the same subgroup.* Since values within each subgroup are judged to be homogeneous they can be used to estimate routine variation. The need for homogeneity within the subgroups will tend to favor smaller rather than larger subgroups.

While the Average and Range Chart is more complex than the *XmR* Chart, it does provide a greater sensitivity to process changes. This increase in sensitivity is proportional to the square root of the subgroup size. Thus, while sensitivity wants a larger subgroup size, the need for homogeneity argues for smaller subgroup sizes, and the best compromise tends to occur when the subgroup size is between *n* = 4 and *n* = 10, where we get a 2 to 3 fold increase in sensitivity without excessively large subgroups.

The Wire Length Data will be used to illustrate the Average and Range Chart. In Table 3.1 these values are arranged into *k* = 20 subgroups of size *n* = 5. The average of the Subgroup Averages, known as the Grand Average, will be our summary statistic for location. Our summary statistic for dispersion will be either the Average Range or the Median Range. As with the *XmR* Chart, the Subgroup Ranges are local measures of dispersion, making the Average Range and the Median Range local measures of dispersion.

The Average Chart uses a running record of the k Subgroup Averages, with a central line equal to the Grand Average and limits of:

$$\text{Upper and Lower Average Limits} \quad = \quad \bar{\bar{X}} \pm A_2\,\bar{R} \quad \text{or} \quad \bar{\bar{X}} \pm A_4\,\tilde{R}$$

The Range Chart uses a running record of the k Subgroup Ranges with a central line equal to the Average Range or the Median Range and limits of:

$$\text{Upper Range Limit} \quad = \quad D_4\,\bar{R} \quad \text{or} \quad D_6\,\tilde{R}$$
$$\text{Lower Range Limit} \quad = \quad D_3\,\bar{R} \quad \text{or} \quad D_5\,\tilde{R}$$

where A_2, A_4, D_3, D_4, D_5, and D_6 are the appropriate scaling factors from Tables A.3 and A.4 in the Appendix.

Table 3.1: The Wire Length Data Arranged into Subgroups of Size 5

Observations					Averages	Ranges
108.5	108.9	107.4	103.8	105.0	106.72	5.1
108.7	109.8	112.5	113.5	110.3	110.96	4.8
102.8	109.7	113.4	108.4	112.4	109.34	10.6
112.1	109.3	110.1	106.8	111.1	109.88	5.3
111.2	113.5	104.9	108.9	116.4	110.98	11.5
110.1	104.8	109.1	112.0	114.8	110.16	10.0
115.2	105.9	110.4	104.1	110.5	109.22	11.1
113.5	105.5	107.4	110.4	110.9	109.54	8.0
107.4	110.6	109.0	110.0	104.1	108.22	6.5
108.3	106.3	111.2	111.9	107.6	109.06	5.6
109.5	108.2	110.2	108.4	110.3	109.32	2.1
106.4	107.8	111.6	108.4	110.6	108.96	5.2
114.1	111.3	108.9	107.1	108.8	110.04	7.0
109.0	109.6	106.1	113.1	110.1	109.58	7.0
110.2	107.9	107.5	108.8	109.3	108.74	2.7
103.2	110.8	114.0	110.3	107.6	109.18	10.8
105.4	111.2	108.9	108.5	108.0	108.40	5.8
110.1	104.5	107.0	105.7	110.6	107.58	6.1
107.0	106.7	108.6	107.9	107.7	107.58	1.9
115.5	113.4	105.0	111.6	106.5	110.40	10.5

For the Wire Length Data the Grand Average is 109.193, the Average Range is 6.88, and for $n = 5$ the scaling factors are $A_2 = 0.577$ and $D_4 = 2.114$. These values yield an Upper Average Limit of 113.16, a Lower Average Limit of 105.22, and an Upper Range Limit of 14.5. There is no Lower Range Limit until n is 7 or larger. The

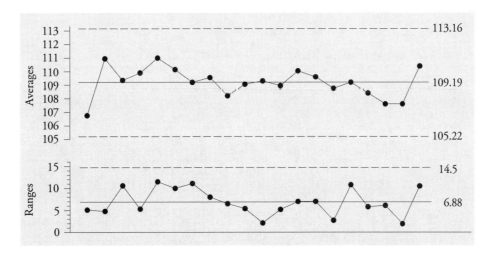

Figure 3.17: The Average and Range Chart for the Wire Length Data

Average and Range Chart for the Wire Length Data is shown in Figure 3.17. Just as was seen on the *XmR* Chart in Figure 3.2, there is no evidence of nonhomogeneity in these data.

If we partition the data for Bead Board No. 7 into $k = 40$ subgroups of size $n = 5$, as shown in Table 3.2, we will end up with the Average and Range Chart shown in Figure 3.18. Twelve of the 40 Subgroup Averages fall outside the limits. These 12 points identify seven excursions in these data. In comparison, the *X* Chart in Figure 3.4 had 11 out of 200 points outside the limits, and these 11 points identified five excursions.

Using Detection Rules One and Two the Average Chart shows a total of ten excursions while the *X* Chart for all 200 values would show only six of these excursions. While five or six excursions is more than enough evidence to justify an investigation into the source of this nonhomogeneity, this example serves to illustrate the greater sensitivity of the Average Chart. In most cases the *XmR* Chart will be sufficient to detect nonhomogeneity. However, if you suspect nonhomogeneity and you can reasonably arrange the data into logical, homogeneous subgroups, you will find the Average Chart to be more sensitive than the *XmR* Chart.

Table 3.2: The Bead Board No. 7 Data

	Observations					Avg.	Range		Observations					Avg.	Range
-1-	9	14	9	12	10	10.8	5	-21-	21	16	16	18	14	17.0	7
-2-	11	7	9	12	13	10.4	6	-22-	14	17	15	18	18	16.4	4
-3-	14	11	10	14	12	12.2	4	-23-	16	16	15	12	16	15.0	4
-4-	11	11	10	13	9	10.8	4	-24-	17	13	14	15	14	14.6	4
-5-	14	17	17	13	13	14.8	4	-25-	9	11	8	7	13	9.6	6
-6-	12	14	16	15	18	15.0	6	-26-	11	10	8	9	9	9.4	3
-7-	12	14	17	12	11	13.2	6	-27-	14	15	13	16	12	14.0	4
-8-	13	15	16	14	13	14.2	3	-28-	15	13	13	16	16	14.6	3
-9-	5	10	9	7	6	7.4	5	-29-	17	19	18	17	19	18.0	2
-10-	6	9	9	10	11	9.0	5	-30-	17	23	19	21	18	19.6	6
-11-	14	14	12	10	13	12.6	4	-31-	16	11	12	12	14	13.0	5
-12-	12	8	9	13	11	10.6	5	-32-	13	15	13	14	15	14.0	2
-13-	16	15	15	15	16	15.4	1	-33-	6	11	12	12	11	10.4	6
-14-	18	18	17	15	17	17.0	3	-34-	11	10	12	9	13	11.0	4
-15-	15	12	16	17	14	14.8	5	-35-	15	12	10	11	12	12.0	5
-16-	12	12	12	18	14	13.6	6	-36-	13	11	13	11	12	12.0	2
-17-	6	9	8	7	5	7.0	4	-37-	16	14	16	17	12	15.0	5
-18-	6	7	3	8	7	6.2	5	-38-	17	14	19	12	17	15.8	7
-19-	15	13	10	10	9	11.4	6	-39-	11	14	14	9	8	11.2	6
-20-	15	14	15	10	13	13.4	5	-40-	17	12	9	9	12	11.8	8

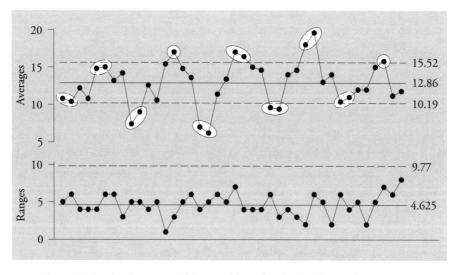

Figure 3.18: An Average and Range Chart for the Bead Board No. 7 Data

3.7 Chunky Data

Most problems with process behavior charts are fail-safe. That is, the charts will err in the direction of hiding a signal rather than causing a false alarm. Because of this feature, when you get a signal you can trust the chart to be guiding you in the right direction.

There is only one exception to this fail-safe feature of the process behavior charts, and that is chunky data. Data are said to be chunky when the distance between the possible values becomes too large. Measuring a person's height to the nearest yard would result in chunky data—an increment of one yard is so large that it will obscure the variation from person to person. Excessive round-off is one way to create chunky data. Using measurement units that are too large is another way.

The effect of chunky data upon a process behavior chart will be illustrated by starting with a set of values that are homogeneous, and then rounding these values off to make them chunky.

Table 3.3: Data Set Eight

214.0	214.3	213.7	213.4	213.5	213.8	214.3	214.3	214.5	214.6
213.9	213.4	214.7	214.8	214.9	214.3	214.1	213.7	213.8	214.0
214.2	214.2	214.5	213.5	213.6	213.6	214.4	214.3	213.6	213.7
214.2	214.7	213.7	214.2	213.8	214.3	213.7	214.5	213.7	213.8
214.1	214.2	214.7	214.0	214.0	214.2	213.7	213.4	214.0	213.2

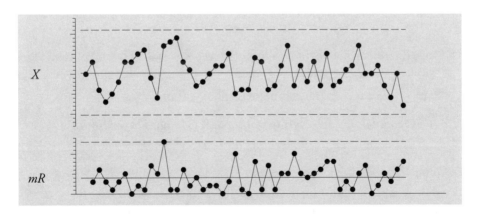

Figure 3.19: The *XmR* Chart for Data Set Eight

The *XmR* Chart for the values in Table 3.3 is given in Figure 3.19. None of the values in Figure 3.19 fall outside the limits.

Next the values from Table 3.3 were rounded off to the nearest whole number. These rounded values are shown in Table 3.4 and were used to create the *XmR* Chart in Figure 3.20. There we see ten individual values and one moving range outside their limits.

Table 3.4: Data Set Eight Rounded to Whole Numbers

214	214	214	213	214	214	214	214	214	215
214	213	215	215	215	214	214	214	214	214
214	214	214	214	214	214	214	214	214	214
214	215	214	214	214	214	214	214	214	214
214	214	215	214	214	214	214	213	214	213

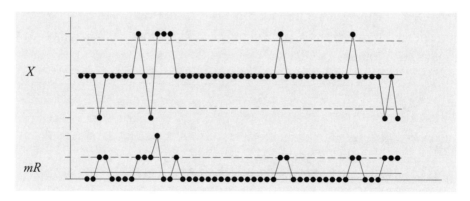

Figure 3.20: The *XmR* Chart for Data Set Eight Rounded to Whole Numbers

The only difference between these two charts is the size of the increments for the values. The points outside the limits in Figure 3.20 have nothing to do with the homogeneity of the data set. They are the result of chunky data.

Chunky data can result in points that fall outside the limits
even when the underlying data set is homogeneous.

Fortunately, when this problem exists it is easy to identify. The way to identify chunky data begins with an inspection of the values to determine the size of the increment present. You want to determine just how close together two of the values could be—what measurement unit is used. You may do this by examining either the individual values or the moving ranges since they will both display the same sized increments. In Table 3.3 the values are recorded to one decimal place. In Table 3.4 the values are given to the nearest whole number.

Next, you will need to determine how many possible range values there are between zero and the Upper Range Limit. Since the ranges will display the same sized increments as the individual values, you can begin with zero and count by increments until you get a value above the *URL*. If the number of possible range values (including zero) within the limits is three or less, then you have chunky data.

In Figure 3.19 the *mR* Chart has an *URL* of 1.31. With an increment of 0.1 there are a total of 14 possible values for the ranges below the limit. In Figure 3.20 the *URL* is 1.00. With an increment of 1.0 there are only two possible values (namely 0 and 1) within the limits of this *mR* Chart.

> *For the XmR Chart your data can be said to be chunky if there are three or fewer possible values below the Upper Range Limit. When this happens the limits for the X Chart will be distorted. In order to be safe from the distorting effects and artificial signals created by chunky data you need to have a minimum of four possible values below the Upper Range Limit.*

Thus, Figure 3.19 is free of the effects of chunky data, while Figure 3.20 suffers the effects of chunky data. Therefore, we cannot safely interpret the signals on Figure 3.20 as being due to nonhomogeneity in the data—the points outside the limits are a consequence of using chunky data to construct the chart.

Of course, when you have chunky data but do not find points outside the limits, it is safe to say that the data are homogeneous. Chunky data simply increases the likelihood of false alarms.

The procedure for checking for chunky data consists of three steps:

1. Determine the increment displayed by the individual values.

2. Determine the Upper Range Limit.

3. Determine the number of possible values for the ranges within the limits. If this number is below the threshold your data are chunky.

> *For Average and Range Charts with subgroups of size n > 2, the data will be said to be chunky when the Range Chart has four or fewer possible values within the limits.*

For Average and Range Charts with subgroups of size n = 2, the data will be said to be chunky when the Range Chart has three or fewer possible values below the Upper Range Limit.

When you have chunky data the remedy is to use smaller increments in the values. If you cannot do this then you will not be able to compute appropriate limits for your process behavior chart.

3.8 Caution Regarding Software

Software companies are not in the business of teaching people the right and wrong ways of computing limits for process behavior charts. They are in the business of selling software. So when a naive customer insists on computing the limits incorrectly (using a global measure of dispersion), they will give the customer what he wants. For this reason many programs that create process behavior charts include options that allow you to compute the limits incorrectly.

- Good software does not allow the limits to be computed incorrectly.
- Acceptable software will default to the correct computations, with a warning on the options that allow the incorrect computations.
- Unacceptable software does not guide the user to the correct computations nor warn when the wrong computations are used.

Some software that correctly computes the limits for the Average and Range Chart will compute limits for the *XmR* Chart incorrectly. The simplest way to verify the computations in any program is to use a data set that is nonhomogeneous for which you know the correct limits and see if the software gives you these correct limits.

There are no shades of gray here. This is not a matter of opinion, but a mathematical fact of life. Limits are either computed correctly, or they are computed incorrectly. And limits computed incorrectly are a sign of either ignorance or dishonesty. Let all users of software beware.

3.9 Where Do We Go from Here?

If your data show evidence of nonhomogeneity you cannot consider them to have come from one universe. This will undermine any attempt to use these data to characterize a universe. The question is not what is the process average, or what is the process dispersion, but rather why are these data not homogeneous?

If your data appear to be homogeneous, then you will have already computed the values you need to characterize the universe from which your data were obtained.

Clearly the *XmR* Chart was created for use with observational studies—studies where you examine the stream of data coming from an existing process. It can also be used with fixed and finite data sets obtained as part of a carefully planned study or experiment. The only requirements are that successive values must be logically comparable and that the moving ranges represent the routine background variation. In the case of a structured study or experiment your knowledge of how the data were obtained must be used to apply the *XmR* Chart correctly. Figure 3.6 illustrates what happens when successive values are not logically comparable—the *XmR* Chart can be fooled when it is used to compare apples and oranges.

Before we can consider questions of statistical inference we will need to understand some of the concepts and nomenclature of probability theory. The objective is not to delve deeply, but simply to develop a framework that we can use in discussing the techniques of statistical inference.

Chapter Four

Statistics, Parameters, and Inference

Statistics allow us to characterize collections of values and to examine those collections for homogeneity. When a data set appears to be homogeneous, we can use the data to characterize the underlying process that generated those data. However, because of the multiplicity of statistics we will need the concept of a probability model and its parameters to organize the characterization.

4.1 The Concept of a Probability Model

Assume that we have a process that is producing some product, and assume that periodic checks are made upon some product characteristic. These checks will result in a sequence of values that can be denoted as:

$$\{ X_1, X_2, \dots, X_i, \dots, X_n, \dots \}$$

While the statistics computed from the first n values of this sequence will characterize the n values there are two questions of interest: 1. How well do these statistics characterize the *process* during the time period covered by the n observations? and 2. How well do they predict future performance? Thus, we routinely need to extrapolate from our data to the underlying process or system that produced those data—we extrapolate from the samples that were measured to the outcomes that were not measured, and we extrapolate from the samples that were measured to those outcomes that have not yet occurred. These extrapolations will be credible only when certain conditions exist.

As outlined in Chapter One, the question of homogeneity directly addresses the issue of this extrapolation. If the data have been found to display homogeneity in the past, and if there is no evidence of a lack of homogeneity in the present, then the extrapolation from the data to the underlying process will be credible.

A concept which is useful in characterizing the extrapolation from the data to the underlying process is the concept of a probability model. The journey from a production process to a probability model can be described as shown in Figure 4.1.

When a production process produces a homogeneous set of measurements that process can be said to be reasonably predictable. Such homogeneous measurements from a predictable process will display a stable, consistent, and recurring pattern of variation.

This persistent pattern of variation will be reflected in a stable histogram that does not change appreciably over time. As a consequence, the histogram may be approximated by any one of a number of arbitrary mathematical functions. Such a function defines a probability model and is denoted by the symbol $f(x)$.

Given a probability model which approximates the histogram of a reasonably predictable process, the parameter which will be used to characterize the "process location" is called the *mean* of $f(x)$. The *mean of the distribution of X* describes the balance point (or center of mass) of the probability model. This parameter will be denoted by the Greek letter mu, μ, or by *MEAN(X)* and is defined as:

$$\mu = MEAN(X) = \int_{all\ x} x\, f(x)\, dx$$

Given a probability model which approximates the histogram of a reasonably predictable process, the parameter which will be used to characterize the "process dispersion" is called the *variance* of $f(x)$. The *variance of the distribution of X* describes the rotational inertia of the probability model. This parameter will be denoted by the square of the Greek letter sigma, σ^2, or by *V(X)* and is defined as:

$$\sigma^2 = V(X) = \int_{all\ x} (x - \mu)^2\ f(x)\, dx$$

Another way of characterizing the dispersion of the process is to use the *standard deviation* of $f(x)$. The standard deviation of the probability model is defined as the square root of the variance of X. This parameter is generally denoted as σ or *SD(X)*. The fact that a parameter and a statistic are *both* called the standard deviation is an everlasting source of confusion. In the interest of clarity the statistic s shall always be referred to as the *standard deviation statistic* in this book.

The usage of Greek letters, such as μ and σ, to denote parameters of a probability model is a common convention in statistical notation.

When a process is predictable,
  the measurements from the product stream…
    $X_1, X_2, X_3, X_4, X_5, X_6, X_7, X_8, … X_n, …$
  will display a consistent and predictable amount of variation.

This implies that periodic histograms of the product measurements . . .

will show a consistent pattern of variation,

so that it is possible to *approximate* this pattern of variation . . .

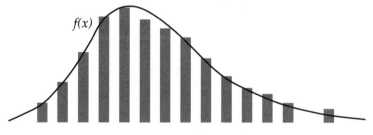

using any one of several mathematical functions, $f(x)$,

which, in turn, may be characterized by parameters . . .

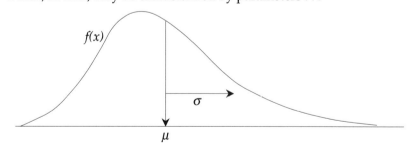

such as the mean, μ, and the standard deviation, σ.

Figure 4.1: The Concept of a Probability Model and Its Parameters

The alternate symbols *MEAN(X), V(X),* and *SD(X)* are also used here because they will provide some additional clarity when working with several different parameters at once.

In contrast to this, Roman letters such as:

$$\bar{X}, R, s, \text{ and } s_n$$

are generally used to denote statistics.

When working with a finite sequence of data we can always compute statistics for location and dispersion. When a process displays a reasonable degree of predictability these measures of location and measures of dispersion may be taken to be estimates of the parameters for some appropriate probability model $f(x)$.

When a process is unpredictable this already tenuous structure falls apart. The unpredictability of the process will result in nonhomogeneous data which will not show a stable and recurring pattern of variation. Therefore, we cannot begin to define a meaningful probability model, $f(x)$, and the notion of the mean and variance of the distribution of X vanishes. Thus, while we may always calculate statistics from the data generated by an unpredictable process, and while these statistics will still describe the historical data after a fashion, they will not be predictive. Such statistics cannot be used to estimate parameters of a probability model because the notion of a probability model for this process is no longer well-defined. The statistics may be used to describe the data, but they cannot be used to extrapolate beyond the data upon which they are based.

This distinction between those situations where we can use statistics to estimate parameters and those situations where we cannot do so is critical to a proper understanding and use of statistical techniques. It also makes it important to distinguish between *statistics* and *parameters*.

Statistics are arithmetic functions of the data. They can be calculated even when the data are a meaningless collection of numbers. The meaning for any statistic can only be derived from the context for the data.

Parameters are descriptive constants for probability models. They exist on the plane of mathematical theory. When it makes sense to use a probability model to approximate reality, we can estimate the parameters for that probability model using the statistics obtained from the data. However, because of the multiplicity of statistics, there are several ways to estimate most of the parameters of a probability model.

Since statistics vary with the data and the parameters for a given model remain constant it is always inappropriate to equate a parameter to a statistic (i.e., do not write any statement of the form [parameter = statistic]). However, since we do use the values of statistics to estimate the value for a parameter it is appropriate to write statements of the form [estimate of parameter = statistic]

In English, the words "average" and "mean" are used interchangeably. In this book the word *average* will be reserved for the *statistic* and the word *mean* will be reserved for the *parameter*.

4.2 Some Cautions Regarding Probability Models

While a probability model, $f(x)$, may be used to approximate the overall pattern of variation for the measurements obtained from a predictable production process, it is merely a mathematical model used for convenience. From the perspective of data analysis there are several things about models and parameters that you should always keep in mind:

1. *The probability model does not generate your data.*

2. While the parameters of the probability model may be used to characterize the "process location" and the "process dispersion" *these parameters are not inherent in the process, but merely part of your approximation to the behavior of the process.*

3. While it is useful to speak about the "process location" and the "process dispersion" for a predictable process, *your data are generated by a process and, like everything in this world, this process is subject to change.*

It is important to also note that the probability model $f(x)$ does not attempt to characterize the time-order sequence for the data. For this reason no model $f(x)$ can be said to be a complete characterization of the process that produced your data. Such models merely attempt to characterize the histogram of the process outcomes.

Probability models and their parameters make it easy to work out theoretical relationships. However, as Walter Shewhart observed, a probability model is a limiting characteristic of an *infinite* sequence of data. It is not a characteristic of any finite portion of that sequence. Therefore, since we shall always have to use finite amounts of data, we can never completely specify a *unique* function $f(x)$ for any process. There will always be some essential arbitrariness connected with the use of any probability model as an approximation for the histogram of data generated by a physical process. For this reason, it is erroneous to think of the parameters of a probability model as the "true values" for process location and process dispersion, or to think that the extreme tails of a probability model will actually describe what you will see in practice.

Another corollary of Shewhart's observation and Item 1 in the list above is that it can never be correct to say that your data follow any particular probability model. While lack-of-fit tests can sometimes identify models that are *inconsistent* with our data, we can never fully specify a unique probability model for any finite data set. Hence, any statement of the form, "These data are normally distributed," can never be anything more than an assumption. So where do probability models get into the act? They are the tools for solving the problem of Probability Theory.

As will be seen in the next section, we can assume that a particular probability model applies and then work out the theoretical relationships that are appropriate for that model. From these relationships we can then develop procedures that are theoretically sound to use with our data. Sometimes these procedures are sensitive to the assumed probability model and sometimes they are not. In either case, the probability models provide a starting point for analysis.

4.3 Elements of Statistical Inference

Probability models are mathematical descriptions of how random samples drawn from a known universe will behave. They define the likelihood of various outcomes in a rigorous manner. By using the properties of these probability models we can develop procedures that are consistent with the laws of probability theory. When we then use these procedures to analyze data we will know that the procedure is mathematically rigorous and reasonable. This keeps us from developing *ad hoc* techniques of analysis that violate the laws of probability theory or that are inappropriate in other ways.

Therefore, probability models are fundamental to the development of sound analysis techniques. We begin with a probability model on the theoretical plane. Using that model we develop some technique or procedure. Then we move from the theoretical plane to the data analysis plane where we use that procedure with our observed values to characterize our data or the process that generated those data.

Since histograms are not, and can never be, the same as the probability models, there will always be some approximation involved in using any statistical procedure. However, if the procedure is theoretically sound, and if it has been proven to be reasonably robust in practice, then we can be confident that our conclusions are reliable.

Clear thinking requires that you always make the distinction between the theoretical plane and the data analysis plane. Probability models and random variables live on the theoretical plane. Histograms and statistics live on the data analysis plane. And statistical inference requires that we jump back and forth between these two planes. This is why a failure to make a distinction between these two planes is the source of much confusion in statistics.

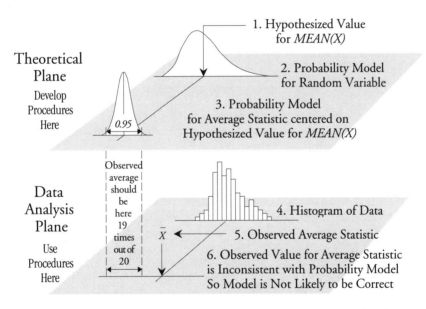

Figure 4.2: The Inductive Inference of a Test of a Hypothesized Value

TESTS OF A HYPOTHESIZED PARAMETER VALUE

One form of statistical inference consists of the examination of some idea about the parameters of a probability model. The argument begins on the theoretical plane with the hypothesized probability model for a random variable and the corresponding probability model for some observable statistic such as the average. Then we find critical values for this second probability model—values which cut off some area in the extreme tails of this distribution. Now we have a procedure we can use: If our original probability model is correct then the average of our observed values should fall between the two critical values in most instances.

Now we shift from the theoretical plane to the data analysis plane. We collect our data, compute our statistic (e.g., the average), and compare this value to the two critical values.

If the statistic falls outside the interval between the two critical values, then we decide that the original probability model is unlikely to be correct. Either the parameter values assumed for the probability model are not right, or else the whole probability model is not right. If we have some prior basis for believing that we have the right probability model, then we can conclude that the hypothesized parameter value is inconsistent with the data.

If the statistic falls within the interval defined by the two critical values we can say that the hypothesized probability model is *one of those models that are consistent with our data*.

Notice the language of the logic here. We can prove that our original assumption is wrong or we can fail to prove that it is wrong: we cannot ever prove that our original assumption is correct. As a result of this we usually formulate the test of a hypothesized value so that the hypothesized value is one that we hope to disprove. Mastering the logic of proof that is part of testing a hypothesized value, and the layers of double negatives which this entails, is another of the hurdles facing students of statistical inference. The careful thinking required and the tortured language are intimidating to many and are not always fully mastered by those who seek to use this form of statistical inference.

For this reason we often turn the inference structure around. Since an inductive inference will usually have many right answers, rather than a single right answer, we might decide to identify a range of parameter values that are consistent with the observed data instead of asking if one particular value is consistent with the data.

INTERVAL ESTIMATES OF A PARAMETER VALUE

To identify such a range of plausible values for *MEAN(X)* we begin with the data and compute the Average. Then, on the theoretical plane, we develop a probability model that is centered on the value of the Average. From this probability model we obtain an expression for random intervals that will bracket the value for *MEAN(X)*

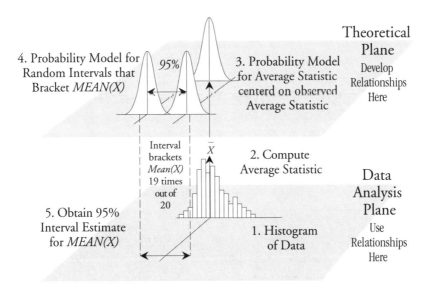

4. Probability Model for Random Intervals that Bracket *MEAN(X)*

95%

3. Probability Model for Average Statistic centerd on observed Average Statistic

Theoretical Plane
Develop Relationships Here

Interval brackets *Mean(X)* 19 times out of 20

$\bar{X}$

2. Compute Average Statistic

Data Analysis Plane
Use Relationships Here

5. Obtain 95% Interval Estimate for *MEAN(X)*

1. Histogram of Data

Figure 4.3: The Inductive Inference of an Interval Estimate

with some specified likelihood [usually denoted as $100(1-\alpha)$%].

When the value of the Average statistic is used to evaluate the expression for this random interval we will have an $100(1-\alpha)$% Interval Estimate for *MEAN(X)*.

This interval estimate will define those parameter values that are consistent with the observed data. While the development is slightly more complex, the application is much easier to use and explain.

Interval estimates differ from tests of a hypothesized value in that their point of departure is the observed statistic rather than some hypothesized value. This makes them easier to use and easier to explain to others. However, the two inference techniques are equivalent: when a hypothesized value does not fall within the interval estimate it can be said to be inconsistent with the observed data. Thus, these two types of statistical inference provide different routes to the same conclusion.

Tests of a hypothesized value may be appropriate in a research setting, but interval estimates are appropriate in both a research setting and in observational studies where we are tracking a phenomenon over time.

Thus, interval estimates are easier to use and have a broader range of application than tests of a hypothesized value. For these reasons I will follow the lead of several other modern authors and use interval estimates as the basic tool of statistical inference. The next two sections will outline the commonly used interval estimates for location and dispersion parameters. Then Section 4.6 will present a practical, unified approach to statistical inference.

4.4 Interval Estimates of Location

As was seen in the previous section, the procedures of statistical inference begin on the theoretical plane with probability models and the relationships between random variables. Then these relationships are used to obtain interval estimates of a parameter value.

This focus on the parameters of a single universe is distinctly different from the question of homogeneity which is concerned with the existence of a single universe. The homogeneity question is essentially nonparametric, while the inferences discussed here are essentially parametric. Once you have decided that the parametric questions make sense for a given data set, techniques like the following will allow you to obtain answers to these questions. This section will focus on parametric inferences concerning a single parameter for location, *MEAN(X)*.

How can we estimate the value of *MEAN(X)*? Once we have satisfied ourselves that the collection of *n* data are reasonably homogeneous and that this question therefore makes sense, it is intuitive that the best point estimate of *MEAN(X)* should be the average of the *n* observations.

$$\text{Estimate of } MEAN(X) \; = \; \overline{X}$$

But how can we describe a range of values for *MEAN(X)* that are consistent with the observed values? To answer this question we proceed as follows. On the mathematical plane we assume that a collection of random variables are independently and identically distributed (homogeneous). The usual probability model used here is the normal distribution having mean μ and standard deviation σ. Next we find the probability model for functions of these random variables.

Let $\overline{X}$ denote the average of *n* independently and identically distributed normal random variables, and let *s* denote the standard deviation statistic computed from these *n* random variables:

$$s \; = \; \sqrt{\frac{\Sigma\,(\,X_i - \overline{X}\,)^2}{n-1}}$$

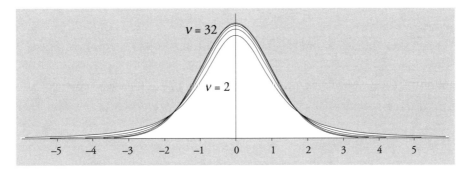

Figure 4.4: Student's *t*-Distribution for 2, 4, 8, 16, and 32 *d.f.*

Then the random variable defined by:

$$t = \frac{\overline{X} - \mu}{s / \sqrt{n}}$$

will follow a Student's *t*-distribution having (*n*-1) degrees of freedom.

Student's *t*-distribution has infinite tails, which means that about all that we can say with certainty is:

$$\text{Probability}\left\{ -\infty < \frac{\overline{X} - \mu}{s / \sqrt{n}} < \infty \right\} = 1$$

Since this is hardly informative, we will need to modify it to make it useful. This is traditionally done by trimming off the most extreme possibilities. By trimming off the most extreme five percent of each tail of the appropriate Student's *t*-distribution we have:

$$\text{Prob}\left\{ -t_{0.05} < \frac{\overline{X} - \mu}{s / \sqrt{n}} < t_{0.05} \right\} = 0.90$$

With a little work on the inequality within the brackets the statement above can be expressed as:

$$\text{Prob}\left\{ \overline{X} - t_{0.05} \frac{s}{\sqrt{n}} < \mu < \overline{X} + t_{0.05} \frac{s}{\sqrt{n}} \right\} = 0.90$$

Thus, the probability that this *random interval* will bracket the process mean is 90 percent. The smaller we make our probability the smaller the interval will be. The interval above is the shortest interval centered on the average that will have a probability of 90 percent.

To this point the argument has been carried out on the theoretical plane. The original values are considered to be observations on random variables which are continuous, independent, and normally distributed. So what happens when we move from the mathematical plane of probability theory down to the data analysis plane where our data are chunky, our histograms are finite, and our data are not generated by a probability model? We use the theoretical relationships above as our guide to practice and compute a 90% Interval Estimate for *MEAN(X)* as:

$$\overline{X} \pm t_{.05} \frac{s}{\sqrt{n}}$$

where $t_{.05}$ is the five percent critical value from a Student's *t*-distribution having *n-1* degrees of freedom. These critical values are given in Appendix Table A.7. In theory, an interval computed in this manner should bracket *MEAN(X)* exactly 90% of the time. Almost a century of practice has shown the interval estimate above to be robust. This means that in practice an interval calculated using the formula above will bracket *MEAN(X) approximately* 90% of the time, more or less.

We will use the data of Table 4.1 to illustrate the construction of interval estimates for *MEAN(X)*. The data of Table 4.1 consist of 500 homogeneous values obtained from Bead Board Number Three while the funnel was centered above bin number 10. These data are reasonably homogeneous—when placed on an Average and Range Chart there are no indications of a lack of homogeneity. Moreover, a histogram involving over 3000 values obtained from this bead board, while the funnel was maintained at the same position, failed to show any detectable departures from a normal probability model. In short, these data are just about as "good" as real data ever get.

If we organize these values into 100 subgroups of size $n = 5$ based on their time-order sequence, we can compute 100 different 90% interval estimates of the process mean. With 4 degrees of freedom, $t_{.05} = 2.132$. Thus our 90% Interval Estiamtes will all have the form:

$$\overline{X} \pm 2.132 \frac{s}{\sqrt{5}}$$

These 90% Interval Estimates are listed in Table 4.1 and shown in Figure 4.5.

Table 4.1: Bead Board No. 3 Data

No.	Values					$\bar{X}$	s	90% Interval Est. μ lower	upper
-1-	12	9	9	8	9	9.4	1.52	7.95	10.85
-2-	11	13	11	11	11	11.4	0.89	**10.55** *	12.25
-3-	14	6	11	8	9	9.6	3.05	6.69	12.51
-4-	10	12	13	8	10	10.6	1.95	8.74	12.46
-5-	11	10	12	11	8	10.4	1.52	8.95	11.85
-6-	7	10	7	7	9	8.0	1.41	6.65	**9.35** *
-7-	12	12	14	7	10	11.0	2.65	8.48	13.52
-8-	11	10	9	10	10	10.0	0.71	9.33	10.67
-9-	9	9	11	11	9	9.8	1.10	8.76	10.84
-10-	11	12	10	9	11	10.6	1.14	9.51	11.69
-11-	9	10	11	11	10	10.2	0.84	9.40	11.00
-12-	9	9	10	11	7	9.2	1.48	7.79	10.61
-13-	7	10	12	11	10	10.0	1.87	8.22	11.78
-14-	8	10	11	9	10	9.6	1.14	8.51	10.69
-15-	10	8	11	12	11	10.4	1.52	8.95	11.85
-16-	11	8	9	11	7	9.2	1.79	7.49	10.91
-17-	9	9	11	11	8	9.6	1.34	8.32	10.88
-18-	12	9	11	10	6	9.6	2.30	7.40	11.80
-19-	12	11	10	15	12	12.0	1.87	**10.22** *	13.78
-20-	9	12	11	9	9	10.0	1.41	8.65	11.35
-21-	13	11	12	7	8	10.2	2.59	7.73	12.67
-22-	9	9	13	8	7	9.2	2.28	7.03	11.37
-23-	10	12	9	11	10	10.4	1.14	9.31	11.49
-24-	8	8	12	10	8	9.2	1.79	7.49	10.91
-25-	9	13	7	10	13	10.4	2.61	7.91	12.89
-26-	11	10	12	10	10	10.6	0.89	9.75	11.45
-27-	11	9	9	8	8	9.0	1.22	7.83	10.17
-28-	11	12	8	12	10	10.6	1.67	9.00	12.20
-29-	11	14	8	13	8	10.8	2.77	8.15	13.45
-30-	14	12	9	9	10	10.8	2.17	8.73	13.87
-31-	9	11	13	10	7	10.0	2.24	7.87	12.13
-32-	10	11	10	12	11	10.8	0.84	10.00	11.60
-33-	9	10	9	13	14	11.0	2.35	8.76	13.24
-34-	12	10	9	8	8	9.4	1.67	7.80	11.00
-35-	9	7	14	12	9	10.2	2.77	7.55	12.85
-36-	9	10	10	11	10	10.0	0.71	9.33	10.67
-37-	11	8	11	9	11	10.0	1.41	8.65	11.35
-38-	12	11	13	8	10	10.8	1.92	8.97	12.63
-39-	9	11	11	11	11	10.6	0.89	9.75	11.45
-40-	13	11	10	7	7	9.6	2.61	7.11	12.09
-41-	10	9	13	10	12	10.8	1.64	9.23	12.37
-42-	8	9	7	10	11	9.0	1.58	7.49	10.51
-43-	7	15	7	8	11	9.6	3.44	6.32	12.88
-44-	11	9	10	11	13	10.8	1.48	9.39	12.21
-45-	10	13	10	9	11	10.6	1.52	9.15	12.05
-46-	12	9	7	13	13	10.8	2.68	8.24	13.36
-47-	9	11	9	10	9	9.6	0.89	8.75	10.45
-48-	8	15	11	10	9	10.6	2.70	8.02	13.18
-49-	7	9	5	12	13	9.2	3.35	6.01	12.39
-50-	10	9	10	11	10	10.0	0.71	9.33	10.67

Table 4.1: Bead Board No. 3 Data

No.	Values					$\bar{X}$	s	90% Interval Est. μ lower	upper
-51-	12	12	10	11	11	11.2	0.84	**10.40** *	12.00
-52-	11	11	12	10	14	11.6	1.52	**10.15** *	13.05
-53-	12	9	12	9	9	10.2	1.64	8.63	11.77
-54-	8	10	14	13	9	10.8	2.59	8.33	13.27
-55-	10	10	10	14	11	11.0	1.73	9.35	12.65
-56-	11	11	8	11	7	9.6	1.95	7.74	11.46
-57-	10	9	11	8	10	9.6	1.14	8.51	10.69
-58-	11	11	10	10	13	11.0	1.22	9.83	12.17
-59-	12	11	5	9	7	8.8	2.86	6.07	11.53
-60-	11	9	9	11	12	10.4	1.34	9.12	11.68
-61-	14	11	14	10	8	11.4	2.61	8.91	13.89
-62-	9	10	10	15	11	11.0	2.35	8.76	13.24
-63-	10	13	7	12	10	10.4	2.30	8.20	12.60
-64-	11	9	12	10	13	11.0	1.58	9.49	12.51
-65-	6	10	11	10	10	9.4	1.95	7.54	11.26
-66-	10	10	11	7	10	9.6	1.52	8.15	11.05
-67-	10	12	12	8	10	10.4	1.67	8.80	12.00
-68-	13	7	11	12	11	10.8	2.28	8.63	12.97
-69-	12	10	7	10	9	9.6	1.82	7.87	11.33
-70-	9	9	9	10	10	9.4	0.55	8.88	**9.92** *
-71-	10	12	11	9	13	11.0	1.58	9.49	12.51
-72-	10	7	11	8	13	9.8	2.39	7.52	12.08
-73-	12	10	9	8	13	10.4	2.07	8.42	12.38
-74-	12	10	11	10	10	10.6	0.89	9.75	11.45
-75-	11	10	12	10	9	10.4	1.14	9.31	11.49
-76-	7	8	12	10	10	9.4	1.95	7.54	11.26
-77-	8	9	11	9	8	9.0	1.22	7.83	10.17
-78-	9	14	12	12	11	11.6	1.82	9.87	13.33
-79-	7	8	9	9	9	8.4	0.89	7.55	**9.25** *
-80-	12	9	10	10	9	10.0	1.22	8.83	11.17
-81-	8	9	9	11	7	8.8	1.48	7.39	10.21
-82-	10	8	12	9	11	10.0	1.58	8.49	11.51
-83-	12	10	10	10	13	11.0	1.41	9.65	12.35
-84-	9	9	10	8	9	9.0	0.71	8.33	**9.67** *
-85-	10	9	7	9	9	8.8	1.10	7.76	**9.84** *
-86-	11	7	5	9	8	8.0	2.24	5.87	10.13
-87-	9	11	11	10	9	10.0	1.00	9.05	10.95
-88-	12	10	13	12	13	12.0	1.22	**10.83** *	13.17
-89-	12	10	11	8	12	10.6	1.67	9.00	12.20
-90-	10	9	12	9	13	10.6	1.82	8.87	12.33
-91-	11	12	9	11	7	10.0	2.00	8.09	11.91
-92-	7	8	13	10	10	9.6	2.30	7.40	11.80
-93-	9	9	8	7	9	8.4	0.89	7.55	**9.25** *
-94-	9	10	11	9	7	9.2	1.48	7.79	10.61
-95-	10	11	11	9	10	10.2	0.84	9.40	11.00
-96-	12	9	13	9	8	10.2	2.17	8.13	12.27
-97-	11	13	11	11	7	10.6	2.19	8.51	12.69
-98-	7	8	9	10	8	8.4	1.14	7.31	**9.49** *
-99-	9	11	12	11	9	10.4	1.34	9.12	11.68
-100-	9	10	9	10	10	9.6	0.55	9.08	10.12

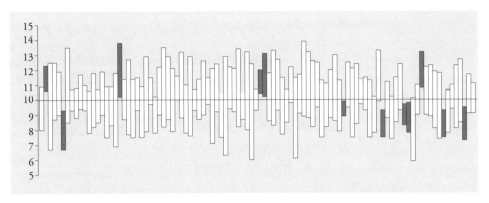

Figure 4.5: 100 90% Interval Estimates of *MEAN(X)* from Table 4.1
Using the Student's *t*-Distribution Method

Eighty-eight of these 100 90% Interval Estimates do contain the process mean of *MEAN(X)* = 10.0. Twelve of these 90% intervals do not contain the value 10. So why did only 88 percent of our 90% Interval Estimates include *MEAN(X)*? Because the value of 90% is a theoretical value that only approximates what happens on the data analysis plane. Theoretical relationships provide a guide for how to actually perform our analysis, but in the end, they are always approximations. Why is this? Because your data will not be generated by a probability model, your histograms will always have finite tails, and your data are never really continuous. So what can we actually say about a 90% Interval Estimate? In practice, we have used a procedure that will result in the shortest intervals centered on the point estimator that will, in theory, bracket the value of the parameter 90% of the time.

- The 90% value defines that proportion of the middle of a probability model that was used to compute the interval.

- The values we get for a 90% Interval Estimate are ***not*** the most likely values for the parameter, rather they define the uncertainty in our point estimate.

- Any interval we may get does ***not*** have a probability of 90% that it will bracket the parameter (each interval is either a hit or a miss, and in practice you will never know which it is).

- The values we get are merely those values that are consistent with the data based on the use of a particular probability model and how much of the model that

we chose to include in our computation of the uncertainty of our point estimate (90%).

The values we get for an interval estimate are the result of a procedure. Change
the model, or change the level of exclusion, and you will get a different interval
estimate from the same data.

The so-called "confidence level" of 90%
tells us nothing about the result—
it simply defines how the interval was computed.

Since 90% Interval Estimates are shorter than 95% Interval Estimates, they are
recommended for general usage by several authors. For example, if we compute one
hundred 95% Interval Estimates for *MEAN(X)* using the data in Table 4.1, 92 of these
100 intervals will actually bracket the value of 10.0, and yet the average length of the
95% Interval Estimates is 30% longer than that for the 90% Interval Estimates. By
accepting the slightly greater risk associated with the 90% Interval Estimates we end
up with substantially shorter intervals.

In the same manner, 99% Interval Estimates will be considerably wider than the
95% Interval Estimates. For Table 4.1 the one hundred 99% Interval Estimates for
MEAN(X) have an average width that is 66% wider than the 95% Interval Estimates,
and 116% wider than the 90% estimates. All of these 99% Interval Estimates do
bracket the value of 10.0, but this improved performance comes with a price tag of
doubling the uncertainty about the value for *MEAN(X)*.

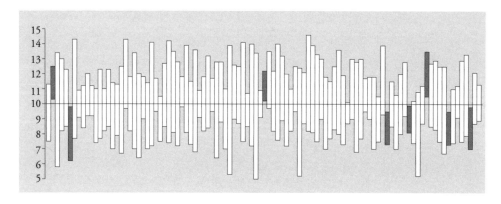

Figure 4.6: 100 95% Interval Estimates of *MEAN(X)* from Table 4.1

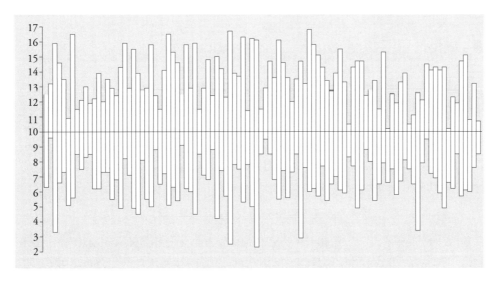

Figure 4.7: 100 99% Interval Estimates of *MEAN(X)* from Table 4.1

In the case of the interval estimates given in this section, the data are just about as perfect as real-world data are ever going to get, and yet the stated probability used to obtain the interval estimate did not match the number of times the interval estimate actually contained the process mean.

Various formulas for interval estimates will be presented throughout this book. In every case the "confidence level" will tell you more about how the interval was computed than it will about the result obtained. The confidence level cannot tell you if your interval actually contains the correct value for the parameter. The "confidence level" of an interval estimate will only give a rough indication of the likelihood that an interval might contain the correct value of the parameter. Therefore, while you might continue to use the terminology of "confidence levels," you should understand that this rather unfortunate terminology applies to the *procedure* rather than the *result*. In the end you simply have a range of values for the parameter computed in a particular manner that are consistent with your data and which have to be interpreted in the context of those data.

4.5 Interval Estimates of Dispersion

How can we estimate the value of $SD(X)$? Once we have satisfied ourselves that the collection of n data are reasonably homogeneous and that this question therefore makes sense, the standard deviation statistic of the n observations, s, is commonly used as a point estimate of $SD(X)$. However, since the variance statistic, s^2, is itself an unbiased estimator of $V(X)$, the standard deviation statistic will always be a biased point estimator of $SD(X)$.

$$\text{Biased Estimator of } SD(X) \;=\; s$$

When s^2 is the variance statistic computed from n independent and identically distributed normal random variables with variance parameter σ^2 the statistic:

$$\chi^2 = \frac{(n-1)\,s^2}{\sigma^2}$$

will follow a Chi-Square distribution having $(n-1)$ degrees of freedom.

The mean of a Chi-Square distribution is equal to its degrees of freedom, while the standard deviation is equal to the square root of the degrees of freedom. Figure 4.8 shows the standardized Chi-Square distributions for 2, 4, 8, 16, and 32 degrees of freedom.

Using the property of independent and identically distributed normal random variables identified above, we can write:

$$\text{Prob}\left\{ \chi^2_{.05} < \frac{(n-1)\,s^2}{\sigma^2} < \chi^2_{.95} \right\} = 0.90$$

where $\chi^2_{.95}$ denotes the 95th percentile and $\chi^2_{.05}$ denotes the 5th percentile for a Chi-Square distribution with $n-1$ degrees of freedom. With a little work on the inequality within the brackets the statement above can be expressed in the following form:

$$\text{Prob}\left\{ \sqrt{\frac{(n-1)\,s^2}{\chi^2_{.95}}} < \sigma < \sqrt{\frac{(n-1)\,s^2}{\chi^2_{.05}}} \right\} = 0.90$$

Under the conditions stated, this *random interval* will bracket the value of σ ninety percent of the time. Therefore, when we shift to the data analysis plane we might compute an interval estimate to characterize the dispersion of a predictable process using:

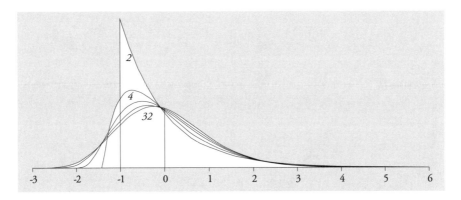

Figure 4.8: Standardized Chi-Square Distributions for 2, 4, 8, 16 and 32 *d.f.*

$$\sqrt{\frac{(n-1)\,s^2}{\chi^2_{.95}}} \;<\; \sigma \;<\; \sqrt{\frac{(n-1)\,s^2}{\chi^2_{.05}}}$$

where s^2 denotes the variance statistic for the n data. The percentiles for Chi-Square distributions may be found in Appendix Table A.8.

When n is large (say $n > 30$) the interval estimate above may be closely approximated by the following:

$$\frac{s\,\sqrt{2n}}{\sqrt{2n}+z_{.05}} \;<\; \sigma \;<\; \frac{s\,\sqrt{2n}}{\sqrt{2n}-z_{.05}}$$

where $z_{.05}$ denotes the upper-tail five percent critical value from a standard normal distribution and s is the standard deviation statistic for the n data.

For the $n = 500$ data of Table 4.1 the standard deviation statistic is 1.814. The five percent critical value for the standard normal distribution is 1.645. Thus we would find a 90% Interval Estimate for the standard deviation of Bead Board No. 3 to be 1.72 to 1.91, based on all 500 data.

For the first subgroup of Table 4.1, consisting of the values {12, 9, 9, 8, 9}, the variance statistic is 2.300. The 0.05 and 0.95 chi-square critical values for 4 degrees of freedom are 0.711 and 9.49. Thus, based on this one subgroup, a 90% Interval Estimate for the standard deviation of Bead Board No. 3 would be 0.98 to 3.60. This interval is wider than the one based on 500 values—with fewer data we have more uncertainty in our estimates.

Continuing in this manner, the 100 subgroups of Table 4.1 yield the interval

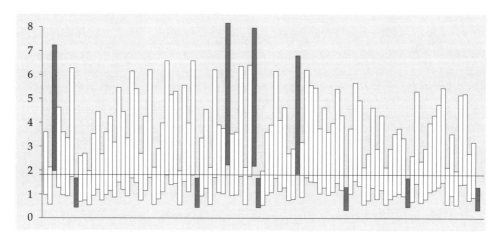

**Figure 4.9: 100 90% Interval Estimates of *SD(X)* from Table 4.1
Using the Chi-Square Distribution Method**

estimates shown in Figure 4.9. Ten of these 100 90% Interval Estimates fail to bracket the point estimate of 1.814.

Parameter values falling within an interval estimate are consistent with the observed data. Parameter values falling outside the interval estimate are inconsistent with the observed data. However, as seen in Figure 4.9, any one interval estimate may fail to bracket the parameter value. The probability used to generate the interval estimate, when subtracted from 1.0, will approximate that proportion of the time that your interval estimate will miss.

4.6 Practical Statistical Inference

So what should we do in practice? Following the lead of others I would like to suggest a simplified approach to parametric inference.

Since both an advocate and a skeptic will usually agree that those parametric values that fall inside a 90% Interval Estimate are consistent with the data, I suggest that you begin with a 90% Interval Estimate and use it as the definition of the basic uncertainty in your point estimate of the parameter value. You (and everyone else) would *fail to reject* any hypothesized values that fall within this 90% Interval Estimate (with an alpha-level of 0.10). These are the parameter values that are most strongly supported by the data.

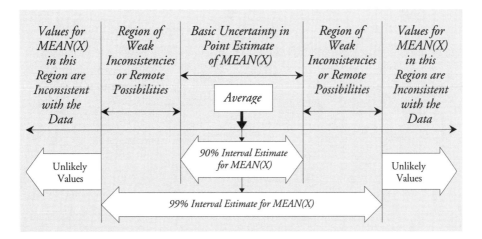

Figure 4.10: Practical Parametric Inference for *MEAN(X)*

Since both an advocate and a skeptic will also usually agree that those parametric values that fall outside a 99% Interval Estimate are definitely inconsistent with the data, I suggest that you next compute a 99% Interval Estimate. Any hypothesized values outside the 99% Interval Estimate will be *rejected* with an alpha-level of 0.01. Virtually everyone will agree that such values are inconsistent with the data.

The only values on which an advocate and a skeptic might disagree are those within the 99% Interval Estimate but outside the 90% Interval Estimate. But since any hypothesized values in this questionable zone will, at most, represent only a weak inconsistency with the data, neither the skeptic nor the advocate should be too dogmatic about these values.

By the time you have computed these two interval estimates, you effectively know the outcome for the test of any particular hypothesized value, and so are prepared to make any statements that need to be made to summarize the analysis of your data.

Using this approach with the first subgroup of Table 4.1 the 90% Interval Estimate for the process mean was 7.95 to 10.85. This range defines our best guess at the value for the process mean based on these data.

A 99% Interval Estimate for the process mean is:

$$\bar{X} \pm t_{0.05}\frac{s}{\sqrt{n}} = 9.4 \pm 2.576\frac{1.52}{\sqrt{5}} = 7.65 \text{ to } 11.15$$

Thus, based on this sample of five measurements, we would say that it is not likely that this process was operating with a mean below 7.65. It is also not likely that this process was operating with a mean above 11.15.

4.7 Interpreting "Degrees of Freedom"

To this point there have been several references to something known as degrees of freedom. These quantities are an integral part of statistical inference because they are most commonly used to define the reference distributions (such as the Chi-Square and Student's t distributions) from which we obtain the critical values for interval estimates. When degrees of freedom are used in this way there is always some formula given that allows you to compute the value for the degrees of freedom. However, since these formulas do not begin to explain what degrees of freedom represent, and since people do not like to use things they do not understand, it is important to take some time to describe what degrees of freedom represent.

Degrees of freedom provide a convenient way to describe the amount of data used by a measure of dispersion and, simultaneously, the coefficient of variation for that measure of dispersion.

But what is a coefficient of variation? Like every other statistic, statistics for dispersion will have a distribution, and these distributions will have their own parameters such as the mean and the standard deviation. In particular, as shown in Appendix Table A.1, the distribution of the standard deviation statistic, s, has:

$$MEAN(s) = c_4\,\sigma \quad \text{and} \quad SD(s) = c_5\,\sigma$$

while the distribution of the range statistic has:

$$MEAN(R) = d_2\,\sigma \quad \text{and} \quad SD(R) = d_3\,\sigma$$

where the bias correction factors c_4, c_5, d_2, and d_3 depend solely upon the amount of data, n, used to compute either s or R; and where σ is the parameter being estimated by the statistics.

The Coefficient of Variation of any statistic is defined to be the standard deviation of that statistic divided by the mean of that statistic. For example, the coefficient of variation for the distribution of the standard deviation statistic is:

$$CV(s) = \frac{SD(s)}{MEAN(s)} = \frac{c_5}{c_4}$$

This ratio will depend solely upon the amount of data used to compute the standard deviation statistic, *s*. In a similar manner, the coefficient of variation for the distribution of the range statistic is:

$$CV(R) = \frac{SD(R)}{MEAN(R)} = \frac{d_3}{d_2}$$

This ratio also depends solely upon the amount of data used to compute the range statistic.

The coefficient of variation is commonly used to characterize the uncertainty in a computed value. Values with a large coefficient of variation are considered to be soft and uncertain. Values with small coefficients of variation will be more reliable. In this case we can use the above coefficients of variation to compare the relative efficiency of *R* and *s*.

It was stated earlier that with small sample sizes the range statistic was essentially as good as the standard deviation statistic. Using the values from Table A.1 we find that for a subgroup of size *n* = 5 the standard deviation statistic will have a coefficient of variation of 0.363, or 36 percent, while the subgroup range will have a coefficient of variation of 0.371, or 37 percent. Thus, for samples of size five the range and the standard deviation statistic contain essentially the same amount of information and have essentially the same amount of uncertainty.

Since the coefficients of variation are functions of the amount of data, and since degrees of freedom are also dependent upon the amount of data, it seems logical that these two quantities might be related to each other. It turns out that for all estimators of *SD(X)* the coefficient of variation can be very closely approximated from the degrees of freedom. In particular, the coefficient of variation for any estimate of *SD(X)* is inversely proportional to the square root of twice the degrees of freedom.

$$C.V. \approx \frac{1}{\sqrt{2 \, d.f.}}$$

This one relationship applies to all estimators of *SD(X)*. (Estimators of *V(X)* have a different relationship.) The relationship above is shown in Figure 4.11. There we see how increased degrees of freedom correspond to reduced uncertainty in our estimates of *SD(X)*. Since this estimate is the foundation of analysis, this curve is a characteristic of all analysis techniques.

Inspection of either the formula or the curve will show that you will have to increase the degrees of freedom four-fold in order to cut the coefficient of variation in

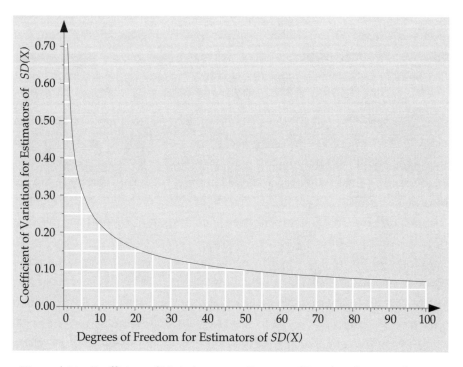

Figure 4.11: Coefficient of Variation versus Degrees of Freedom for Est. of *SD(X)*

half. This non-linear nature of the effect of degrees of freedom is very important.

Clearly the greatest reduction in the coefficient of variation occurs with the first few degrees of freedom. After that we face diminishing returns. Once we have 30 to 40 degrees of freedom, additional degrees of freedom become superfluous. This curve is the basis for using small amounts of data to characterize predictable processes.

Figure 3.10 is the same curve as that shown in Figure 4.11. In Figure 3.10 we saw that limits for process behavior charts based on fewer than 6 degrees of freedom were said to be soft. Limits based on 7 to 12 degrees of freedom were said to have begun to gel. Limits based on 12 to 30 degrees of freedom were said to be solidifying, and limits based on more than 30 degrees of freedom were said to be very solid. Formulas for approximating the degrees of freedom for the limits of a process behavior chart are given in Appendix Tables A.2 to A.6. Using those formulas you can verify that Figures 3.1 and 3.2 have very soft limits while the limits of Figure 3.5 have 21 degrees of freedom.

All other charts in Chapter Three have limits based on 30 or more degrees of freedom.

While we will work with degrees of freedom, we should think in terms of the curve in Figure 4.11 when interpreting what those degrees of freedom mean in practice. While 100 degrees of freedom sound like many more than 50 degrees of freedom, an appreciation of Figure 4.11 will help you to understand that both are more than sufficient to give you very solid limits and reasonable inferences about an underlying predictable process.

4.8 Summary

Statistics are functions of the data. They live on the data analysis plane. Parameters are descriptive constants for a probability model. They live on the theoretical plane. It does not do to confuse statistics and parameters.

Statistical inference involves the use of procedures and relationships developed on the theoretical plane with data and statistics. As such it involves switching back and forth between the theoretical plane and the data analysis plane. Any failure to distinguish between these two planes is likely to result in considerable confusion.

Alpha-levels for tests of hypotheses and confidence levels for interval estimates do not describe any property of the results. They merely characterize the manner in which the procedure was carried out. They describe how you have computed your decision criterion or your interval estimate, but they do not characterize the result of your inference. These numbers are inputs on the theoretical plane, not descriptions of what happened on the data analysis plane.

Since interval estimates are easier to obtain and much easier to explain to others, and since they work in both experimental situations and with observational studies, they will be the primary tool of statistical inference used in this book.

Degrees of freedom characterize the amount of data used by an estimator of *SD(X)* and also the uncertainty in that estimator.

The following chapters will provide a road map for when and how to use both process behavior charts and the traditional techniques of statistical inference to analyze different types of data.

PART TWO

THE TECHNIQUES
OF
DATA ANALYSIS

Part Two provides an overview of those basic techniques of data analysis that will serve for most situations.

Chapters Five through Eight present techniques for analyzing data that consist of measurements of some quantity. Chapter Five looks at data collected under one condition. Chapter Six compares data collected under two conditions. Chapter Seven compares data collected under three or more conditions. And Chapter Eight looks at issues related to the use of simple linear regression.

Chapters Nine through Eleven present techniques for analyzing data that are based on counts. Chapter Nine looks at data based on counts of items when those data are collected under one, two, and three or more conditions. Chapter Ten looks at data based on counts of events when those data are collected under one, two, and three or more conditions. Chapter Eleven presents techniques for analyzing data that consist of counts for three or more categories.

Since analysis consists of both discovery and the communication of those discoveries, these chapters describe both the traditional techniques and alternative approaches that use familiar techniques for analysis. People do not often act on what they do not understand, and the most brilliant analysis is worthless if it is not understood by those who need to take action.

If you torture the data long enough,
they will surrender.

Chapter Five

Data Collected Under One Condition

5.1 What Can We Say About Our Process?

When you have a collection of measurements that were all obtained under what you believe to be one set of conditions, you should begin with a histogram and an *XmR* Chart of these values. These two basic graphs can show you unexpected things in your data that you need to know about in order to perform an appropriate analysis.

If the *XmR* Chart reveals evidence of nonhomogeneity your primary objective should be to identify the cause of the lack of homogeneity.

If the *XmR* Chart does not reveal any evidence of nonhomogeneity, and the histogram does not show any unusual behaviors or any unexpected values, then you may proceed to use the data to characterize the process or system that generated your data.

Questions of interest for a predictable process are outlined below, along with ways to answer these questions.

1. **"What is the process mean?"** Having used a process behavior chart to determine that your data appear to represent a predictable process, the simplest and best estimate of the process mean is the central line from either the X Chart or the Average Chart.

2. **"What is the process variation?"** If all you need is a point estimate of $SD(X)$ you can use either the Average Range divided by d_2 or the Median Range divided by d_4. When either of these chart-based estimates has a reasonable number of degrees of freedom it will be a reliable point estimate.

3. **"What range of process outcomes should we expect in the future from this process under this one set of conditions?"** The Natural Process Limits for the X Chart already estimate this range. If you used an Average and Range Chart to determine that the data are homogeneous, then you will need to compute the Natural Process Limits for your data using the formula: *Grand Average* ± 3 *Sigma(X)*. A knowledge of the Natural Process Limits will naturally lead to questions of process capability. These will be addressed in Chapter 13.

4. **"What range of values for the process mean is consistent with these data?"** A 90% Interval Estimate of *MEAN(X)* will answer this question. These are the values that virtually everyone will agree upon as being consistent with your data. These values can be said to be *not detectably different from the process mean* (even at an exploratory 10% level). In computing this and the following interval estimates it is best to use the global standard deviation statistic, s, called for by the formulas.

5. **"Is the process mean greater than (or less than) some value?"** Those values that fall outside a 99% Interval Estimate for *MEAN(X)* are those values that virtually everyone will agree upon as being inconsistent with your process data. These values can be said to be *detectably different from the process mean* (at a conservative 1% level).

6. **"What range of values for the process variation is consistent with these data?"** A 90% Interval Estimate of *SD(X)* will answer this question.

7. **"Is the process variation greater than (or less than) some value?"** Those values that fall outside a 99% Interval Estimate for *SD(X)* are those values that are inconsistent with your process data. These values can be said to be detectably different from the process variation (at a conservative 1% level).

Of course, the answers to all of these questions should only be applied to the one set of conditions studied. In the case of a pilot program or a process evaluation, this will often be sufficient.

Thus, Questions 1, 2, and 3 are automatically answered by the computations used to construct the *XmR* Chart. Questions 4 through 7 are answered by the practical approach to inference outlined in Section 4.6. It really is this simple when the data have been collected under one condition.

◆ ◆ ◆

The Wire Length Data, given in Table 1.1, has the histogram and *XmR* Chart shown in Figure 5.1. The *XmR* Chart shows no evidence of nonhomogeneity, and the histogram reveals a reasonably well formed mound shape. With nothing out of the ordinary in either graph, it is reasonable to use these data to characterize the underlying process as follows.

1. **The Average of 109.19 is our best point estimate of the process average.**

2. **The *Sigma(X)* value of 2.85, with 61 degrees of freedom, is a reasonably good estimate of the process dispersion.**

The *mR* Chart gives us: *Sigma(X)* = 3.21/1.128 = 2.85. From Table A.2 this value is found to have 0.62(99) = 61 degrees of freedom. The global standard deviation statistic of *s* = 2.86, has 99 degrees of freedom. Recall that (from Figure 4.11) 99 *d.f.* is only slightly better than 61 *d.f.* (The coefficient of variation for *Sigma(X)* is 9.0% while that for the *s* statistic is 7.1%.)

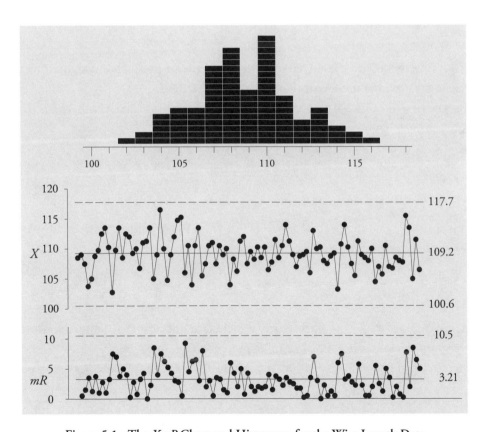

Figure 5.1: The *XmR* Chart and Histogram for the Wire Length Data

3. **The range of process outcomes that we should expect in the future from this process under this one set of conditions is given by the Natural Process Limits from the X Chart: 100.6 to 117.7.**

As three-sigma limits, these two values should bracket virtually all of the process outcomes (99 percent or more) as long as the process remains unchanged. Of course, if a boundary condition falls within these two values the boundary would take precedence. However, since the histogram does not show any evidence of the existence of such a barrier with these data, it is reasonable to use both Natural Process Limits in this case.

In many instances, by the time you have a point estimate of the process location, a point estimate of the process dispersion, and Natural Process Limits for a predictable process, you will know what you wanted to know, and your analysis will be complete. Natural Process Limits may be compared to specification limits, and the estimates of the process average and dispersion will facilitate other computations you may wish to make. You do not have to use all the analysis tools on every data set.

4. **Allowing for 90% of the uncertainty attached to our point estimate, the process mean is estimated to be within one-half unit of 109.2.**

For Data Set Two the global standard deviation statistic is $s = 2.862$ with 99 *d.f.* Thus the 90% Interval Estimate for the process mean is:

$$\bar{X} \pm t_{.05} \frac{s}{\sqrt{n}} \quad = \quad 109.19 \pm 1.645 \frac{2.862}{\sqrt{100}} \quad = \quad 108.72 \text{ to } 109.66$$

Values for the process mean in this interval are consistent with the process data.

5. **It is unlikely that the process mean is less than 108.45 or greater than 109.93.**

The 99% Interval Estimate for the process mean for Data Set Two is:

$$\bar{X} \pm t_{.005} \frac{s}{\sqrt{n}} \quad = \quad 109.19 \pm 2.576 \frac{2.862}{\sqrt{100}} \quad = \quad 108.45 \text{ to } 109.93$$

6. **Allowing for 90% of the uncertainty attached to our point estimate, the process standard deviation is estimated to be between 2.56 and 3.24.**

The 90% Interval Estimate for the process standard deviation for Data Set Two is:

$$\frac{s \sqrt{2n}}{\sqrt{2n} \pm z_{.05}} \quad = \quad \frac{2.862 \sqrt{200}}{\sqrt{200} \pm 1.645} \quad = 2.56 \text{ to } 3.24$$

To reduce this uncertainty in the estimate of the standard deviation will require a greater amount of data.

7. **Values for the process standard deviation that fall below 2.42, or above 3.50, are inconsistent with these data.**

The 99% Interval Estimate for the process standard deviation for Data Set Two is:

$$\frac{s \sqrt{2n}}{\sqrt{2n} \pm z_{.005}} = \frac{2.862 \sqrt{200}}{\sqrt{200} \pm 2.576} = 2.42 \text{ to } 3.50$$

We have now answered the seven basic inferential questions about the process that produced the Wire Length Data.

- We estimate that this process has an average of 109.2 ± 0.5, and a standard deviation of 2.85 −0.3/+0.4.

- We expect about two-thirds of the process outcomes to be in the interval 109.2 ± 2.85 ≈ 106.3 to 112.1.

- We expect about 95% of the process outcomes to fall in the interval 109.2 ± 2(2.85) ≈ 103.4 to 115.0.

- Virtually all of the process outcomes will fall between 100.5 and 117.9.

- We can be reasonably certain that the process average is not below 108.5, nor is it above 109.9.

- We can also be reasonably sure that the process variation is not greater than 3.5, nor is it less than 2.4.

What more do you need to know about the length of wires produced by this process? Between the histogram, the process behavior chart, and these summary statements you will have a very complete summary of the performance of this process.

5.2 But What About the Significance Levels?

When we talk about significance levels for a test of hypothesis we commit two lies with two words. When a statistician says significant what he or she means is "detectable." When a test statistic exceeds its critical value we have detected a difference between the hypothesized value and the summary statistic used. Since the common usage for the word "significant" applies to the practical importance of the result, rather to the fact of whether or not we can detect the result, we can easily appear to be lying with statistics when we start to talk about "statistical significance." Hence, the absence of these words throughout this book.

But then what about the alpha-levels? In the manual version of testing hypotheses we had to choose a critical value to use in the comparison. We would choose an alpha-level and then find the corresponding critical value. These alpha-levels were simply an indication of how conservatively we approached the decision problem. In practice, it is only when the signals are small, relative to the noise, that the alpha-level is of any import. When the signals are strong, relative to the noise, the test statistics will so far exceed the critical values that our choice of alpha-level becomes immaterial. So if you need to be concerned about the alpha-level, you do not have really strong signals.

The objective here is not to calculate probabilities, but to make decisions, and this approach to practical inference allows you to make rational decisions that are consistent with the data. In science and in industry the most reliable confirmatory tool is the nontrivial replication of results, not the significance level of the result. Since Six Sigma programs are about improving production, you should have plenty of data to confirm whether or not you have made things better. If you haven't, it doesn't matter what your alpha-level was. If you have, then it also doesn't matter what your alpha-level was.

5.3 Bead Board No. 3

Table 4.1 listed 500 observations from Bead Board No. 3. The first 25 of these values, along with their summary statistics, are given in Table 5.1. These data result in the histogram and Average and Range Chart shown in Figure 5.2, where we find no evidence of a lack of homogeneity.

The Average Range is 4.60. Using the formula from Table A.1 we get:

$$Sigma(X) = 4.60/2.326 = 1.978.$$

From Table A.3 we see that with $k = 5$ subgroups of size $n = 5$ this value has 18 degrees of freedom.

Since the data display no evidence of a lack of homogeneity we expect the global standard deviation statistic, s, to be similar to $Sigma(X)$, and it is: $s = 1.904$ with 24 degrees of freedom.

1. Our point estimate of the process mean is 10.28.

2. As a simple point estimate of the process standard deviation we can use either the value of *Sigma(X)* = 1.98 or the value of *s* = 1.90.

3. An estimate of the expected range of process outcomes is:

$$10.28 \pm 3\,(1.90) = 4.6 \text{ to } 16.0 \text{ or } 5 \text{ to } 16$$

4. The basic uncertainty in our estimate of the process mean is ± 0.6:

$$\bar{X} \pm t_{.05}\frac{s}{\sqrt{n}} = 10.28 \pm 1.645\frac{1.904}{\sqrt{25}} = 9.65 \text{ to } 10.91$$

5. A 99% Interval Estimate for the process mean is:

$$\bar{X} \pm t_{.005}\frac{s}{\sqrt{n}} = 10.28 \pm 2.58\frac{1.904}{\sqrt{25}} = 9.30 \text{ to } 11.26$$

Values for the process mean that are below 9.30 are inconsistent with these data. Values for the process mean that are above 11.26 are also inconsistent with these data.

Table 5.1: Five Subgroups from the Bead Board No. 3 Data

Subgroup No.	Observed Values					$\bar{X}$	R
-1-	12	9	9	8	9	9.4	4
-2-	11	13	11	11	11	11.4	2
-3-	14	6	11	8	9	9.6	8
-4-	10	12	13	8	10	10.6	5
-5-	11	10	12	11	8	10.4	4

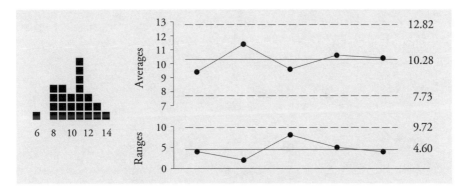

Figure 5.2: Histogram and Average and Range Chart for Table 5.2

6. The basic uncertainty in our estimate of the process standard deviation is −0.36/+0.60:

$$\sqrt{\frac{(n-1)\,s^2}{\chi^2_{.05}}} \; < \; \sigma \; < \; \sqrt{\frac{(n-1)\,s^2}{\chi^2_{.95}}} \; = \; 1.54 \ \text{to} \ 2.50$$

7. A 99% Interval Estimate for the process standard deviation is:

$$\sqrt{\frac{(n-1)\,s^2}{\chi^2_{.005}}} \; < \; \sigma \; < \; \sqrt{\frac{(n-1)\,s^2}{\chi^2_{.995}}} \; = \; 1.38 \ \text{to} \ 2.96$$

Thus, values for the process standard deviation below 1.38 and values above 2.96 are inconsistent with these data.

By answering these seven questions we have a good idea about the parametric values for this predictable process. Consider how these estimates, based on 25 values, stack up against the complete data set of 500 values shown in Figure 5.3.

- Using 25 values we estimated the process mean to be 10.28 ± 0.6. Using all 500 values in Table 4.1 we find an average of 10.08.

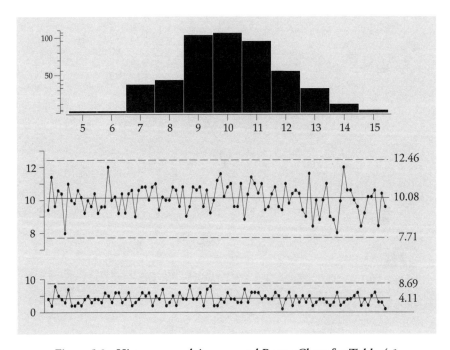

Figure 5.3: Histogram and Average and Range Chart for Table 4.1

- Using 25 values we estimated the process standard deviation to be about 1.90, with our uncertainty placing it in the range of 1.54 to 2.50. Using all 500 values in Table 4.1 we find a global standard deviation statistic of 1.814.

- Using 25 values we would predict that about two-thirds of the values should fall within the interval 10.28 ± 1.90 = 8.38 to 12.18 or 9 to 12. In Figure 5.3 a total of 363 values occur at 9, 10, 11, or 12, which is 73%.

- Using 25 values we would predict that around 95% of the values should fall within the interval 10.28 ± 2(1.90) = 6.48 to 14.08 or 7 to 14. In Figure 5.3 a total of 481 values occur at these values which is 96% of the values.

- Using 25 values we predicted that virtually all of the process outcomes would fall within the interval 4.6 to 16.0. The 500 values of Figure 5.3 range from 5 to 15.

Since the Average and Range Chart shown in Figure 5.3 shows no evidence of a lack of homogeneity, it is reasonable to use all 500 data to characterize Bead Board No. 3. As an exercise use all 500 data to answer the seven questions about the process listed below.

For the 100 Subgroups of size $n = 5$ in Figure 5.3: the Average Chart shows the Grand Average to be 10.084; the Range Chart shows the Average Range to be 4.11 and this statistic has 362 degrees of freedom. The global standard deviation statistic is 1.814 with 499 degrees of freedom.

1. What is an estimate of the process mean?

2. What is an estimate of the process variation?

3. What range of process outcomes should we expect in the future from this process under this one set of conditions?

4. What range of process means are consistent with these data?

5. Is the process mean detectably greater than (or detectably less than) some value?

6. What range of values for the process variation is consistent with these data?

7. Is the process variation detectably greater than (or detectably less than) some value?

So what did we gain by using all 500 data as compared with using the first 25 data? The point estimates did not change appreciably, but the interval estimates got dramatically tighter. A *twenty-fold* increase in the amount of data resulted in *five-fold* reductions in the width of the 90% interval estimates for the process mean and the process standard deviation!

Here we see the law of diminishing returns in action. In different forms we continually bump into the curve shown in Figure 4.11. The first 10 degrees of freedom allow our estimates to congeal. The next 20 degrees of freedom allow them to solidify. After that, additional data will only improve our estimates very slowly.

Of course, the only reason that the 25 data and the 500 data told the same story is that these data are homogeneous and the underlying process is predictable. Without a reasonable degree of homogeneity all of the computations above would be worthless.

5.4 The Data for NB10

Around 1940 the National Bureau of Standards obtained a ten-gram weight made out of chrome-steel alloy. This weight was designated as NB10 and was weighed once a week.

The values in Table 5.2 consist of 100 consecutive weighings, performed by a Mr. Almer or a Mrs. Jones, at the Bureau during 1962 and 1963. All weighings were made on the same instrument, in the same room, using the same procedure. All factors known to affect the results, such as air pressure and temperature, were held as constant as possible. Since NB10 seems to weigh a little bit less than a full 10 grams the values in Table 5.1 are number of *micrograms* by which the weight of NB10 exceeds 9.999 grams or 9,999,000 micrograms. The values are in time order by column.

Table 5.2: 100 Weighings of NB10 (9,999,xxx micrograms)

1-10	11-20	21-30	31-40	41-50	51-60	61-70	71-80	81-90	91-100
591	602	592	597	595	596	596	588	592	599
600	597	601	600	591	594	595	594	594	593
594	593	601	590	601	593	608	591	599	588
601	598	598	599	598	595	593	600	588	625
598	599	601	593	593	589	594	592	607	591
594	601	603	577	594	590	596	596	563	594
599	600	593	594	587	590	597	599	582	602
597	599	599	594	591	590	592	596	585	594
599	595	601	598	596	599	596	592	596	597
597	598	599	595	598	598	593	594	599	596

First, we need to know if these values are homogeneous. In this case, since NB10 is presumably not changing the repeated measurements provide a check on the measurement process. An instrument that can determine the weight of a ten-gram item (approximately the weight of two nickels) to one part in ten million is a very high-precision instrument! But are these scales operated consistently and predictably over time?

The X Chart limits in Figure 5.4 are based on all the observations and the Median Moving Range value of 4.0. There are five, and possibly six, excursions in these data.

- Weeks 21 to 26 show a run of 4 out of 5 values more than one sigma above the central line.
- Week 36 had an exceptionally low value.
- Weeks 55 to 58 show a run of four successive values more than one sigma below the central line.
- Week 63 shows a value that is right on the upper limit.
- The high value in Week 85, followed by three low values, looks like a classic example of over-adjustment.
- Finally, Week 94 is another signal of a problem with this measurement system.

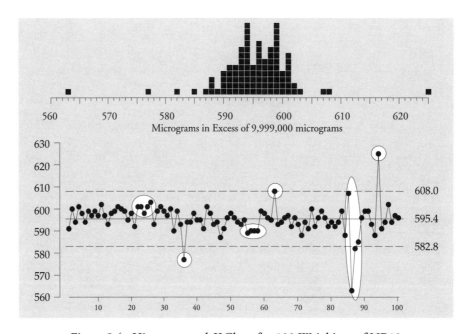

Figure 5.4: Histogram and *X* Chart for 100 Weighings of NB10

Each of these excursions presented an opportunity for the Bureau of Standards to learn how to perform this operation better. There is no evidence that they took advantage of any of these opportunities. They were not operating this measurement system up to its full potential. While the limits approximate the potential for the measurement process, the actual performance falls short of this potential.

In addition, if we assume that NB10 was *certified* to be 10 grams, the *X* Chart suggests that the *measurement system* used by the U. S. Bureau of Standards is likely to differ from the one used to certify NB10 by approximately 400 micrograms—even when it is operated predictably.

The unpredictable nature of the measurement process makes the use of the NB10 data to compute interval estimates highly questionable. Which portion of the data would you use? Which period of operation would the estimates be characterizing? Do they seem to be performing this measurement with greater consistency at the end of this two-year period than they did at the beginning?

In one textbook these data were used to illustrate the technique of removing *outliers* from the data prior to computing estimates of the process parameters. The absurdity of this approach is revealed by the X Chart. While we can reasonably state that the bias of this measurement system is approximately 400 micrograms, we cannot put too fine a point on this number since we have concrete evidence that the measurement system has been operated differently at various times.

Thus, since a lack of homogeneity for the data will undermine our ability to answer the seven questions outlined at the beginning of this chapter, any attempt to compute estimates prior to checking for homogeneity is equivalent to the old joke about "Ready, Fire, Aim!"

5.5 Summary

If your data have been collected under one condition, yet are not homogeneous, then you have multiple universes. When this happens your data may provide a description of the past, but they will not provide a rational basis for characterizing what to expect in the future.

If your data have been collected under one condition and are homogeneous, then you may use those data to characterize the underlying process. The characteristics of interest are usually:

- a point estimate of process location;
- a point estimate of process dispersion;
- an estimate of the range of process outcomes to expect in practice.

In addition we will sometimes also want to add to our list the following:

- a characterization of the basic uncertainty in the estimate of location (based on a 90% Interval Estimate for the mean);

- a characterization of those values for process location that are inconsistent with the data (using a 99% Interval Estimate for the mean);

- a characterization of the basic uncertainty in the estimate of dispersion (based on a 90% Interval Estimate for the standard deviation);

- a characterization of those values for process dispersion that are inconsistent with the data (using a 99% Interval Estimate for the standard deviation).

Once you have the information above, you will have extracted virtually all of the useful information that you can obtain from the data. The rest of the job of data analysis consists of interpreting this information in the context of the data.

Once we have characterized our process as operating predictably or unpredictably we know whether or not it makes sense to use the numerical summaries to characterize the underlying process.

If we have a predictable process, knowledge of the process location and the process dispersion will be sufficient to tell us what to expect from this process in the absence of any process changes.

Knowledge of the uncertainty in our estimates of location and dispersion will allow us to understand and express the limitations on our estimates and to identify those process parameter values that are *inconsistent* with our data.

Further analysis of our data collected under one condition will be more of an exercise in computation than a voyage of discovery. For example, estimates of the so-called shape parameters are notoriously unreliable, and using them to custom-fit a probability model to your data will not tell you any more about your process behavior than you can learn from the simple histogram. In fact such fitted curves are often more misleading than helpful since the probability model does not generate your data. While an ungrouped histogram is a fact of life, a fitted model is merely a mathematical abstraction that may or may not be appropriate.

As was pointed out in the previous chapter, we use probability models to develop procedures to use in data analysis. This is distinctly different from trying to figure out which probability model might approximate our histogram of data. Probability models are important in theory. They do not have a direct role in actually performing the analysis.

BOX AND WHISKER PLOTS

Another graphic technique that is found in many statistics textbooks is the box and whisker plot. This plot uses five summary statistics to represent a data set in a stylized manner. These five statistics are the minimum, the lower quartile, the median, the upper quartile, and the maximum. The plot usually consists of a box drawn between the quartiles to represent the middle 50% of the data, with the median value shown as a line through this box, and with two whiskers attached to the ends of the box to represent the upper and lower 25% portions of the data. If the summary statistics are to be more than a trivial reexpression of the data you will need to have a healthy number of observations in the data set before this plot is appropriate. (Why draw a box and whisker plot when you could easily plot all of the data with less effort?)

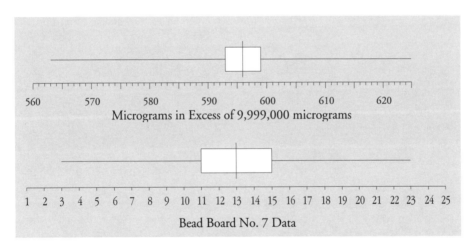

Figure 5.5: Box and Whisker Plots for NB10 and Bead Board No. 7

The box and whisker plots for the 100 values of the NB10 data and the 200 values of the bead Board No. 7 Data are shown in Figure 5.5. Recall that both of these data sets are not homogeneous. While we might be tempted to compare the length of the whiskers to the width of the box, such comparisons cannot be relied upon to tell you if a data set is homogeneous. In fact, all box and whisker plots implicitly assume that the data are homogeneous, and yet the box portion gives greater visual weight to the middle 50% of the data while the whiskers tend to make the outer 50% of the data vanish. This differential treatment of data that are assumed to be homogeneous has never seemed to make much sense to this author. The box and whiskers plot may have been easier to create than a histogram when things were done by hand, but with computer generated graphics this simplification does not seem to serve any useful purpose.

Finally, since box and whisker plots do not provide any basis or context for performing an analysis of the data they must be considered to be descriptive graphic techniques. While it may well make sense to occasionally use numerical summaries to describe our data, it seems a bit excessive to discard the data entirely in order to draw a graph to represent those data using nothing but some summary statistics.

Chapter Six

Data Collected Under Two Conditions

The usual purpose for collecting data under two different sets of conditions is to make a comparison between the outcomes associated with the two sets of conditions. We want to know if the two different conditions can be said to have outcomes with different averages, or if their outcomes have different amounts of variation, or both. Unfortunately, since two data sets will always have different averages and different standard deviations, even when they are collected under the same set of conditions, we cannot simply compare the statistics for the two sets of values. We have to have a difference that is greater than can be attributed to chance before we can say that the two conditions are different. And this is the origin of Axiom 8 given in Chapter One: You must *detect* a difference before you can legitimately *estimate* that difference, and only then can you *assess the practical importance* of that difference.

There are many different ways of detecting a difference between two collections of values. Since the best analysis is the simplest analysis that provides the needed insight, and since the various techniques for detecting differences differ in sensitivity and complexity, we will begin with the simplest and work our way up to the most sensitive.

6.1 Detecting a Difference with Histograms

The simplest way to compare two conditions is to draw two histograms (using ungrouped or minimally grouped data). If these two histograms do not overlap, and if each histogram contains at least 20 values, then it is safe to say that the two conditions are detectably different. In fact this condition is strong enough to be used in reverse to *define* two conditions that are different even if they might have been thought to be the same.

An example of this is seen in the data of Table 6.1. These values are the counts of the number of blemishes per roll for 50 consecutive rolls produced on one line. For these 50 rolls we might compute an average number of blemishes per roll of 29.16,

Table 6.1: Numbers of Blemishes per Roll

Roll	1	2	3	4	5	6	7	8	9	10	11	12	13	14	15	16	17
Count	33	37	24	35	22	23	25	23	32	34	33	37	26	36	35	23	26

Roll	18	19	20	21	22	23	24	25	26	27	28	29	30	31	32	33	34
Count	22	33	36	38	22	21	23	35	26	35	24	33	21	35	27	26	25

Roll	35	36	37	38	39	40	41	42	43	44	45	46	47	48	49	50
Count	24	23	34	35	34	21	23	34	30	22	25	35	36	37	34	25

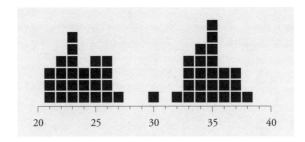

Figure 6.1: The Number of Blemishes per Roll

and a global standard deviation statistic of $s = 5.808$. However, when we plot these 50 counts in a simple histogram we find that they clearly represent two different things.

With no further information you can, at this point, claim that there are two different modes of operation occurring with this line. Moreover the global average of 29.16, and the global standard deviation statistic of $s = 5.8$ do not begin to characterize either one of the two distinct processes that are operating on this one line.

Without a graph to guide you, you can easily compute meaningless numerical summaries.

Another example of how a histogram can provide clues to the presence of two conditions is the histogram of the Hot Metal Delivery Times shown in Figure 2.8 and reproduced here as Figure 6.2. Here there are *at least* two different conditions present. The upper 23 values do not appear to belong to the same histogram defined by the lower 118 values. The trips taking over 95 minutes to complete are clearly different from the bulk of trips taking about one hour or less. Yet the average delivery time is 59.9 minutes! One glance at this histogram and the question shifts from "What is the average?" to "Why does this difference exist?" No further analysis is needed to prove that there is a difference.

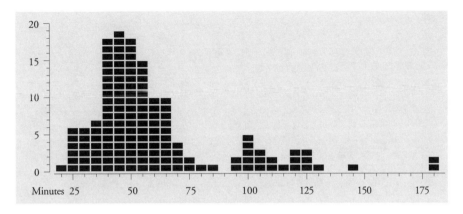

Figure 6.2: The Hot Metal Delivery Times Data

When a data set consisting of a reasonable number of values contains differences that are dramatic enough to create non-overlapping mounds on a histogram it is no stretch to say that the distinct mounds represent different conditions.

6.2 Detecting a Difference with *XmR* Charts

For the sake of clarity say that we have n_1 observations collected under Condition One and n_2 observations collected under Condition Two. The easiest way to compare these two conditions is to use two *XmR* Charts. Here we place the observations for each condition on a single *XmR Chart* with limits computed for each condition separately.

- If Condition One has one or more points outside the limits for Condition Two, then the two conditions are detectably different.

- If Condition Two has one or more points outside the limits for Condition One, then the two conditions are detectably different.

- If either condition shows points outside its own limits we have evidence of nonhomogeneity which deserves to be investigated.

- If none of the above happens then we have only failed to detect a difference; we have not proved the two conditions to be the same.

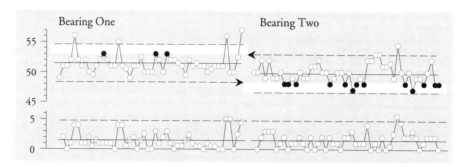

Figure 6.3 *XmR* Charts for Comparing Bearings One and Two

As an example, consider the data for Camshaft Bearing Diameters One and Two, given in Table 2.4. The *XmR* Charts for these two sets of values is shown in Figure 6.3. Bearing One has an Average of 51.46 and an Average Moving Range of 1.49 units. Bearing Two has an Average of 49.78 and an Average Moving Range of 1.51 units. Even though both bearings have points outside their own limits, Figure 6.3 shows that there is also a detectable difference in the average diameters for Bearings One and Two. While the exceptional values for each bearing show that these processes are being operated erratically, both bearings show periods of consistent operation as well. The basis for saying that the two bearing processes have detectably different averages is not the exceptional values from each bearing, but rather the three routine values for Bearing One that exceed the upper limit for Bearing Two and the thirteen routine values for Bearing Two that fall below the lower limit for Bearing One. In addition, the Moving Range Charts show that the two bearing processes have essentially the same amount of variation.

Given a detectable difference in averages along with the unpredictable operation, a reasonable estimate of the amount by which the two bearing processes differ can be obtained by comparing their medians: (51 – 50) = 1 unit. Thus we have detected a difference between these two process averages that amounts to one ten-thousandth of an inch.

◆ ◆ ◆

The advantages of using an *XmR* Chart to make comparisons are simplicity of technique, the power of having a picture to show when presenting your results, the ability to detect the flaws in the data, and the ability to carry out a reasonable analysis in spite of those flaws.

◆ ◆ ◆

To further illustrate the use of the *XmR* Chart in making comparisons consider comparing Bearing Two and Bearing Three. Bearing Three has an Average of 48.20 units and an Average Moving Range of 2.67 units. The chart is shown in Figure 6.4.

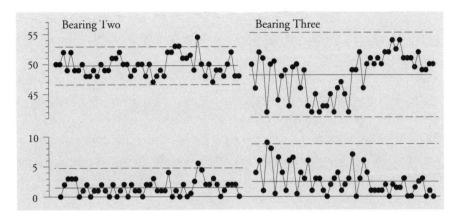

Figure 6.4: *XmR* **Charts for Comparing Bearings Two and Three**

Bearing Three has only one moving range outside the limits, yet we cannot claim that the Bearing Three process is operating predictably. The runs of 12 and 19 successive values on the *X* Chart and the large swings at the start of the chart all combine to show a process that is very unpredictable. This makes the comparison of *process parameters* highly questionable. (What number would you use to characterize the "location" of the Bearing Three Process? The Average of 48.2 can hardly be said to characterize the last 19 values.)

Overall, Figure 6.4 makes it clear that the process for Bearing Three is not operating with the same consistency as the process for Bearing Two. The two conditions are definitely different, but these differences are not easily quantified by comparing averages or comparing variation. The graph shows the *qualitative* difference that we need to know about while all of our numerical summaries fail to capture the essence of this difference.

◆ ◆ ◆

The use of *XmR* Charts to make comparisons will allow you to detect all but the smallest of any detectable differences that exist. It will allow you to show those differences to others. It will allow you to assess the degree of homogeneity within the data sets, and it will allow you to make qualitative as well as quantitative comparisons. If you fail to detect a difference between two homogeneous data sets using the *XmR* Chart, then you may go on to use other techniques of statistical inference, but in practice you will rarely need to do so.

6.3 Using an Average and Range Chart

The use of the *XmR* Chart will be most satisfactory when you have more than 10 observations for each condition. With fewer values it will become increasingly difficult to detect a lack of homogeneity within either category.

If you are willing to assume that the data for each condition are homogeneous, and if you have the same amount of data for each condition (that is $n_1 = n_2$), then you could use an Average and Range Chart to compare the location and dispersion of the outcomes for the two conditions.

◆ ◆ ◆

Table 6.2 contains two subgroups of size five from Table 4.1. When we place these two subgroups of size $n = 5$ on an Average and Range Chart we get Figure 6.5.

Table 6.2: Two Subgroups from Bead Board No. 3

						Average	Range	Variance
Subgroup 71	10	12	11	9	13	11.0	4	2.50
Subgroup 72	10	7	11	8	13	9.8	6	5.70

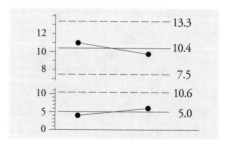

Figure 6.5: Average and Range Chart for Table 6.2

Figure 6.5 shows no detectable difference between these two data sets, which is appropriate since they were both collected from the same process during a period of predictable operation (see Figure 5.3 for the Average and Range Chart using all the data from Bead Board No. 3).

Average and Range Charts having fewer subgroups than the number of data within a subgroup will be very conservative (that is, when $k < n$). This means that when we use an Average and Range Chart to compare two conditions false alarms will be very, very rare. Therefore, those differences that we detect will tend to be real.

The effective alpha-levels for Average and Range Charts used with finite amounts of data (as opposed to an ongoing stream of data) are listed in Tables A.9 and A.10 in the Appendix. These values are the theoretical probabilities that you will have a false alarm on such a chart. From Table A.9 we find that the Average Chart in Figure 6.5 has an alpha-level of 0.003. This means that only about 3 charts in 1000 such charts (with $k = 2$, $n = 5$) will have a false alarm.

With only two subgroups the Range Chart can detect differences in dispersion only when the subgroup size exceeds $n = 6$.

Whenever the subgroup size exceeds $n = 15$ the Standard Deviation Chart will be a more sensitive chart for examining dispersion than the Range Chart will be.

The data of Table 6.3 will be used to illustrate using both an XmR Chart and an Average Chart for making comparisons. The first 20 values were collected under Condition One and have an Average of 11.05 and an Average Moving Range of 2.42. The second set of 20 values were collected under Condition Two and have an Average of 14.30 and an Average Moving Range of 2.16. Are these two conditions detectably different?

Table 6.3: The First Forty Values from Bead Board No. 7

Condition One:	9	14	9	12	10	11	7	9	12	13
	14	11	10	14	12	11	11	10	13	9
Condition Two:	14	17	17	13	13	12	14	16	15	18
	12	14	17	12	11	13	15	16	14	13

We begin by placing these 40 values on an XmR Chart with two sets of limits. The chart is shown in Figure 6.6. Each X Chart has one point outside the limits for the other condition. Thus we find a detectable difference between the averages for Conditions One and Two and no detectable difference in dispersion between the two conditions. Our best estimate of the difference between the averages for these two conditions is $14.3 - 11.05 = 3.25$ units.

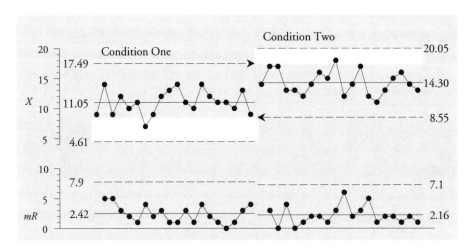

Figure 6.6: *XmR* Charts for Comparing Conditions in Table 6.3

If we use an Average and Standard Deviation Chart to compare these two conditions we would have $k = 2$ and $n = 20$. Condition One has an average of 11.05 and a
standard deviation statistic of $s = 1.959$. Condition Two has an average of 14.30 and a
standard deviation statistic of $s = 2.003$. Therefore, the Grand Average is 12.675, and
the Average Standard Deviation Statistic is 1.981. From Table A.5 we find:

$$Upper\ Average\ Limit = 12.675 + 0.680\,(1.981) = 14.02$$
$$Lower\ Average\ Limit = 12.675 - 0.680\,(1.981) = 11.33$$
$$Upper\ Std.\ Dev.\ Limit = 1.49\,(1.981) = 2.95$$
$$Lower\ Std.\ Dev.\ Limit = 0.51\,(1.981) = 1.01$$

The chart in Figure 6.7 tells the same story as that in Figure 6.6. Both charts just
barely show a detectable difference between the averages for the two conditions, and
no detectable difference in dispersion. Table A.9 does not go out to cover $n = 20$, but

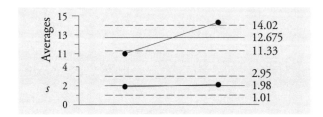

Figure 6.7: Average and Std. Dev. Chart for Comparing Conditions in Table 6.3

inspection of the tabled values shows that our alpha-level for the Average Chart of Figure 6.7 will be smaller than 0.0005.

While the difference between the two conditions is made clearer in Figure 6.7 than it appears in Figure 6.6, Figure 6.7 does not provide any check on the internal homogeneity of the two subgroups. For this reason, you may wish to use both charts—the *XmR* Chart to see what is going on within the data and the Average and Standard Deviation Chart to present your results to others.

The *XmR* Chart is the appropriate technique for evaluating the homogeneity of our two data sets. Furthermore, since the limits on an *XmR* Chart are intended for judging additional individual values, using the limits for one condition to evaluate the points from the other condition is appropriate and perfectly within the scope of the way these charts were meant to be used.

However, using the Average Chart to compare two averages is clearly an adaptation of the chart. The fixed-width limits on the Average Chart are intended for use with an ongoing stream of averages. They are not fine-tuned for making comparisons between two averages. So while the fixed-width limits of an Average Chart are conservative when $k = 2$, and while we can safely use this simple approach, we might wish to adjust the width of the limits according to our choice of an alpha-level for the comparison. To do this will require the Analysis of Means.

6.4   The Analysis of Means

The Analysis of Means is an extension of the adaptation of the Average Chart described in the previous section. Given a finite data set consisting of k homogeneous sets of data, each containing n values, we can identify which of the k averages are detectably different from the Grand Average while controlling the theoretical risk of a false alarm.

The Analysis of Means (ANOM) looks like an Average Chart and is interpreted like an Average Chart. The only difference between an ANOM Chart and an Average Chart is the way we compute the limits.

For *any number of subgroups of size n* the Average Chart has fixed width limits of the form:

$$\text{Grand Average} \ \pm \ 3 \ \text{Estimated } SD(\overline{X})$$

For *exactly k subgroups of size n* the ANOM Chart will have variable width limits that depend upon:

      (1) the number of subgroup averages, k, that are compared by the chart,

      (2) the degrees of freedom for the estimate of $SD(X)$, and

      (3) the overall alpha-level for the comparison.

These limits will have the form:

$$\text{Grand Average} \pm H \text{ Estimated } SD(\overline{X})$$

As with the Average Chart, tables of quick scaling factors are available for constructing an ANOM Chart so that we do not have to work with H directly. These scaling factors will depend upon which local measure of dispersion you choose to use.

VERSION ONE: WHEN USING THE AVERAGE RANGE:

The ANOM Chart detection limits can be found using the formula:

$$\text{Grand Average} \pm ANOM_\alpha \ \overline{R}$$

where the quick scaling factor $ANOM_\alpha$ depends upon n, k, and α. These scaling factors may be found in Appendix Table A.11.

VERSION TWO: WHEN USING THE POOLED VARIANCE:

$$\text{Pooled Variance Estimate of } SD(X) = s_p = \sqrt{\overline{s^2}}$$

The ANOM Chart detection limits may be found using:

$$\text{Grand Average} \pm H_2 \ s_p$$

where the quick scaling factor H_2 depends upon n, k, and α. These scaling factors may be found in Appendix Table A.12.

ANOM Chart limits based on an alpha-level of 0.01 will detect those differences that are large enough to be beyond dispute. Small alpha-levels are used when you have to convince a skeptic and additional data will not be available to confirm your findings. ANOM Chart limits based on larger alpha-levels will detect smaller differences, and will, therefore, be more sensitive. However, they will also have a correspondingly greater risk of a false alarm. Larger alpha-levels are recommended when your findings can be confirmed by subsequent operations.

Table 6.2 (repeated): Two Subgroups from Bead Board No. 3

						Average	Range	Variance
Subgroup 71	10	12	11	9	13	11.0	4	2.50
Subgroup 72	10	7	11	8	13	9.8	6	5.70

For the data of Table 6.2 the Average Range is 5.0 (with 7 degrees of freedom). The Grand Average is 10.4. With an alpha-level of 0.01, $k = 2$, and $n = 5$, Table A.11 gives a quick scaling factor of 0.448 and our ANOM detection limits are:

$$\text{Grand Average} \pm ANOM_\alpha \ \bar{R} \ = \ 10.4 \pm 0.448 \,(5.0) \ = \ 8.16 \text{ to } 12.64$$

This ANOM Chart is shown in Figure 6.8. It tells the same story as the Average Chart in Figure 6.5, but with tighter limits.

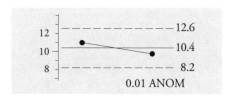

Figure 6.8: ANOM for Comparing Conditions in Table 6.2

Using the pooled variance we find s_p for Table 6.2 to be 2.025 (with 8 degrees of freedom). With an alpha-level of 0.01, $k = 2$, and $n = 5$ we find a quick scaling factor of 1.063 from Table A.12 and compute virtually the same ANOM detection limits:

$$\text{Grand Average} \pm H_2 \ s_p \ = \ 10.4 \pm 1.063 \,(2.025) \ = \ 8.25 \text{ to } 12.55$$

The difference in these two sets of limits is due to the difference in the two estimates of dispersion, not to any inherent difference in the techniques.

◆ ◆ ◆

Table 6.3 (repeated): The First Forty Values from Bead Board No. 7

Condition One:	9	14	9	12	10	11	7	9	12	13
	14	11	10	14	12	11	11	10	13	9
Condition Two:	14	17	17	13	13	12	14	16	15	18
	12	14	17	12	11	13	15	16	14	13

For the data of Table 6.3 the pooled variance estimate of $SD(X)$ is 1.981 with 38 degrees of freedom. The Grand Average is 12.675. With an alpha-level of 0.01, $k = 2$, and $n = 20$, Table A.12 gives a scaling factor of 0.428 and our ANOM detection limits are:

$$\text{Grand Average} \pm H_2 \; s_p = 12.675 \pm 0.428 \; (1.981) = 11.83 \text{ to } 13.52$$

This ANOM plot is shown in Figure 6.9 along with the Average Chart shown in Figure 6.5. Comparing the ANOM plot with the Average Chart will reveal the conservative nature of the Average Chart when $k = 2$, and it will show the increased sensitivity to be had by using the Analysis of Means.

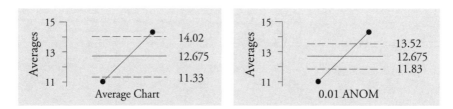

Figure 6.9: Average Chart and ANOM for Comparing Conditions in Table 6.3

The ANOM approach combines the advantage of having a picture to use in sharing your findings with others with the ability to choose a definite alpha-level for your procedure. As was noted earlier, the alpha-level does not tell you anything about your results, but it does tell others how you computed your detection limits.

In order for ANOM to work as advertised, and for the resulting plot to make sense, each of the k subgroups used will need to have a reasonable degree of internal homogeneity. It is the homogeneity of each subgroup that justifies the use of descriptive statistics in analysis. If the subgroup average is not a reasonable statistic for summarizing the location of the subgroup, the ANOM will not make sense.

6.5 The Two-Sample Student's *t*-test

The classical technique for comparing two averages is a two-sample Student's *t*-test. Given n_1 homogeneous observations collected under one set of conditions with average $\bar{x}_1$ and standard deviation statistic s_1; and given n_2 homogeneous observations collected under another set of conditions with average $\bar{x}_2$ and standard deviation statistic s_2; and given that you wish to examine the idea that the average values for all such data collected under these two sets of conditions might be the same, then begin by computing a pooled estimate of dispersion:

$$ s_p = \sqrt{\frac{(n_1 - 1)\, s_1{}^2 + (n_2 - 1)\, s_2{}^2}{n_1 + n_2 - 2}} $$

A 100(1–α)% Interval Estimate of the difference between the mean for Condition One and the mean for Condition Two, [$\mu_1 - \mu_2$] will be:

$$ (\bar{x}_1 - \bar{x}_2) \quad \pm \quad t_{\alpha/2} \; s_p \sqrt{(1/n_1) + (1/n_2)} $$

where the critical value $t_{\alpha/2}$ comes from a Student's *t*-distribution with degrees of freedom equal to $(n_1 + n_2 - 2)$.

Values within a 90% Interval Estimate will define those values that are consistent with these data. If zero is contained in this interval you cannot detect any difference between the means for the two conditions.

Values outside a 99% Interval Estimate are those values for the difference that are clearly inconsistent with these data. If zero is outside this interval estimate, then you have a detectable difference between the means for the two conditions.

If the value zero falls within the 99% Interval Estimate, but outside the 90% Interval Estimate, then you have a remote possibility that the two conditions are the same, or a weak signal that they are different—take your choice.

◆ ◆ ◆

Table 6.2 (repeated): Two Subgroups from Bead Board No. 3

						Average	Range	Variance
Subgroup 71	10	12	11	9	13	11.0	4	2.50
Subgroup 72	10	7	11	8	13	9.8	6	5.70

The first subgroup of Table 6.2 has an average of 11.0 and a variance statistic of s^2 = 2.50 with 4 degrees of freedom. The second subgroup has an average of 9.8 and a variance statistic of s^2 = 5.70 with 4. degrees of freedom. The pooled variance estimate of *SD(X)* therefore has 8 degrees of freedom and is:

$$ s_p = \sqrt{\frac{(n_1 - 1)\, s_1{}^2 + (n_2 - 1)\, s_2{}^2}{n_1 + n_2 - 2}} = 2.025 $$

So our 90% Interval Estimate of $[\,\mu_1 - \mu_2\,]$ will be:

$$(\bar{x}_1 - \bar{x}_2) \quad \pm \quad t_{\alpha/2} \; s_p \sqrt{\; (1/n_1) + (1/n_2)}$$

$$= (11.0 - 9.8) \pm 1.860 \,(2.025)\sqrt{0.4}$$

$$= 1.20 \pm 2.38 \; = \; -1.18 \text{ to } 3.58$$

Since this interval contains zero, we have failed to detect a difference between the averages of these two subgroups.

Table 6.3 (repeated): The First Forty Values from Bead Board No. 7

Condition One:	9	14	9	12	10	11	7	9	12	13
	14	11	10	14	12	11	11	10	13	9
Condition Two:	14	17	17	13	13	12	14	16	15	18
	12	14	17	12	11	13	15	16	14	13

Condition One of Table 6.3 has an average of 11.05 and a variance statistic of $s^2 = 3.8395$ with 19 *d.f.* Condition Two has an average of 14.3 and a variance statistic of $s^2 = 4.0105$ with 19 *d.f.* The pooled variance estimate of $SD(X)$ therefore has 38 *d.f.* and is:

$$s_p \;=\; \sqrt{\frac{(n_1 - 1)\,s_1{}^2 + (n_2 - 1)\,s_2{}^2}{n_1 + n_2 - 2}} \;=\; 1.9812$$

The 0.005 critical value from a Student's *t*-distribution with 38 degrees of freedom is approximately 2.72, so our 99% Interval Estimate of $[\,\mu_1 - \mu_2\,]$ will be:

$$(\bar{x}_1 - \bar{x}_2) \quad \pm \quad t_{\alpha/2} \; s_p \sqrt{\; (1/n_1) + (1/n_2)}$$

$$= (11.05 - 14.30) \pm 2.72\,(1.981)\sqrt{0.10}$$

$$= -3.25 \pm 1.70 \; = \; -4.95 \text{ to } -1.55$$

Since this interval does not include zero we decide that there is a detectable difference between the averages for these two conditions, and our best estimate of that difference is that the average for Condition Two exceeds that of Condition One by 3.25 units.

6.6 The Paired *t*-test

The two-sample *t*-test given in the previous section uses the variation within each condition to determine if an observed difference is likely to be due to chance. As noted earlier, this procedure is intended for use when it makes sense to assume that the data for each condition are internally homogeneous. However, there are situations where this assumption does not make sense.

Assume that you have *n* experimental units and that each of these experimental units is used to obtain observations under each of the two conditions. If we simply took the *n* observations for Condition One and the *n* observations for Condition Two, and used the procedure of the previous section, we could end up with a very insensitive test.

The problem of using the two-sample *t*-test here is the problem of whether or not the *n* experimental units are all alike. When these units differ their differences will inflate the pooled variance and reduce the sensitivity of the two-sample *t*-test. Thus, to get around this problem we change the structure of the comparison. Instead of averaging *across* the *n* experimental units for each condition, we compare the two conditions *within* each experimental unit by computing differences, averaging the differences, and using an interval estimate on the average of the differences.

Say that under Condition One you collect the values $\{ x_1, x_2, \ldots, x_n \}$ from the *n* experimental units, while you collect the values $\{ y_1, y_2, \ldots, y_n \}$ from the same *n* experimental units under Condition Two. (That is both x_i and y_i are obtained from the *i* th experimental unit.)

To examine the idea that the average for all such data collected under these two sets of conditions might be the same, we compute the differences:

$$\{ d_1 = x_1 - y_1, \quad d_2 = x_2 - y_2, \quad \ldots, \quad d_n = x_n - y_n \}$$

If this set of differences is homogeneous we can use the average, $\bar{d}$, and the standard deviation statistic, s_d, to obtain a $100(1-\alpha)\%$ Interval Estimate for the mean difference between the two conditions:

$$\bar{d} \pm t_{\alpha/2} \frac{s_d}{\sqrt{n}}$$

where the critical value $t_{\alpha/2}$ comes from Student's *t*-distribution with $(n-1)$ d.f.

Notice that the homogeneity requirement applies to the differences, not the original data sets { x_1, x_2, ... , x_n } and { y_1, y_2, ... , y_n }. This technique, when appropriate, lets you make comparisons in spite of any lack of homogeneity among the experimental units.

◆ ◆ ◆

To illustrate the paired *t*-test, the data in Table 6.4 consists of the diameters of Bearings One and Two for 20 camshafts. Recall that the *XmR* Charts for both Bearing One and Bearing Two contained points outside the limits.

Table 6.4: Bearing Diameters One and Two for 20 Camshafts (1.37xx inches)

Camshaft	1	2	3	4	5	6	7	8	9	10
Bearing 1	49	51	51	52	56	52	51	52	50	49.5
Bearing 2	50	50	52	49	52	49	49	50	48	48
Difference	−1	1	−1	3	4	3	2	2	2	1.5

Camshaft	11	12	13	14	15	16	17	18	19	20
Bearing 1	51	52	53	52	51	51	55	51	50.5	49
Bearing 2	49	48	50	49	49	51	51	52	50	50
Difference	2	4	3	3	2	0	4	−1	0.5	−1

The *X* Chart for 20 differences in Table 6.4 is shown in Figure 6.10. It shows no evidence of nonhomogeneity.

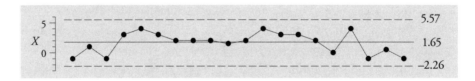

Figure 6.10: *X* Chart for Differences for Pairings Between Bearings One and Two

The average of the differences is 1.65 units, and the standard deviation statistic for these $n = 20$ differences is computed to be $s_d = 1.733$ (19 *d.f.*). A 99% Interval Estimate for the mean difference between Bearing One and Bearing Two is:

$$\bar{d} \pm t_{\alpha/2} \frac{s_d}{\sqrt{n}} = 1.65 \pm 2.861 \frac{1.733}{\sqrt{20}} = 0.54 \text{ to } 2.76$$

Since this interval does not contain zero we can say that the two bearings are detectably different. A reasonable estimate of this difference can be obtained from a 90% Interval Estimate for the mean difference between Bearing One and Bearing Two:

$$\bar{d} \pm t_{\alpha/2}\frac{s_d}{\sqrt{n}} = 1.65 \pm 1.729\frac{1.733}{\sqrt{20}} = 0.98 \text{ to } 2.32$$

Thus, while our point estimate suggests that Bearing One averages 1.65 units larger than Bearing Two, differences in the range of 1.0 to 2.3 units are consistent with these data.

◆ ◆ ◆

Table 6.5: Bearing Diameters Two and Three for 50 Camshafts (1.37xx inches)

Camshaft	1	2	3	4	5	6	7	8	9	10
Bearing 2	50	50	52	49	52	49	49	50	48	48
Bearing 3	50	46	52	51	42	50	50.5	44	48	49
Difference	0	4	0	−2	10	−1	−1.5	6	0	−1
Camshaft	11	12	13	14	15	16	17	18	19	20
Bearing 2	49	48	50	49	49	51	51	52	50	50
Bearing 3	43	49.5	50	46	49	43	42	45	42	43
Difference	6	−1.5	0	3	0	8	9	7	8	7
Camshaft	21	22	23	24	25	26	27	28	29	30
Bearing 2	48	49	50	50	48	50	47	48	49	48
Bearing 3	43	45	42	46	47	45	42	49	49	52
Difference	5	4	8	4	1	5	5	−1	0	−4
Camshaft	31	32	33	34	35	36	37	38	39	40
Bearing 2	52	52	53	53	51	51	51.5	49	54.5	50
Bearing 3	46	50	51	50	51	50	52	52	54	52.5
Difference	6	2	2	3	0	1	−0.5	−3	0.5	−2.5
Camshaft	41	42	43	44	45	46	47	48	49	50
Bearing 2	48	50	47	49	49	48	50	52	48	48
Bearing 3	54	51	51	51	49.5	52	49	49	50	50
Difference	−6	−1	−4	−2	−0.5	−4	1	3	−2	−2

If we try the same type of comparison between Bearing Two and Bearing Three, using all 50 pairings from Table 6.5, the X Chart for the 50 differences in Figure 6.11 shows runs of (a) nine successive values above the central line and (b) 13 successive values below the central line. This nonhomogeneity of the *differences* undermines the use of the pairings as a basis for comparing Bearing Two with Bearing Three. While the average of the 50 differences is 1.58 units, which differences are represented by the average of 1.58? The long runs on the X Chart undermine the interpretation of this average as an estimate of an underlying, *constant* difference between the two bearings. While Bearings Two and Three are different, the difference is a qualitative one that cannot be characterized by parametric comparisons.

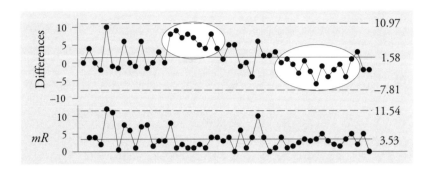

Figure 6.11: Differences for Pairings Between Bearings Two and Three

6.7 NB10 Revisited

The X Chart in Figure 5.4 shows a definite upset at Week 36. Examination of the chart also shows a possible shift in level that coincides with that upset. Therefore, it might be interesting to compare those measurements made prior to Week 36 with those made following Week 36.

Since there is a potential upset in Week 63, the simplest way to make the comparison above would be to compute limits based on the first 35 values and also to compute limits based on Weeks 37 to 62. This was done, and the results are shown in Figure 6.12. For simplicity, the data for Weeks 63 to 100 are not included in Figure 6.12.

No points from one set fall outside the limits from the other set (except for Week 36 which we already know is different). However, Weeks 7 to 12, Weeks 14 to 18, Weeks 22 to 26, and Weeks 28 to 32 are four runs of 5 or 6 successive values that are more than one sigma above the central line for the second set of limits, while Week 51 starts a run of 8 weeks that are below the central line of the first set of limits. Thus there are several indications of a detectable difference between the weights recorded for NB10 prior to the upset in Week 36 and the weights recorded for NB10 following that upset.

Since both sets of weighings are internally homogeneous, we might use a two-sample *t*-test to confirm what the chart shows. The first 35 weeks have an average of 597.69 and a standard deviation statistic of 3.341. The 26 weeks from Week 37 to Week 62 have an average of 594.23 and a standard deviation statistic of 3.433.

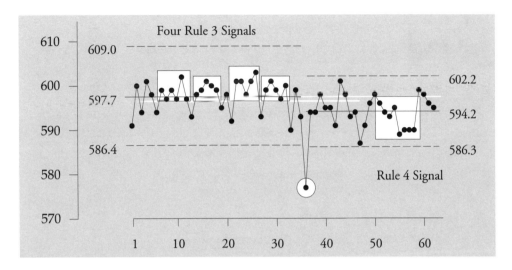

Figure 6.12: *X* **Chart Comparing Weeks 1-35 with Weeks 37-62**

This results in a pooled estimate of dispersion of

$$s_p = \sqrt{\frac{(n_1 - 1)s_1{}^2 + (n_2 - 1)s_2{}^2}{n_1 + n_2 - 2}} = 3.380$$

With 59 degrees of freedom our 99% Interval Estimate for the difference in the two averages is:

$$(\bar{x}_1 - \bar{x}_2) \pm t_{\alpha/2}\, s_p \sqrt{(1/n_1) + (1/n_2)}$$

$$= (597.69 - 594.23) \pm 2.662\,(3.380) \sqrt{1/35 + 1/26}$$

$$= 3.46 \pm 2.33 = 1.13 \text{ to } 5.79$$

Therefore, using either the *XmR* Chart or the two-sample Student's *t*-test, we detect a difference in the average weights before and after Week 36. The measurement system used to weigh NB10 gave readings that averaged about 3.5 micrograms less following the upset in Week 36 than it gave prior to the upset.

This scale is not being operated up to its full potential, nor is it being operated consistently over time.

6.8   Summary of Comparing Two Conditions

The best analysis is the simplest analysis that gives the needed insight.

The following list is arranged in order of increasing complexity and increasing sensitivity. Differences detected by one technique will generally be detected by all of the following techniques that apply. However techniques further down the list may detect differences that are missed by the less sensitive techniques.

Histograms

> Detect and portray large differences
>
> Qualitative and quantitative differences can be seen
>
> Best with reasonably large data sets
>
>> (you will need enough data to show both the clustering and the gaps)
>
> Easy to explain to others

XmR Charts

> Detect and portray most differences that are large enough
>> to be of practical importance
>
> Detect any lack of homogeneity within the data
>
> Reveal any qualitative differences present
>
> Best with more than 10 values per condition
>
> Can use with unequal amounts of data from two conditions
>
> Can detect differences in dispersion
>
> Easy to explain to others

Average Chart

> Detects most differences that are large enough to be of practical importance
>
> Portrays the differences between conditions more clearly than *XmR* Charts
>
> Need to have equal amounts of data from two conditions
>
> Assumes homogeneity within each condition
>
> Very conservative limits when $k = 2$
>
> Easy to explain to others

Range Charts

    Check for homogeneity within conditions

    Can detect large differences in dispersion when $n \geq 7$

    Use Standard Deviation Chart for $n \geq 16$

    Must have equal amounts of data from the two conditions

    Easy to explain to others

ANOM

    More sensitive than Average Chart

    Assumes homogeneity within each condition

    You choose alpha-level for ANOM limits

    Still gives a picture of the differences

    Needs to have equal amounts of data from the two conditions

    Easy for others to interpret

Two-Sample *t*-Test

    Assumes homogeneity within each condition

    Sensitivity similar to ANOM

    Works with small amounts of data

    Can have unequal amounts of data from two conditions

    No picture

    Not easy to explain to the uninitiated

Paired *t*-Test

    Data have to possess paired structure

    Differences have to be homogeneous

    Can remove effects of nonhomogeneous experimental units

        (and thereby improve the sensitivity of the analysis)

    Works with small amounts of data

    No picture

    Not easy to explain to the uninitiated

When the two conditions are found to be detectably different you may wish to use the questions of Chapter Five to summarize each of the two groups of data. Otherwise you may wish to combine the two groups and apply the techniques of Chapter Five to the combined set of data.

Chapter Seven

Data Collected Under
Three or More Conditions

This chapter will cover the analysis of data collected under three or more categorical conditions (commonly referred to as treatments). In the interest of clarity, a single treatment may consist of a combination of values for several independent variables, or it may be one in a set of mutually exclusive categories. If you are interested in analyzing data collected at three or more *values* of a single independent variable, you might wish to use the techniques in the next chapter.

As with data collected under two conditions, we will want to know if differences in the response variable can be attributed to the different treatments. If we can detect such differences, then, as stated in Axiom 8, we will want to estimate those differences and assess their practical importance.

7.1 *XmR* Charts for Each Treatment

If there are at least six or more values for each treatment, you may place the data for each treatment on its own *XmR* Chart. If these charts are all plotted in sequence on the same vertical scale it will facilitate comparisons between treatments while also checking for homogeneity within each treatment. For those treatments that appear to be internally homogeneous these charts will also provide estimates of location and dispersion. Furthermore, as we saw in the previous chapter, by showing all of the data the *XmR* Charts will allow you to spot both qualitative and quantitative differences between the treatments.

Assume that the 40 data of Table 7.1 consist of four sets of ten observations each collected under four different treatments. These values are the first 40 values from Table 2.2: Bead Board No. 7 Data.

Table 7.1: **Data for Four Treatments from Bead Board No. 7**

	Values and Moving Ranges										$\bar{X}$	$\overline{mR}$	R
Treatment A	9	14	9	12	10	11	7	9	12	13	10.6		7
mR		5	5	3	2	1	4	2	3	1		2.89	
Treatment B	14	11	10	14	12	11	11	10	13	9	11.5		5
mR		3	1	4	2	1	0	1	3	4		2.11	
Treatment C	14	17	17	13	13	12	14	16	15	18	14.9		6
mR		3	0	4	0	1	2	2	1	3		1.78	
Treatment D	12	14	17	12	11	13	15	16	14	13	13.7		6
mR		2	3	5	1	2	2	1	2	1		2.11	

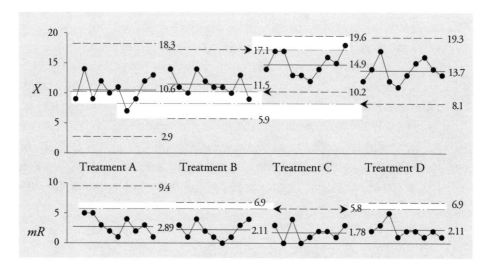

Figure 7.1: *XmR* Charts for Table 7.1

The *XmR* Charts for these four treatments are shown in Figure 7.1. All four data sets appear to be internally homogeneous. The *mR* Charts do not show any detectable differences in dispersion between these four treatments. Using the *X* Charts to compare the four treatments results in the following: we see no detectable difference in location between Treatments A and B; we do find that Treatment C has a detectably higher average than both Treatment A and Treatment B; and we see that Treatment D has a detectably higher average than Treatment A. Thus, of the six pairwise comparisons between these four treatments, three show detectable differences in location:

In addition to these detectable differences, we have a picture to show to others that will support this analysis, making it easy to communicate our findings.

Since the risk of finding a difference where none exists will increase geometrically with the number of treatments compared, this technique is not recommended for use with a large number of treatments.

7.2 Average and Range Charts

If you have the same amount of data collected under each treatment, and are willing to assume internal homogeneity for the data from each treatment, then you could compare the treatment averages and the treatment ranges with an Average and Range Chart. As long as the number of treatments, k, is smaller than the subgroup size, n, this adaptation of the Average and Range Chart will be reasonably conservative (having an effective alpha-level of 2% or less—see Table A.9).

Points outside the limits on the Average Chart will identify those treatments whose averages are detectably greater or less than the Grand Average. Once you have detected a difference, the treatment averages will be the best estimates of the treatment means.

Points outside the limits on the Range Chart will identify those treatments with variation that is detectably different from that level of variation represented by the Average Range.

❖ ❖ ❖

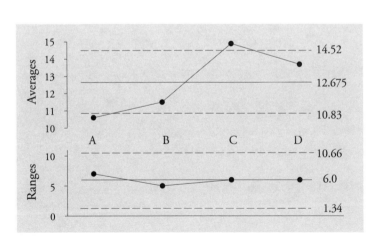

Figure 7.2: **Average and Range Chart for Table 7.1**

The Average and Range Chart for the four treatments of Table 7.1 is shown in Figure 7.2. Treatments A and C have averages that are detectably different from the Grand Average. (Notice that the comparisons here are different than those made with the four *XmR* Charts. Rather than directly comparing treatments, we are now comparing each treatment with the Grand Average.) In Figure 7.2, with $n = 10$ and $k = 4$, the Average Chart has an overall alpha-level of 0.006, while that of the Range Chart is 0.003. With such conservative alpha-levels, it is safe to assume that the signals are real.

7.3 Analysis of Means

The Analysis of Means is an extension of the adaptation of the Average Chart described in the pervious section. Given k homogeneous sets of data, each containing n values, we can identify which of the k averages are detectably different from the Grand Average while *choosing* the overall alpha-level for the analysis.

As explained in the previous chapter, ANOM looks like an Average Chart, and it is interpreted like an Average Chart. The only difference between an ANOM Chart and an Average Chart is the way we compute the limits. While an Average Chart always uses fixed three-sigma limits, an ANOM Chart uses variable width limits that depend upon k, α, and the degrees of freedom for the estimate of $SD(X)$. Quick scaling factors given in the Appendix simplify the creation of an ANOM Chart.

VERSION ONE: WHEN USING THE AVERAGE RANGE:

The ANOM Chart detection limits can be found using the formula:

$$\text{Grand Average} \pm ANOM_\alpha \, \overline{R}$$

where the quick scaling factor $ANOM_\alpha$ depends upon n, k, and α. These scaling factors may be found in Appendix Table A.11.

VERSION TWO: WHEN USING THE POOLED VARIANCE:

$$\text{Pooled Variance Estimate of } SD(X) \; = \; s_p \; = \; \sqrt{\overline{s^2}}$$

The ANOM Chart detection limits may be found using:

$$\text{Grand Average} \pm H_2 \, s_p$$

where the quick scaling factor H_2 depends upon n, k, and α. These scaling factors may be found in Appendix Table A.12.

◆ ◆ ◆

For the data of Table 7.1 the Grand Average is 12.675 and the Average Range is 6.00. With an alpha-level of 0.10, $n = 10$, and $k = 4$ we find a quick scaling factor from Table A.11 to be 0.202, giving ANOM limits of:

$$\text{Grand Average} \pm ANOM_\alpha \, \overline{R} \ = \ 12.675 \pm 0.202\,(6.0) \ = \ 11.46 \text{ to } 13.89$$

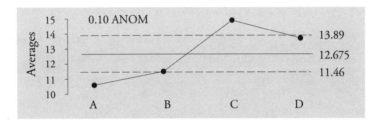

Figure 7.3: ANOM Chart for Table 7.1

This ANOM has a larger alpha-level than the Average Chart in Figure 7.2. As a result it also has tighter limits. Treatments A and C are detectably different from the Grand Average, while Treatments B and D are borderline.

7.4 Analysis of Variance

The extension of the two-sample t-test to handle k samples is known as the One-Way Analysis of Variance (One-Way ANOVA). This procedure uses the difference between the global and local measures of dispersion. It is built on the fact that when the data are not homogeneous the global measure of dispersion will be inflated relative to the local measure. Since differences in treatment means are one type of non-homogeneity, the One-Way ANOVA is structured to isolate these differences into one measure of dispersion and to compare this with a local measure of dispersion. This comparison is then used as an indicator of the differences between the treatment means.

In effect, the One-Way ANOVA partitions a global measure of variation into two components. One component is completely obtained from within the treatments and the other is completely attributable to the differences between the treatment averages.

1. Say that we have k treatments and for each of these treatments we have n observations of a response measure. Then $N = nk$ will denote the total number of observations in the study. The global measure of dispersion, known as the *Total Variation*, will have $(N-1)$ degrees of freedom and can be described as the numerator of the global variance statistic computed using all N observations:

$$Total\ Variation\ =\ (N-1)\,s^2$$

This Total Variation is going to be partitioned into two components.

2. The local component is known as the *Within Treatment Variation*. It will have $k(n-1)$ degrees of freedom and is the numerator of the pooled variance statistic:

$$Within\ Treatment\ Variation\ =\ k(n-1)\ \overline{s^2}$$

3. The other component is known as the *Between Treatment Variation*. It will have $(k-1)$ degrees of freedom and is found by subtracting the Within Treatment Variation from the Total Variation:

$$Between\ Treatment\ Variation\ =\ [\,(N-1)\,s^2\,]\ -\ [\,k(n-1)\ \overline{s^2}\,]$$

4. Under the condition that all treatment means are the same, the N data should be homogeneous, and each of the three quantities above, when divided by their degrees of freedom, will provide an estimate of $V(X)$ for the one universe represented by these N data. In practice we only work with the *Within* and *Between* estimates:

$$Within\ Est.\ V(X)\ =\ \overline{s^2}$$

$$Between\ Est.\ V(X)\ =\ \frac{[\,(N-1)\,s^2\,]\ -\ [\,k(n-1)\ \overline{s^2}\,]}{(k-1)}$$

When some of the treatment means differ from the others the N data will no longer be homogeneous: The global measure of dispersion will be inflated by this difference (relative to the local measure of dispersion), and rather than being similar, the Between Treatment Estimate of $V(X)$ will be substantially larger than the Within Treatment Estimate of $V(X)$.

5. These two estimates of $V(X)$ are compared using a ratio. This ratio is known as the F-ratio in honor of Sir Ronald Fisher.

$$F\text{-ratio} = \frac{Between\ Est.\ V(X)}{Within\ Est.\ V(X)}$$

Homogeneous data sets will result in F-ratios in the neighborhood of 1.0. Differences between the treatment means will inflate the F-ratio.

For our first example of a One-Way ANOVA, consider the first 30 values from a data set we have already found to be homogeneous, the Wire Length Data. Assume that these 30 values represent 10 observations collected under each of three treatments, so that $n = 10$, $k = 3$, and $N = 30$.

Table 7.2: Three Treatments from the Wire Length Data

A	108.5	108.9	107.4	103.8	105.0	108.7	109.8	112.5	113.5	110.3
B	102.8	109.7	113.4	108.4	112.4	112.1	109.3	110.1	106.8	111.1
C	111.2	113.5	104.9	108.9	116.4	110.1	104.8	109.1	112.0	114.8

1. The global variance statistic for these 30 values is $s^2 = 10.88685$.
   The Total Variation has $N-1 = 29$ *d.f.* and is:

   $$Total\ Variation = (N-1)\,s^2 = \textbf{315.7187}$$

2. When all treatments have the same number of observations the pooled variance is the average of the s^2 values computed for each of the three treatments separately:

   $$\overline{s^2} = \frac{8.9471\ +\ 9.6277\ +\ 14.8357}{3} = 11.1368$$

   So that the Within Treatment Variation has $k(n-1) = 27$ *d.f.* and is:

   $$Within\ Treatment\ Variation = k(n-1)\,\overline{s^2} = \textbf{300.6940}$$

3. Which gives us a Between Treatment Variation with $(k-1) = 2$ *d.f.* of

   $$Between\ Treatment\ Variation = Total\ Var. - Within\ Treatment\ Var.$$
   $$= (N-1)\,s^2 - k(n-1)\,\overline{s^2}$$
   $$= 315.7187 - 300.694 = \textbf{15.02467}$$

4. Since the Wire Length Data is homogeneous, we should find that each of the three

quantities above, when divided by their degrees of freedom, are quite similar. The Total Variation divided by 29 is 10.88. The Within Variation divided by 27 is 11.14. The Between Variation divided by 2 is 7.51.

5. Thus our *F*-ratio is in the vicinity of 1.0 and we detect no difference:

$$F\text{-ratio} = \frac{Between\ Est.\ V(X)}{Within\ Est.\ V(X)} = \frac{7.51}{11.13} = 0.675$$

In order to organize the various steps in the One-Way ANOVA it is customary to place the various numbers in an ANOVA Table. The first column identifies the type of variation in each row of the table—Between Treatments, Within Treatments, and Total Variation. The second column presents the breakdown of the Total Variation into the Between and Within components. These values are commonly referred to a "Sums of Squares." The third column presents the degrees of freedom for each row. The fourth column generally presents the two estimates of $V(X)$ based on the Between component and the Within component. These estimates are commonly referred to as "Mean Squares." Finally the last two columns contain the *F*-ratio and its P-value. The One-Way ANOVA Table for the data of Table 7.2 is:

Source	Sums of Squares	d.f.	Mean Squares	F-ratio	P-value
Between	15.02467	2	7.51	0.675	0.518
Within	300.69400	27	11.13		
Total	315.71867	29			

The *F*-ratio in the ANOVA Table is compared to a critical value from an F-distribution having 2 and 27 degrees of freedom:

$$F_{.05}\ (2,\ 27) = 3.35$$

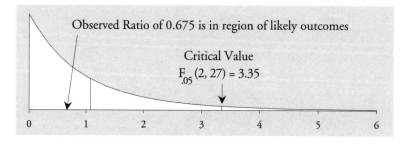

Figure 7.4: The F-Distribution with 2 and 27 Degrees of Freedom

These critical values are given in Appendix Table A.13. When a computed F-ratio exceeds this value it is in the extreme upper five percent of the theoretical distribution for ratios of this type. Since the *F*-ratio fails to exceed this critical value, we say there are no detectable differences between the treatment averages in this case.

◆ ◆ ◆

To illustrate how the One-Way ANOVA detects differences between treatment means, we return to the data of Table 7.1. There we had 10 observations collected under each of four treatments, so that $n = 10$, $k = 4$, and $N = 40$. These 40 values and a schematic representation of their Analysis of Variance are shown in Figure 7.5.

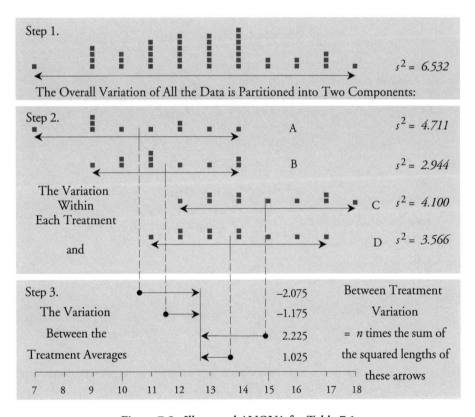

Figure 7.5: Illustrated ANOVA for Table 7.1

Table 7.1: Data for Four Treatments from Bead Board No. 7

	Values										$\bar{X}$	R
Treatment A	9	14	9	12	10	11	7	9	12	13	10.6	7
Treatment B	14	11	10	14	12	11	11	10	13	9	11.5	5
Treatment C	14	17	17	13	13	12	14	16	15	18	14.9	6
Treatment D	12	14	17	12	11	13	15	16	14	13	13.7	6

1. Using all 40 values, the global variance statistic is $s^2 = 6.53269$. The Total Variation is thus:

$$Total\ Variation\ =\ (N{-}1)\,s^2\ =\ 39\,(6.53269)\ =\ \mathbf{254.775}$$

2. With equal n the pooled variance is the average of the s^2 values computed for each of the four treatments separately:

$$\overline{s^2}\ =\ \frac{4.7111 + 2.9444 + 4.100 + 3.5666}{4}\ =\ 3.83056$$

So that the Within Treatment Variation is:

$$Within\ Treatment\ Variation\ =\ k(n{-}1)\ \overline{s^2}\ =\ 4\,(9)\,(3.83056)\ =\mathbf{137.9000}$$

3. Which gives us a Between Treatment Variation of

$$Between\ Treatment\ Variation\ =\ (N{-}1)\,s^2\ -\ k(n{-}1)\ \overline{s^2}$$
$$=\ 254.775 - 137.900\ =\ \mathbf{116.875}$$

4. & 5. Using the numbers shown in boldface above we can now fill in the One-Way ANOVA Table for the data of Table 7.1:

Source	Sums of Squares	d.f.	Mean Squares	F-ratio	P-value
Between	116.875	3	38.96	10.17	.0005
Within	137.900	36	3.83		
Total	254.775	39			

For an F-distribution with 3 and 36 degrees of freedom the 5% upper-tail critical value is about 2.9. Since the computed *F*-ratio exceeds this critical value, or equivalently, since the P-value is less than the traditional alpha-level of 0.05, we have detectable differences between the treatment means. In fact, no matter which of the commonly used alpha-levels you might choose, this computed ratio will exceed the critical value.

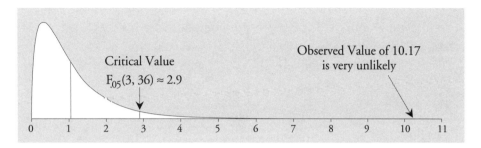

Figure 7.6: The F-Distribution with 3 and 36 Degrees of Freedom

Notice that unlike the other techniques (*XmR* Charts, Average and Range Charts, and ANOM Charts) the One-Way ANOVA does not tell you *which* treatments differ. The One-Way ANOVA merely provides a green light to look for differences between the treatment means. Thus we need a way of making comparisons after the One-Way ANOVA indicates that detectable differences exist. One such technique is the Tukey Post-Hoc Test.

Since even spreadsheet programs provide us with the ability to obtain a One-Way ANOVA, very few people will ever compute the ANOVA quantities manually. Therefore I will not dwell on the formulas or the modifications needed to handle unequal numbers of observations per treatment. Most software will produce a One-Way ANOVA table that is recognizably similar to the one above. However there is one thing that is different with software-generated ANOVA Tables. Rather than looking up a critical value and comparing the computed *F*-ratio to that value, software programs will usually convert the *F*-ratio into something known as the probability of exceedence. The probabilities of exceedence for the preceding examples are shown in the ANOVA tables in the last column labeled P-values.

When a procedure for testing a hypothesized parameter value is carried out manually it is common to compute a test statistic and then to compare that test statistic with some critical value that depends upon our choice of an alpha-level for the test. In effect, the alpha-level defines our standard of evidence—what will it take for us to say we have a detectable difference from the hypothesized value of the parameter?

When such a procedure is automated the basic computations are the same, but the results are reported differently. Instead of comparing the test statistic with a tabled critical value, most software packages will report the *probability of exceedence for the test statistic*. The probability of exceedence is the theoretical probability of getting a test result that is more extreme than the one you have just obtained when the hypothesized parameter value is correct. If the probability of exceedence is small, then your data are not consistent with the hypothesized parameter value.

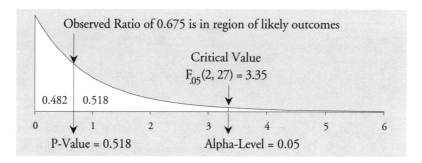

Figure 7.7: The P-Value for the ANOVA for the Data of Table 7.2

It is important to avoid confusing the probability of exceedence with the alpha-level of the test. The alpha-level defines your decision criterion while the probability of exceedence is the transformed test statistic. Whether we compare the test statistic with the critical value, or compare the probability of exceedence with the alpha-level, we are making the same comparison. The test statistic and the probability of exceedence are observed quantities that are dependent upon the data. The alpha-level and the associated critical value define a decision criterion.

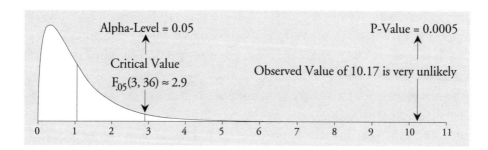

Figure 7.8: The P-Value for the ANOVA for the Data of Table 7.1

With the One-Way ANOVA, the F-test evaluates the likelihood that all the treatments have the same mean. When the *F*-ratio exceeds the critical value from an F-distribution we can say that we have detectable differences between the treatment means. Likewise, when the probability of exceedence for the F-ratio is smaller than the alpha-level we have chosen we can say that we have detectable differences between the treatment means.

7.5 The Tukey Post-Hoc Test

The Tukey Post-Hoc Test provides a way to make all possible pairwise comparisons between k treatment averages when every treatment average is based on n data (each treatment has the same number of observations). The threshold for what constitutes a detectable difference is Tukey's Honestly Significant Difference (HSD):

$$HSD = q\,[\,\text{Est. } SD(\bar{X})\,] = q\sqrt{\frac{MSW}{n}}$$

where MSW is the Mean Square Within (the Within-Treatment estimate of $V(X)$ from the One-Way ANOVA) and where q is a critical value from the Studentized Range Distribution. These critical values depend upon α, the overall alpha-level for the procedure; k, the number of treatment averages being compared; and v, the degrees of freedom for the estimate of $SD(X)$. These critical values may be found in Appendix Table A.14.

The One-Way ANOVA for the data of Table 7.1 showed a detectable difference between the four treatment averages. The Mean Square Within was 3.83 with 36 degrees of freedom. The number of treatments is $k = 4$, each based on $n = 10$ data. With an overall alpha-level of $\alpha = 0.05$, with $k = 4$, and with 36 degrees of freedom, interpolation in Table A.14 gives the Studentized Range critical value of approximately $q = 3.81$. This gives an Honestly Significant Difference of:

$$HSD = q\sqrt{\frac{MSW}{n}} = 3.81\sqrt{\frac{3.83}{10}} = 2.36$$

Any two treatment averages that differ by more than 2.36 units may be said to be detectably different. Treatment A has an Average of 10.6. Treatment B has an Average of 11.6. Treatment C has an Average of 14.9. Treatment D has an Average of 13.7.

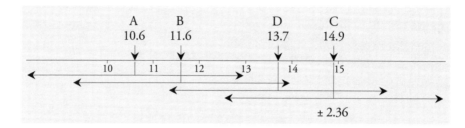

Figure 7.9: The Tukey Post-Hoc Test for the Data of Table 7.1

Only three pairwise comparisons show detectable differences: C is detectably greater than A and B, and D is detectably greater than A. These are exactly the same results we found using the *XmR* Charts in Section 7.1.

Many other post-hoc tests exist. This merely serves to illustrate how post-hoc tests are intended to finish the job that was begun with the One-Way ANOVA.

7.6 NB10 Again

Returning to the NB10 Data of Table 5.2, we see in Figure 7.10 that there are several upsets in this time series. In Section 6.7 we examined the averages before and after the upset at Week 36.

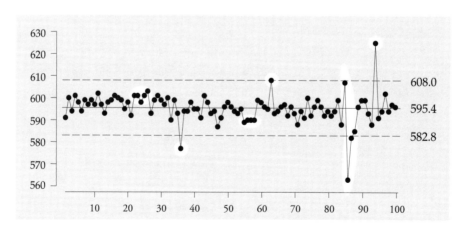

Figure 7.10: The *X* Chart for 100 Weighings of NB10

In addition to the upset in Week 36, there is another in Week 63, followed by a period of inconsistent readings during Weeks 85 to 88. Finally there is another exceptionally large value in Week 94. These upsets break the data set into logical segments, and raise the question of whether or not this measurement system was operated the same way in between the upsets.

How could you answer this question? If you performed an ANOVA you might detect a signal, but the unequal number of values would preclude a Tukey Post Hoc Test. The quick tables for ANOM also require equal subgroup sizes. But the simple *XmR* Chart still works.

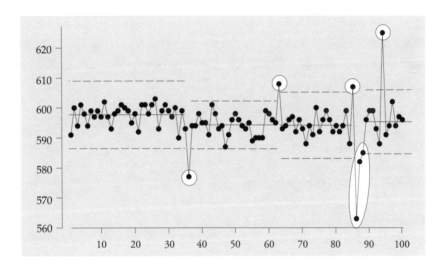

Figure 7.11: The *X* Chart for 100 Weighings of NB10 with Four Sets of Limits

The limits shown in Figure 7.11 are based on the 93 values not circled. Weeks 1 to 35 were used for the first set of limits. Weeks 37 to 62 we used for the second set of limits. Weeks 64 to 84 were used for the third set of limits. And Weeks 89 to 100, except for Week 94, were used for the fourth set of limits.

Interpreting these limits, we see that the first upset changed the average (this change was detected beyond a reasonable doubt in Section 6.7 and was estimated to be equivalent to about 4 micrograms). However, as can be seen from the chart, the subsequent upsets do not seem to have had any demonstrable impact upon the average. (While the last set of limits has a slightly higher average, this average is based on so few values that it is unlikely that there is a detectable difference here.)

Notice how the *X* Chart not only helps us understand the data well enough that we can ask the interesting questions, but it also provides us with a way to answer those questions. The graphic nature combined with the versatility and simplicity of this technique make it one of the most important tools in the data analysis tool kit. Use it and learn things. Ignore it and you may, like others, end up lost within the jungle of data analysis.

7.7 Summary of Comparing Several Conditions

The following list is arranged in order of increasing complexity and increasing sensitivity. Differences detected by one technique will generally be detected by all of the following techniques that apply. However techniques further down the list may detect differences that are missed by less sensitive techniques.

XmR Chart

> Detects and portrays most differences that are
> > large enough to be of practical importance
>
> Detects any lack of homogeneity within the data
> Reveals any qualitative differences present
> Need at least 6 values per treatment or condition
> Best with more than 10 values per treatment
> Can detect differences in dispersion
> Easy to explain to others
> Not recommended for large numbers of treatments

Average Chart

> Identifies Treatment Averages that differ from the Grand Average
> Assumes homogeneity within each condition
> Conservative limits when $k < n$
> Needs equal number of values per condition
> Easy to explain to others

Range Chart

> Checks for homogeneity within conditions
> Can identify treatments having excessive variation
> Use Standard Deviation Chart for $n \geq 16$
> Needs equal number of values per condition
> Easy to explain to others

ANOM

>   Can be made more sensitive than Average Chart
>   Assumes homogeneity within each condition
>   You choose the alpha-level
>   Still gives a picture of the differences
>   Can be adapted for unequal numbers of values per condition
>   Easy for others to interpret

One-Way ANOVA

>   Assumes homogeneity within each condition
>   Sensitivity similar to ANOM
>   Results are not specific as to which treatments differ
>   Can be adapted for unequal numbers of values per condition
>   No picture of the data given
>   Not easy to explain to the uninitiated

Tukey Post-Hoc Test

>   Makes all possible pairwise comparisons between k treatments
>   Treatments must have equal n
>   Sensitivity similar to ANOM
>   Not easy to explain to the uninitiated

The best analysis is the simplest analysis that gives the needed insight.

Chapter Eight

Data Collected at
Three or More Values for X

In the previous chapter techniques were presented that may be used to make comparisons between three or more treatments or conditions. In the special case where the three or more treatments consist of three or more levels of a single independent variable, there are two additional techniques that are of interest: scatterplots and simple linear regression.

Regression is said to be *simple* regression when the response variable is expressed as a function of a single independent variable. When a response variable is considered as a function of several independent variables the regression is said to be *multiple* regression. Regression is said to be *linear* regression when the equation is linear in the parameters, β.

Regression modeling is one of the most widely used statistical tools. It allows us to express the relationship between a response variable and one or more independent variables in terms of an algebraic function. One reason for the popularity of regression modeling is the ability to summarize relationships found in experimental, observational, or historical data in simple, elegant equations. And in these equations we find both the strength and the danger of regression analysis.

8.1 The Universe Had a Definite Beginning

In 1929 Edwin Hubble announced that there was a proportionality between the distance to a galaxy and the velocity with which that galaxy is receding from our galaxy. The distances were based on the apparent magnitude of the galaxies, and the velocities were based on the red-shifts measured in the spectrum of each galaxy. Table 8.1 contains the measured red shifts and the estimated distances (as of 1976) for

22 "local" galaxies. The red shifts are expressed as the ratio of the shift in wavelength divided by the unshifted wavelength. The distances are in millions of light years.

Table 8.1: Red Shifts and Distances to 22 Local Galaxies

Red Shift	Dist.	Red Shift	Dist.	Red Shift	Dist.
0.005	89	0.030	584	0.072	1160
0.013	260	0.034	587	0.065	1255
0.018	307	0.030	659	0.078	1551
0.022	312	0.035	709	0.072	1558
0.017	321	0.043	750	0.083	1624
0.017	335	0.053	979	0.094	1724
0.018	419	0.052	1118		
0.022	500	0.044	1145		

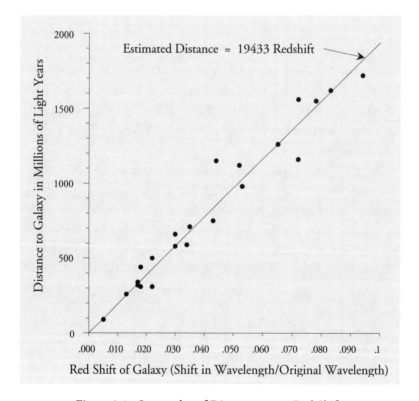

Figure 8.1: Scatterplot of Distance versus Red Shift

The scatterplot of these 22 pairs of values is shown in Figure 8.1. Based on this scatterplot Hubble's conjecture seems quite reasonable: Distance is proportional to red shift. But how can we find the equation of the line that best fits these data? Today this process is highly automated, but the steps involved are is as follows.

Inspection of Figure 8.1 will show that while the points do not all fall on a straight line, a straight line model is reasonable. We could think of each observation on Y as consisting of some linear function of X plus some observational error, e:

$$y_i = \beta_0 + \beta_1 x_i + e_i$$

If we interpret this model as a deterministic relationship, with some observational errors on the Y values thrown in, then our regression equation:

$$\hat{y}_i = b_0 + b_1 x_i$$

will approximate the deterministic relationship. Thus, the problem of regression is the problem of selecting b_0 and b_1 such that the resulting line will "fit" the data. Whatever line we may choose, the amount by which the observations deviate from the regression line will be called the residuals:

$$r_i = y_i - \hat{y}_i = y_i - [\, b_0 + b_1 x_i \,]$$

These residuals will characterize the fit between any line we use and the observations. Different ways of obtaining values for b_0 and b_1 will result in different lines with different sets of residuals. For the past two hundred years the most common approach to finding values for b_0 and b_1 is the one that will minimize the sum of the squared residuals:

$$Sum\ of\ Squared\ Residuals = \Sigma\,(\,y_i - b_0 - b_1 x_i\,)^2$$

This approach, pioneered by Legendre and Gauss, is known as the least-squares approach.

Today we let a computer do the actual estimation after we have specified the form of the model. When a proportional model is assumed, there will be no intercept term since proportionality between X and Y means that the line goes through the origin. Leaving the intercept term out of the regression model will force the regression line through the origin. Placing the data of Table 8.1 in a spreadsheet and fitting a model of the form:

$$Distance = \beta_1\ Redshift + e$$

(where β_1 is the constant of proportionality) we obtain the equation:

$$Estimated\ Distance = 19433\ Redshift$$

With the model above, the physics of the situation implies that a point estimate of the age of the universe would be $[\pi/2 - 1]\,\beta_1$. The fitted value of $b_1 = 19433$ million years suggests an age for the universe of 11.1 billion years. (While today's best estimate is 13.7 billion years, the compelling nature of the graph in Figure 8.1 made the idea of a definite beginning for the universe so unavoidable that it changed the whole course of cosmology.)

8.2   Evaluating Terms in the Model

For the data of Table 8.1 we could have fit a model of the form:

$$Distance = \beta_0 \; + \; \beta_1 \; Redshift \; + \; e$$

which would have resulted in the regression equation:

$$Estimated \; Distance \; = \; 21 + \; 19058 \; Redshift$$

So how can we decide which regression equation is best for these data?

Notice that the result we obtain depends upon the model that we choose to fit. The second model, with an intercept term β_0, is more flexible and is generally the preferred model. However, in this case the conjecture was that of proportionality, which would not involve an intercept term. So how can we decide if an intercept term is needed?

If the intercept term β_0 is actually zero, then we do not need to estimate it with a b_0 value. A test of the hypothesis that $\beta_0 = 0$ is provided by the probability of exceedence attached to the b_0 value found with the second model.

- If we get a small probability of exceedence, then it is unlikely that $\beta_0 = 0$.

- If we get a large probability of exceedence, then it is likely that $\beta_0 = 0$.

In general, both skeptics and advocates will agree that an intercept term is needed when its probability of exceedence is less than 0.01.

But what is the problem with just leaving the intercept term in anyway? If we include a term in our model when it is not needed we will be fitting our regression equation to the noise in the data. In the model above, the intercept term of $b_0 = 21$ has a probability of exceedence of 0.64 or 64%.

Thus, while in general the proportional model:

$$\hat{y}_i = \; b_1 \, x_i$$

will be less flexible than the model with an intercept term, in this case not only is it consistent with Hubble's conjecture, but it also fits the data better.

In the same way, we can evaluate the possibility that the slope term is meaningful. A regression equation might be fit to data for which there is no underlying relationship between X and Y. In this case the slope term β_1 would be zero. Yet the regression equation might have a non-zero b_1 term. We evaluate the hypothesis $\beta_1 = 0$, the slope is zero, using the probability of exceedence attached to the b_1 term. Once again, a small probability means that $\beta_1 = 0$ is unlikely. For the proportional model above the probability of exceedence for the b_1 term was very, very small [1.8×10^{-22}].

Thus, by looking at the probabilities of exceedence for the various parameters in the regression model you can determine if the estimates for each of those parameters are detectably different from zero or not. When one of these parameters could be zero the corresponding term in the model should be deleted. (If you leave a term in the model when the estimate is not detectably different from zero you are simply fitting noise with your regression equation.)

THE COEFFICIENT OF DETERMINATION

In addition to the probabilities of exceedence, another useful numerical summary for a regression model is the Coefficient of Determination, commonly denoted as R^2. This one number expresses the proportion of the total variation in the data that has been explained by the regression equation.

The proportional model for the data of Table 8.1 has a Coefficient of Determination of 95.55%. This means that the regression equation:

$$\hat{y}_i = \textit{Estimated Distance} = 19433 \ \textit{Redshift}$$

explains 95.55 percent of the variation of the responses about the origin. The formula for the Coefficient of Determination for this proportional model is

$$R^2 = \frac{\Sigma \hat{y}_i^2}{\Sigma y_i^2}$$

However, when the model includes an intercept term the formula for the Coefficient of Determination changes to:

$$R^2 = \frac{\Sigma (\hat{y}_i - \bar{y})^2}{\Sigma (y_i - \bar{y})^2}$$

This ratio defines that proportion of the total variation of the responses *about their mean* that has been explained by the regression equation.

The slope and intercept model for the data of Table 8.1 has a Coefficient of Determination of 95.60%. This means that the regression equation:

$$\hat{y}_i = \text{Estimated Distance} = 21 + 19058 \text{ Redshift}$$

explains 95.6% of the variation of the responses about their mean. These two R^2 values are essentially the same since, in this case, the intercept term is trivial and the two sets of estimated distances are essentially the same.

The square root of the coefficient of determination (for the slope and intercept model) is the correlation coefficient between the estimated values and the responses.

As can be seen from the formulas above, the Coefficient of Determination for the proportional model will generally not be directly comparable with that of the slope and intercept model. It is possible, for example, to get a large coefficient of determination when fitting a proportional model and a much smaller coefficient of determination when fitting a slope and intercept model.

A word of caution is appropriate before we get carried away by the job of interpreting the many different numerical summaries that are commonly produced by regression software. The scatterplot is your reality, and every regression equation you compute is merely an approximation to this reality. Therefore, the first and most important graph you will need to use is the scatterplot with the regression line superimposed. Other plots may be useful, and numerical summaries and test values will help, but the scatterplot with the regression equation is absolutely essential. For more about this see Section 8.9.

8.3 Regression: One Line or Two?

Consider the data in Table 8.2. If we fit a regression equation expressing Y as a function of X we get:

$$\hat{y}_i = b_0 + b_1 x_i = 0.7978 + 0.6742 x_i$$

But if we fit a regression equation expressing X as a function of Y we get:

$$\hat{x}_i = a_0 + a_1 y_i = 0.4348 + 0.8696 y_i$$

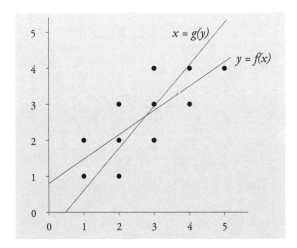

Figure 8.2: Scatterplot of Data Set Nine With Two Regression Lines

The scatterplot in Figure 8.2 shows that these two regression lines are distinctly different. The first equation, based on the model of $y = f(x)$, minimizes the sum of the squared residuals when the residuals are measured in a *vertical* direction. The second equation, based on the model of $x = g(y)$, minimizes the sum of the squared residuals when the residuals are measured in a *horizontal* direction. The method of least squares will give you either line. What these lines represent will depend upon the nature of the data and how they were obtained.

Table 8.2: Data Set Nine

X	1	1	2	2	2	3	3	3	4	4	5
Y	1	2	1	2	3	2	3	4	3	4	4

We may think of the two models $y = f(x)$ and $x = g(y)$ as inverses of each other, but the way in which we estimate the slope and intercept for each of these models will always result in two different regression equations. Why does this happen? To answer this question we can begin with either one of the two models and invert it. Consider the first model $y = f(x)$:

$$Y = \beta_0 + \beta_1 X + e$$

isolate the term involving X to get:

$$(Y - \beta_0 - e) = \beta_1 X$$

When we solve this expression for X we get:

$$X = \frac{(Y - \beta_0 - e)}{\beta_1}$$

$$= \frac{-\beta_0}{\beta_1} + \frac{Y}{\beta_1} + \frac{-e}{\beta_1}$$

$$= \alpha_0 + \alpha_1 Y + \delta$$

And the parameters of this last equation, α_0 and α_1, are non-linear functions of the original parameters. Thus, the inversion of the equation of a straight line requires a non-linear transformation of the slope and intercept parameters.

The estimates obtained by the least squares procedure are unbiased estimates of the parameters in the model used. Since the property of being unbiased is a property that is only preserved by linear transformations, any non-linear combination of unbiased estimates will yield a biased estimate. One of the two regression lines provides unbiased estimates for one form of the relationship, while the other regression line provides unbiased estimates for the other form of the relationship.

When the Coefficient of Determination is close to 1.0 these two regression lines will be close together. (The Coefficient of Determination for Data Set Nine is only 59%.) However, even when these two lines converge, it is important to understand the difference between them. The interpretation of these two regression lines will depend upon the nature of the observations on X and Y and what type of relationship exists between them. The next three sections will outline three different ways of interpreting the two regression equations.

8.4   A Deterministic Relation with Controlled X

Case One exists when X and Y are deterministically related and X is controlled or observed without error (or with very little error relative to the errors of observation for Y).

An example of this would be the data of Table 8.1. While there is considerable uncertainty in the distance values, the red shifts are measured with reasonable precision. Since the regression equation explains 95.6% of the total variation for these data there is only a slight difference between the two regression lines that could be fitted to these data.

Another example would be the data of Table 8.3 which come from a undergraduate physics lab session in which an experiment was performed to illustrate Hooke's Law: the stretch of a spring is proportional to the load. Various weights were attached to a piano wire, and the length of the piano wire was measured (fairly imprecisely).

Table 8.3: Hooke's Law

Weight (kg)	2	4	6	8	10
Length (cm)	439.2	439.2	439.3	439.5	439.5

Since the weights are known, while the lengths are observed with error, we will expect that the points of the scatterplot will deviate vertically from the underlying deterministic relationship. Therefore, it is appropriate to minimize the sum of the squared residuals in a vertical direction, and the correct model to use is the one that considers length as a function of weight plus some measurement error:

$$Length = \beta_0 + \beta_1\ Weight + e_i$$

The least squares regression equation for this model is:

$$Length = 439.07\ \text{cm} + 0.045\ \text{cm/kg}\ Weight$$

This regression equation provides an unbiased estimate of the deterministic relationship between length and weight.

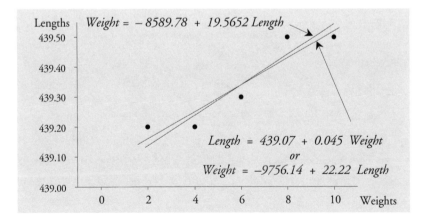

Figure 8.3: Two Regression Lines for Hooke's Law

The least squares regression equation of Weight (X) as a function of Length (Y) will yield a *biased* estimate of the deterministic relationship, and is therefore not the preferred approach for this case. If we wanted to express Weight as a function of Length we would simply invert the regression equation of Length upon Weight given above to get:

$$Weight = \frac{[\,Length - 439.07\text{ cm}\,]}{0.045\text{ cm}/\text{kg}}$$
$$= -9756.14 + 22.22\text{ kg}/\text{cm } Length$$

Thus, when the X values are essentially known without error, and the Y values are only known with error, and we think that X and Y are deterministically related, the regression of Y as a function of X will provide an unbiased estimate of that underlying deterministic relationship.

8.5 A Deterministic Relation with Uncertain X Values

Case Two exists when X and Y are deterministically related and both X and Y are observed with error.

As an example of this case consider the data of Table 8.4. There a careful but complicated laboratory analysis known as "bottle loss" is compared with an auto-mated, on-line measure known as "cup loss." Since both analyses are measuring the same property of the product, and since the on-line test is quicker and easier to obtain, the question of how these two analyses are related is of interest. Fourteen production samples were split and measured each way. Since the objective is to predict the bottle loss from the cup loss, let the bottle loss be the "dependent" variable.

The regression of Bottle Loss as a function of Cup Loss is:

$$Est.\ Bottle\ Loss = 0.2097 + 0.8585\ Cup\ Loss$$

This regression equation is a *biased* estimate of the relationship between Bottle Loss and Cup Loss. This bias occurs because, while there is uncertainty in both X and Y, the equation above only minimizes the sum of squared residuals in a vertical direction.

Since X and Y are deterministically related with uncertainty in both values, we find the regression of Cup Loss (X) as a function of Bottle Loss (Y) and invert the resulting regression equation to get:

$$\text{Est. Bottle Loss} = -0.2013 + 0.9776 \, \text{Cup Loss}$$

Since this equation has minimized the sum of squares of the horizontal residuals it also provides a *biased* estimate of any underlying deterministic relationship that exists.

Table 8.4: Bottle Loss (*Y*) and Cup Loss (*X*)

X	3.1	3.9	3.4	4.0	3.8	3.6	3.3	3.5	2.9	3.6	4.1	3.1	3.2	2.8
Y	2.7	3.6	3.0	3.5	3.7	3.4	3.1	3.2	2.6	3.3	3.7	3.0	2.8	2.8

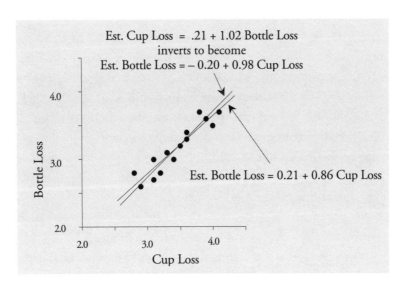

Figure 8.4: Regressions of Bottle Loss upon Cup Loss

The actual relationship between the Cup Loss measurements and the Bottle Loss values will probably fall somewhere in between the two regression lines shown in Figure 8.4. The slope is probably somewhere between 0.86 and 0.98 while the intercept is somewhere between 0.2 and −0.2. If one of the two variables displays more variation than the other, then that regression which treats the variable with the greater variation as the dependent variable will probably be closer to the actual relationship.

In this case, the scatterplot shows about the same variation in each direction. So we might choose to use the average of the two regression lines in production and end up with a proportional model that relates the Bottle Loss to the Cup Loss:

Est. Bottle Loss = 0.92 Cup Loss

When a deterministic relationship exists between X and Y and when both X and Y are observed with error, the two least squares equations provide biased estimates of the underlying deterministic relationship.

8.6 X and Y are Random Variables

Case Three exists when X and Y can be described as random variables having a bivariate normal joint probability distribution.

In this case, while X and Y are said to be *correlated*, there is *no functional relationship* that exists between values of X and values of Y. Given any particular value for X, the corresponding values for Y will follow a normal probability distribution, and given any particular value for Y, the corresponding values for X will follow a normal probability distribution. In both cases these normal probability distributions are known as conditional distributions since they depend upon the value of the other value. Specifically, the means of the conditional distributions for Y given X will be a linear function of the X values, and the means of the conditional distributions of X given Y will be a linear function of the Y values.

An example of this case might consist of the heights of fathers and their sons. Forty such pairings are given in Table 8.5 and shown in Figure 8.5.

The regression equation of Y as a function of X will estimate the line that defines the conditional means of Y given X. This regression line estimates the mean height

Table 8.5: Heights of Fathers and Sons

Fathers	Sons	Fathers	Sons	Fathers	Sons	Fathers	Sons
63.5	66.25	66.5	67	69	66.5	65.5	67.75
63.5	65	67	66.25	69.5	69	66	65.5
63.5	67.75	67.25	69.5	69.5	71.5	66	69.25
63.5	68.5	67.25	67.5	69.5	73.25	68.75	71
64	64	67.5	70	69.75	68.75	68.75	70.5
65	70.75	67.75	64.75	69.75	70.25	69	69.5
65	67.25	68	67	70	68	68.5	73
65	66.25	68.25	68.5	70.75	74	72.5	71.75
65.25	65.25	68.25	66.75	71.25	70.5	71.75	69.5
65.5	69.5	68.5	68	71.25	72.5	71.25	71.5

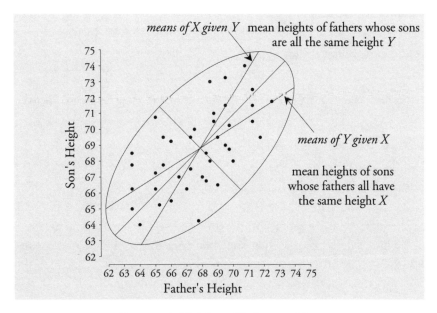

Figure 8.5: Heights of Fathers and Sons

of the sons for fathers of a specific height:

$$Est.\ Mean\ Height\ of\ Sons\ =\ 26.9\ +\ 0.617\ Height\ of\ Fathers$$

Both the slope and intercept terms are meaningful (the p values are less than 0.003) and this regression has a Coefficient of Determination of 39%. Sons whose fathers are 72 inches tall will average 71.3 inches in height, while sons whose fathers are 64 inches tall will average 66.4 inches tall.

The regression of X as a function of Y will estimate the line that defines the conditional means of X given Y. This regression line estimates the mean height of the fathers whose sons all have a specific height:

$$Est.\ Mean\ Height\ of\ Fathers\ =\ 24.3\ +\ 0.631\ Height\ of\ Sons$$

Once again, both the slope and intercept terms are meaningful (the p values are less than 0.009). Thus, we estimate that fathers whose sons are 72 inches tall will average 69.7 inches tall, while fathers whose sons are 64 inches tall will average 64.7 inches tall.

In trying to determine if a data set might be reasonably approximated by a bivariate normal distribution you might try to superimpose an ellipse like the one in

Figure 8.5 upon the scatterplot. The centroid of the ellipse will be the point defined by the average of the X values and the average of the Y values. If the scatterplot has a positive slope the Major Axis will pass through the point:

$$[\ \bar{x} + s_x\ ,\ \bar{y} + s_y\ ]$$

If the scatterplot has a negative slope the Major Axis will pass through the point:

$$[\ \bar{x} + s_x\ ,\ \bar{y} - s_y\ ]$$

If an ellipse that satisfies these constraints provides a reasonable fit to the scatterplot then the use of the regression equations to approximate the conditional means of X given Y and of Y given X will be appropriate.

Thus, in this case, while there is no underlying deterministic relationship, the two regression equations do represent two different sets of conditional means.

The *regression fallacy* occurs when someone tries to use the major axis in Figure 8.5 to relate the values of X to the values of Y. While this may be visually appealing, it is wrong. As shown in Figure 8.6 the conditional distributions of Y given X are not centered on the major axis. The are instead centered on the line connecting the two points on the ellipse having vertical tangents, which is the regression line of Y as a function of X.

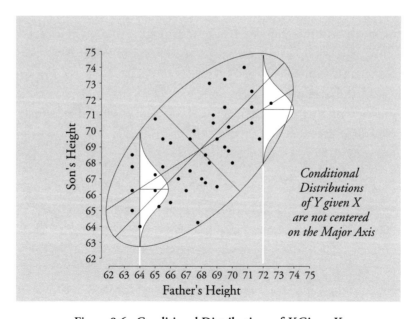

Figure 8.6: Conditional Distributions of Y Given X

Thus, the regression of Y upon X provides an unbiased estimate of mean values for Y that occur in conjunction with a particular value of X.

Likewise, the regression of X as a function of Y is the line that connects the two points on the ellipse having horizontal tangents. This line is an unbiased estimate of the mean values for X that occur in conjunction with a particular value of Y. The conditional distributions of X given Y are not centered on the major axis of the ellipse. The major axis does not describe the behavior of either variable as a function of the other variable.

Figure 8.7 illustrates the *regression to the mean* phenomenon that occurs with pairs of random variables. Very tall fathers will tend to have shorter sons, and very short fathers will tend to have taller sons. Of course, as a group, the sons average about one inch taller than their fathers, but for any vertical slice through Figure 8.7 (any one value of X other than the average) the conditional mean of Y will be closer to the overall mean of Y than the value of X will be to the overall mean of X. This tendency was labeled the "regression to mediocrity" by Sir Francis Galton in 1875.

Thus, while there are two different least squares equations that we can fit to any given scatterplot, the interpretation of these two regression equations will depend upon the nature of the relationship between X and Y and how the observed values

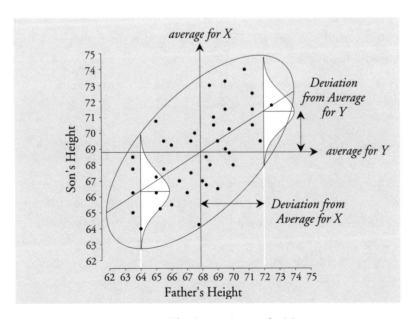

Figure 8.7: The Regression to the Mean

for *X* and *Y* were obtained. A failure to understand this can lead to many errors of interpretation and usage.

8.7 Data Snooping

When you start rummaging around in a database to discover if you can use some variables to "predict" other variables you are data snooping (an activity more recently dignified by the term data mining). Of course the problem of data snooping is that of separating those relationships that are serendipitous from those that are real. Two variables that move around together may have a direct or indirect deterministic relationship, or they may have a probabilistic relationship, or they may have no relationship at all. Just because we have a nice regression equation with a large Coefficient of Determination does not mean that *X* is related to *Y*. Once again, we come back to the first axiom of data analysis: no data have meaning apart from their context. It is the context that gives meaning to any regression equation and determines how to interpret the regression equation in practice. Careful consideration of the nature of *X* and *Y*, and the type of relationship that is reasonable, will be required to make sense of any regression equations you may find while data snooping.

As an example of this, consider the data of Table 8.6. There the millions of pounds of steam used in a chemical plant each month over the past 24 months is shown along with the average monthly temperature for the plant site.

Table 8.6: Steam Usage and Average Monthly Temperature

Temp. °F	35	30	31	59	61	71	74	77	71	58	46	29
Steam M lbs.	11.0	11.1	12.5	8.4	9.3	8.7	6.4	8.5	7.8	9.1	8.2	12.2
Temp. °F	28	39	47	49	59	70	70	75	72	58	45	33
Steam M lbs.	11.9	9.6	10.9	9.6	10.1	8.1	6.8	8.9	7.7	8.5	8.9	10.4

While it makes sense that the temperature will have an impact upon steam usage in the plant, there are many other possible independent variables that should also affect steam usage: such as the amount of product produced, the days of operation each month, the quality of the feed stock, etc. Since it is logical to consider the steam usage as the dependent variable and the temperature as the independent variable, we would find the regression of steam usage as a function of temperature:

Est. Average Steam Usage = 13.68 − 0.0807 *Avg. Monthly Temp.*

This regression equation may estimate an underlying deterministic relationship, but it is at best a partial relationship—some, but not all, of the steam usage probably depends directly upon the site temperature. Thus, we should only claim that the *average* steam usage is characterized by this line, and treat the regression equation more like those found when X and Y are random variables.

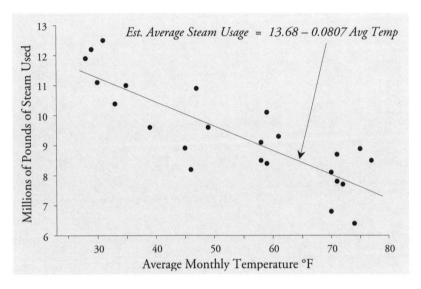

Figure 8.8: Regression of Steam Usage upon Average Temperature

Another example of regression as a data snooping tool is given in Table 8.7. There the number of tax returns filed (in thousands) and the number of passenger vehicles registered (in thousands) are listed for each county in one state. The scatter-plot of these 38 pairs of values is seen in Figure 8.9. The regression of the number of tax returns as a function of the number of registered autos is:

$$\text{Est. Average No. Tax Returns} \ = \ 4.42 + 0.514 \ \text{Autos Registered}$$

Clearly automobile registrations do not cause tax returns to be filed, but there is enough of a correlation here to use one variable to approximate the other. The State Department of Revenue might find an equation like this to be useful even though it is not certain whether this equation will hold true from one year to the next.

On the other hand, the county clerks might find the regression of automobile registrations upon tax returns to be helpful:

Est. Average No. Auto Registrations = 3.34 + 1.58 *Tax Returns Filed*

Table 8.7: Registered Autos and Tax Returns Filed by County

Autos	Returns	Autos	Returns	Autos	Returns
76	23	80	37	94	27
32	11	56	21	50	31
64	13	238	67	72	15
98	31	56	13	58	8
18	11	38	17	120	38
112	33	140	27	34	11
126	38	10	5	28	10
36	9	36	17	126	48
272	70	26	8	66	30
236	48	154	32	20	7
182	36	52	10	186	91
118	35	162	39	174	84
378	98	354	93		

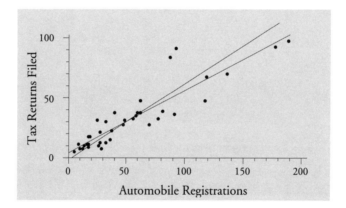

Figure 8.9: Regressions Relating Tax Returns and Auto Registrations

Both of these regression equations have intercept terms that might well be zero (large P-values), but in the absence of some definite mechanism linking these two variables it is better to leave the intercept terms in the equations. Removing the intercept terms would restrict the equations to a model of strict proportionality and we do not know enough about this relationship to make this kind of assumption.

RESTRICTED RANGES

Another problem with data snooping is the problem of restricted ranges. If Y depends upon X, but in the data base the values for X are restricted in some way, we

Table 8.8: Restricted Heights of Fathers and Their Sons

Fathers	Sons	Fathers	Sons	Fathers	Sons	Fathers	Sons
72.5	71.75	69	66.5	70	68	69.5	69
69.5	71.5	70.75	74	69.5	73.25	69.75	68.75
71.75	69.5	69.75	70.25	69	69.5	71.25	70.5
		71.25	72.5	71.25	71.5		

might find either a distorted relationship or no relationship at all.

For example, consider the data from Table 8.5, but let us say that the study was conducted using fathers who were members of a police force that only accepted applicants that were at least 69 inches tall. Then our data would look like those in Table 8.8 and Figure 8.10.

The regression equation shown has a P-value for the slope of 0.14, meaning that there is no detectable relationship between X and Y.

Thus, when an input variable has a restricted range you might not find a relationship even when a definite relationship exists. This is one of the hazards of data snooping with multiple linear regression. You should always use common sense, process knowledge, and sound theory in interpreting what your regression analysis produces.

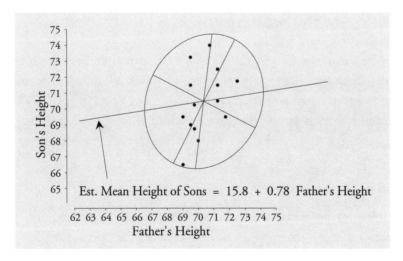

Est. Mean Height of Sons = 15.8 + 0.78 Father's Height

Figure 8.10: Regressions When Fathers' Heights are Restricted

8.8 Trends

An even more uncertain usage of regression equations is that of trend lines. When we fit a trend line to a time-series we are using the time period as the independent variable, even though we know that the time period does not cause the trend. Here, the time period is merely a surrogate for the underlying system of cause-and-effect relationships that is creating the trend. With trend lines, the emphasis is always upon prediction and forecasting, yet this is exactly where the trend line gets dicey. Extrapolation of a regression equation is always a risky business, even when there is an underlying cause-and-effect relationship. Extrapolation of a trend line may be necessary in some instances, but users of trend lines must understand the inherent uncertainties and implicit assumptions.

The simplest and easiest way to detect a trend in a time-series is to place the values on an *XmR* Chart and see if there are one or more points below the limit at one end and one or more points above the limit at the other end. When a regression equation is used to estimate a trend line you can check for a detectable (nonzero) trend using the P-value for the slope term.

8.9 The Role of the Scatterplot

Once upon a time, when this author was much younger, he was working with some civil engineers to analyze data on midblock traffic accidents. One investigator stated that the width of the street would have an effect upon the midblock accident rate. This author quickly sorted the data by width of street and had the computer produce a regression of accident rate as a function of street width. The resulting equation was:

$$\textit{Est. Mean Accident Rate} = 3.57 - 0.036 \textit{ Width}$$

The accompanying analysis showed a correlation of 22 percent between these two variables and a P-value of 0.44 for the estimated slope parameter. In other words, the regression line did not have any detectable slope (it was estimating a horizontal line). Based upon this equation I reported that there was no relationship between the accident rate and the street width. The engineers strongly disagreed.

Following this disagreement, I decided to look at the scatterplot, and found the picture shown in Figure 8.11.

If I had started with the scatterplot the whole fiasco could have been avoided. There is clearly a relationship between street width and midblock accident rates, but it is not a simple linear relationship. If you assume the wrong shape for your regression equation you are very likely to end up with egg on your face.

Regression equations are no better than the model you use.

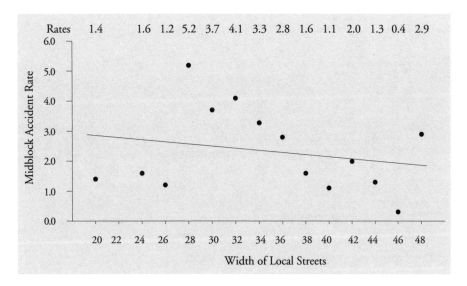

Figure 8.11: Midblock Accident Rates as a Function of the Width of Local Streets

8.10 The Problem of Regression Models

We have obtained a simple equation that uses the redshift of a galaxy to characterize its distance from our galaxy. This model explains 95.6 percent of the variation in these distances, and it provides an estimate of the age of the universe which is reasonable in the light of subsequent work. But the equation would not have been of any interest had it not continued to work with additional data. Table 8.9 provides an additional 34 pairs of observations on redshift and distance (once again, for the sake of comparison, these are the estimated distances as of 1976).

Table 8.9: Red Shifts and Distances to 34 Additional Galaxies

Red Shift	Dist.	Red Shift	Dist.	Red Shift	Dist.
0.131	2232	0.168	3704	0.175	4175
0.135	2273	0.175	3704	0.281	4535
0.143	2305	0.196	3755	0.254	4555
0.137	2695	0.202	3843	0.198	4662
0.136	2797	0.206	3950	0.226	4815
0.159	2888	0.200	3968	0.291	4837
0.153	2915	0.228	4061	0.226	4973
0.150	2997	0.265	4098	0.241	5631
0.172	3167	0.236	4131	0.392	6496
0.192	3331	0.206	4155	0.360	8563
0.183	3347	0.173	4155	0.461	9520
0.165	3619				

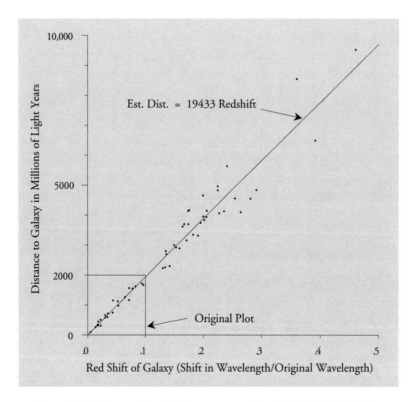

Figure 8.12: Scatterplot of Distance versus Red Shift for 56 Galaxies

The data of Tables 8.1 and 8.9 are shown in Figure 8.12, along with the original regression model. Refitting this model using all the data changes the slope from 19433 to 19493, a change of less than one-third of one percent!

Thus, there is a proportionality, and our estimates of that proportionality are characterizing a real, persistent, and fundamental relationship.

No matter how large your Coefficient of Determination, no matter how well your regression equation may fit your data, it only characterizes the data it has been given. The ability to use the regression model with other data, or possibly with other values for X, will depend more upon the nature and pedigree of the data, and the processes that generated those data, than it will upon any of the numbers on the printout of the regression analysis.

The extrapolation seen in Figure 8.12 works because the regression model was estimating a universal relationship. It started as a conjecture, but with each additional point it became more firmly established as a fact.

In most cases we are not as fortunate as Edwin Hubble. We do not commonly encounter data that reveal such a simple and profound universal relationship. While we may occasionally experiment with fundamental cause-and-effect relationships, we more often work with data from processes that change over time. These conditions will limit our use of any regression model.

When working with a fundamental cause-and-effect relationship we will need to be careful to avoid extrapolation on the predictor variable. While our regression model may work well in the range studied, it may not work at all outside that range.

When working with data from processes that may change over time we need to consider any regression model to be tentative and provisional. If the underlying processes remain the same, then the regression model will probably work. If the processes change, the old model is not likely to still be appropriate. Regression models seek to fit your data—they do not examine those data for homogeneity over time. Yet, as we have seen it is the homogeneity over time that allows us to extrapolate into the future.

Thus, the greatest danger of a regression model is the temptation to think that, because you can express a relationship in an equation, you understand that relationship. While regression models may be used to characterize fundamental relationships, even when the exact form of those relationships are unknown; while regression models may be used to discover coincidental relationships that can be used to optimize or predict other variables; and while regression models can provide new insights into complex relationships; all regression models are limited by the quality of the data and the perseverance of the conditions represented by those data. All data are historical. All analyses of data are historical. And the one constant of history is change.

After all, the whole universe is expanding.

Chapter Nine

Count-Based Data

The preceding chapters have outlined various analysis techniques that may be used when the response variable is a measurement. This chapter will consider what happens when the response variable is either a count of items or a proportion based on a count of items. The next chapter will deal with counts of events or rates based on counts of events. In the interest of clarity we need to begin with the distinction between these two types of counts.

9.1 Two Types of Counts

There are two types of counts; *counts of items having some attribute* and *counts of events*. These counts differ in what is being counted, and they differ in the nature of their areas of opportunity.

COUNTS OF ITEMS

When you are characterizing each item in a set of **n** items according to whether or not that item possesses some attribute, and counting the number of items with that attribute, your count will be a *count of items*. For example, the count of the number of orders incorrectly filled last month, or the number of employees who retired during the past year, would be counts of items.

Since counts of items are limited by the number of items inspected, counts of items will always have a finite counting number, **n**, as their area of opportunity—the count may be any counting number from 0 to **n**. In the examples above, the value for **n** would be, respectively, the number of orders filled last month or the number of employees at the start of the year. (Note that this use of the letter "n" is different from its use to denote the number of measurements in a data set. Here you have a single count, and **n** is the area of opportunity for that count. To distinguish these two uses of the letter "n" I will use a boldface **n** for the area of opportunity of a count of items and an italicized *n* for the number of measurements in a data set.)

With counts of items you can count the number of items, out of **n** items, that possess some attribute, or you can count the number of items *not* having that attribute. Since these two numbers must always add up to **n**, they both contain the same information. In other words, you could insert the word "not" into the description of a count of items and still have a meaningful statement.

Since counts of items are actually "counts of items having some attribute," they are sometimes referred to as "attribute data." With a count of items, each item will contribute either a zero or a one to the total count. Thus, after considering **n** items we do not have **n** measurements, but rather a single value, Y, which is the total count obtained by summing up all those zeroes and ones. This total count is both a single observation and a summary statistic.

COUNTS OF EVENTS

In addition to counts of items, there are also counts of events. While many books refer to counts of events as attribute data, they are actually something quite different.

Since you cannot have half of an event, events are inherently countable, so we must use the counting numbers to keep track of events. However, unlike attributes where you can count the *presence* or *absence* of the attribute, you cannot count the *nonevents*. Since the count here refers to the event, rather than to some attribute of an item, counts of events are not attribute data.

This difference in what is being counted provides a helpful way of making a distinction between counts of items and counts of events. If you can insert a negation in the definition of what is being counted, you are counting items with (or without) an attribute. If you cannot insert a negation and have something that makes sense, then you are counting events. For example, we cannot count the number of non-complaints, yet we can count the number of employees retiring or *not* retiring. We cannot count the number of non-accidents, but we can count the number of orders correctly or incorrectly filled.

The area of opportunity for a *count of events* is the region within which the events occurred. This region might be a finite region of space and time, a finite region of product, or a finite number of manhours worked, but it is always a finite portion of some underlying continuum within which the events occur.

When working with counts of events the definition of the area of opportunity can be vague. In fact, for any given count, it may be defined in different ways. The area of opportunity for the number of transactions might be the number of hours the business was open, or it might be the number of manhours worked. Either could serve as the area of opportunity for this count. The key to defining the area of opportunity for counting events is that it must be some finite region of space, or time, or production, or activity, which serves to define the region within which the events occur.

COUNTS OF ITEMS OR EVENTS

Some counts can be either a count of items or a count of events depending on how we define the count and the area of opportunity. Errors in order fulfillment could belong to either category. If you count all types of errors, so that a single order could have more than one error, then this might be considered a count of events. However, if you count the number of orders with errors, you have a count of items.

If you count the number of sales per week, you are counting events. If you count the number of visitors to the store who made a purchase, you are counting items.

Finally, we can occasionally treat counts of items as if they are counts of events. This happens when the counts are small relative to **n**, so that **n** does not actually place a practical upper bound on the values for the counts. An example of this might be the number of absences for a given company on a given day. The actual number of absences will (usually) be so much smaller than the possible number that it will not matter much whether we consider this count to be a count of items or a count of events.

When working with counts it is critical to know the size of the area of opportunity for each count. The distinction between counts of items and counts of events is important since we will use different inferential techniques with each.

9.2 Interval Estimates for Universe Proportions

With count data there is a danger of combining counts from different universes. For example, a daily summary for a plant might show a total of 85 units, out of 17,022 units produced, failed their final test, resulting in a failure rate of $85/17,022 = 0.005$ or one half of one percent. However, if 70 failures came from Line One, which made 6905 units, and 15 failures came from Line Two, which made 10,117 units, what can you do with the ratio of 85/17,022 = 0.005? While it is true that on this one day this plant did have one-half percent defective, is Line One operating with one-half percent defective? Is Line Two? Once again, while the *descriptive* statistic summarizes the day's output, it does not give you any leverage for *analysis* since it does not characterize the underlying processes that produced the count.

If the area of opportunity for a count represents more than one universe, then that count cannot provide any information about *any* of the universes. Such a count may be descriptive, but it cannot be used for data analysis.

> *A count can be used to characterize an underlying process*
> *only when the area of opportunity for that count*
> *represents a single universe.*

If you have a count of items, Y, with an area of opportunity, **n**, and if that area of opportunity represents a single universe, then the statistic:

$$\bar{p} = \frac{Y}{\mathbf{n}}$$

is the traditional estimate of the parameter, **p**, for the proportion of items in the universe which possess the attribute. This statistic is commonly known as the *binomial point estimate*.

As long as both Y and $(\mathbf{n}-Y)$ are greater than 5 we can obtain an approximate $100(1-\alpha)\%$ Interval Estimate for the universe proportion **p** using:

$$\bar{p} \pm z_{\alpha/2} \frac{\sqrt{\bar{p}(1-\bar{p})}}{\sqrt{\mathbf{n}}}$$

where $z_{\alpha/2}$ denotes the upper-tail critical value from a standard normal distribution. (These values may be found in the last row of Table A.7.) This formula is known as the *Wald Interval Estimate* for **p** and is the one given in most textbooks.

Inspection of the above formula will show that the Wald Interval Estimate will always result in an interval that is symmetric about the binomial point estimate. However, exact interval estimates for **p** will only be symmetric when **p** is equal to 0.50. The approximate nature of the Wald Interval Estimate, connected with the fact that it uses a symmetric interval to estimate an asymmetric interval, has resulted in the development of many other approximations. Only one of these maintains the simplicity of the Wald estimate while providing a better interval estimate for **p**.

A better approximation to a $100(1-\alpha)\%$ Interval Estimate for the universe proportion, **p**, that will work for any value of Y and $(\mathbf{n}-Y)$ may be found by simply adding two successes and two failures to the binomial point estimate:

$$\tilde{p} = \frac{Y+2}{\mathbf{n}+4}$$

and then using the formula:

$$\tilde{p} \pm z_{\alpha/2}\frac{\sqrt{\tilde{p}\,(1-\tilde{p}\,)}}{\sqrt{\mathbf{n}+4}}$$

This adjustment will provide a closer approximation to the interval estimate for **p** when Y or $(\mathbf{n}-Y)$ is small. As Y and $(\mathbf{n}-Y)$ get larger this adjustment will disappear. This point estimate is known as the *Wilson Point Estimate*, and the interval estimate above will be known as the *Wilson Interval Estimate*, after E. B. Wilson, who proposed this approach in 1927. This interval estimate is still a symmetric interval, but it is no longer symmetric about the binomial point estimate. By shifting the center of our interval estimate we end up with a better approximation without undue complexity.

In the interest of clarity and simplicity I recommend that you use $\bar{p}$ as your point estimate. However, when drawing inferences about the proportion in a single universe having a specific attribute, I recommend the use of the Wilson Interval Estimate.

◆ ◆ ◆

For Line One, our point estimate for the fraction defective would be $70/6905 = 0.0101$ or 1%. (With such large values for Y and **n** the addition of two successes and two failures will result in a trivial change.) A 99% Interval Estimate for **p** would be:

$$\tilde{p} \pm z_{.005}\frac{\sqrt{\tilde{p}\,(1-\tilde{p}\,)}}{\sqrt{\mathbf{n}+4}} = 0.0104 \pm 2.576\frac{\sqrt{.0104\,(.9896)}}{\sqrt{6909}} = 0.0072 \text{ to } 0.0136$$

Therefore we would definitely reject the idea that Line One was operating with a fraction defective as small as one-half percent.

For Line Two, our point estimate for the fraction defective would be $15/10,117 = 0.0015$ or 0.15%. A 99% Interval Estimate for **p** would be:

$$\tilde{p} \pm z_{.005}\frac{\sqrt{\tilde{p}\,(1-\tilde{p}\,)}}{\sqrt{\mathbf{n}+4}} = 0.0017 \pm 2.576\frac{\sqrt{.0017\,(.9983)}}{\sqrt{10121}} = 0.0006 \text{ to } 0.0027$$

Therefore we would definitely reject the idea that Line Two was operating with a fraction defective as large as one-half percent. Moreover, since these two 99% Interval Estimates do not overlap, it would appear that the Line One and Line Two have definitely different failure rates.

Of course these inferences about Lines One and Two make an implicit assumption that each line is operating with a consistent fraction defective throughout the day. If a line has different fractions defective at different times of the day then all of the above computations for that line are meaningless.

9.3 Homogeneity for Counts

The question of homogeneity for count data comes down to a question about whether or not the area of opportunity represents a single universe. With small areas of opportunity we can usually justify the assumption that the area of opportunity represents a single universe. However, as the area of opportunity gets larger this assumption becomes more questionable. This is the major problem with the use of inspection data for inferential calculations. Inspection data may provide descriptive statistics for how many defectives were produced on a given day, but without homogeneity the descriptive statistics do not characterize the underlying process.

A series of counts of the same attribute or event, over smaller areas of opportunity, will allow you to check for the homogeneity that is required to use count data for analysis. By placing these counts on an *XmR* Chart you can explicitly check for homogeneity over time. If the counts display homogeneity, then they may be combined into global summaries and used for analysis. If they are nonhomogeneous, then you need to find out why. The only limitation on the use of an *XmR* Chart with count data is the problem of chunky data. This problem will usually occur when the average count falls to the neighborhood of 1.0 or below.

Line One averages about 450 units per half-hour. Each unit is subjected to an automated on-line inspection. By recording the number of units produced and the number that failed inspection each half-hour, the operators of Line One obtained the data of Table 9.1 for one eight-hour day. The *X* Chart for these data is shown in Figure 9.1 with limits based on the Median Moving Range.

Table 9.1: Number Failing On-Line Test for Line One

Period	1	2	3	4	5	6	7	8	9	10	11	12	13	14	15	16
No. Failed	1	0	2	3	1	0	2	3	2	0	4	14	21	2	12	3
No. Made	432	435	427	409	415	433	438	452	457	441	451	402	398	460	412	443

Figure 9.1: *X* **Chart for Number Failed Each Period on Line One**

Figure 9.1 shows a run of eleven points below the central line and three points above the upper limit. Line One cannot, by any stretch of the imagination, be said to have been operated consistently during the course of this day. No computation we can make will permit us to characterize the actual performance of Line One with a single set of summary statistics. Until we find out why Line One is operating, or is being operated, inconsistently we should expect continued chaos.

We may compute a descriptive statistic for Line One and say that we had 70/6905 = 0.010 that failed today, but the lack of homogeneity for these counts prevents us from using this value as an estimate of the inherent failure rate for Line One. Line One does not have one failure rate—it has many different failure rates, *none of which are characterized by the binomial point estimate of 0.010.* You need to find out why Line One is operating unpredictably before you can ever get Line One to operate up to its full potential.

◆ ◆ ◆

The same data collection scheme was used for Line Two and resulted in the data shown in Table 9.2 and Figure 9.2.

With an average count just below 1.0 we use the moving range chart to check for chunky data. With an Upper Range Limit of 3.3 we still have four possible values for the moving ranges within the limits. Thus while we are on the borderline, we do not have a problem with chunky data in this case.

Table 9.2: Number Failing On-Line Test for Line Two

Period	1	2	3	4	5	6	7	8	9	10	11	12	13	14	15	16
No. Failed	0	0	0	1	2	0	2	1	3	1	1	1	2	0	0	1
No. Made	625	643	616	596	683	611	605	568	665	652	625	621	650	635	628	694

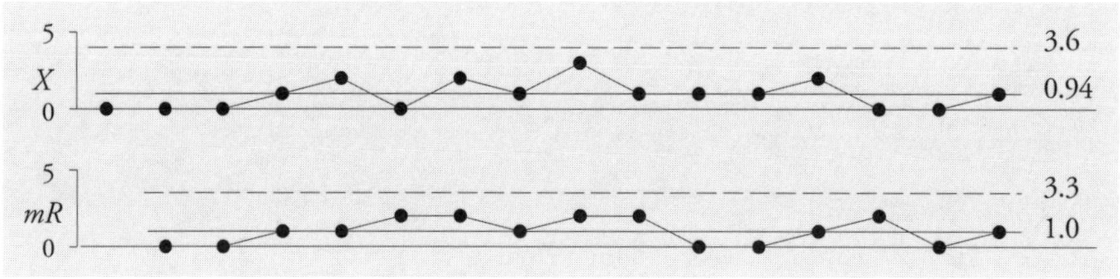

Figure 9.2: *X* Chart for Number Failed Each Period on Line Two

Since Line Two shows no evidence of inconsistent operation, we can combine all of the data from Table 9.2 to obtain a global proportion to characterize the operation of Line Two. The overall proportion failing the on-line test is the binomial point estimate of the failure proportion **p** for Line Two:

$$\bar{p} = \frac{15}{10117} = 0.00148$$

Based on the *X* Chart in Figure 9.2, you should expect an average of one failure per half-hour, with a maximum of three failures on any single half-hour period from Line Two. Based on the 99% Interval Estimate found earlier we can say that it is unlikely that Line Two has a failure proportion below 0.0006, and it is unlikely that it has a failure proportion above 0.0027.

Notice that it is the homogeneity of these counts, demonstrated by the *X* Chart, that justifies using them collectively to estimate the proportion **p** that are failing on Line Two.

9.4 Should I Compare Counts or Rates?

In the two examples in the previous section, the counts for each half-hour did not have equal sized areas of opportunity—the number of units made in each period differed. In spite of this we compared the counts on the *X* Charts. In general, whenever the areas of opportunity are reasonably close to being the same size we can compare the counts directly. The usual guideline here is that the sizes of the areas of opportunity should differ by no more than ± 20 percent from some average sized area of opportunity. So if the largest area of opportunity is less than 1.2 times the average size of all the areas of opportunity, and if the smallest area of opportunity is greater than 0.8 times the average size of all of the areas of opportunity, it is considered acceptable to compare the counts directly.

Table 9.3: Number Failing On-Line Test for Line One

Period	1	2	3	4	5	6	7	8	9	10	11	12	13	14	15	16
No. Failed	1	0	2	3	1	0	2	3	2	0	4	14	21	2	12	3
No. Made	432	435	427	409	415	433	438	452	457	441	451	402	398	460	412	443
Failure Rate	2.3	0.0	4.7	7.3	2.4	0.0	4.6	6.6	4.4	0.0	8.8	34.8	52.8	4.3	29.1	6.8

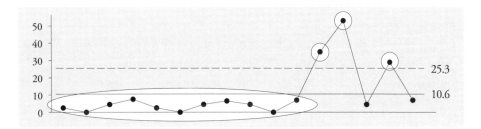

Figure 9.3: *X* Chart for Parts Per Thousand Failure Rates on Line One

When the areas of opportunity vary by more than ± 20 percent, then it is customary to convert the counts into rates before comparing them. The rate is simply the count divided by its own area of opportunity. For counts of items these rates are also known as proportions. Table 9.3 shows the data for Line One converted into rates and expressed in parts per thousand. Figure 9.3 shows these values on an *X* Chart with limits based on the Median Moving Range.

While the scale has changed, the graph and the story it tells are essentially the same as in Figure 9.1. This is as expected since the areas of opportunity were all reasonably similar. While Line One may have averaged 10.6 failures per thousand on this one day, the *process* is not operating with a failure rate of 10.6 per thousand.

9.5 A Caution Regarding Counts on an *XmR* Chart

The first axiom of data analysis requires you to always consider the context for your data as part of the analysis. When dealing with counts of items the possible values for any count are 0 to **n**. When **n** is not too small, say **n** ≥ 20, there will be a sufficient number of possible values for the counts so that they can reveal gross changes in the underlying process.

This means that if, from a practical perspective, the successive values are radically different, then the *XmR* Chart may not be needed—a simple running record may suffice to tell the story.

An example of just such a running record is shown in Figure 9.4. Each point represents from 32 to 108 attempted installations of a pal-nut on a trim panel for a car door. When the percentages are changing from single digits to over 40% we do not need limits to know that the process is changing! The data for April 3, April 12, and April 15 show that this process is capable of operating with a very low percentage of missed installations. The data for the other days show that those responsible for operating this process do not have a clue about how to operate it consistently. Any objective evaluation of the percentages shown in Figure 9.4 will result in the assessment that the process is changing. While we could compute an Upper Natural Process Limit of 0.285 for Figure 9.4, we do not need this limit to understand the erratic nature of this production process. Some signals are so clear that they are visible to the naked eye.

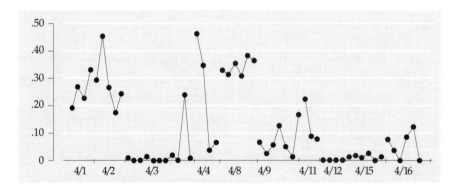

Figure 9.4: Percentage Missed Installations per Cycle for Panel A

However, if instead of using the data for each cycle, we summarized the data for each day we would have the values and *X* Chart shown in Figure 9.5. There the huge day-to-day swings create limits that contain all of the points. Regardless of how we might interpret the *X* chart, any contextual interpretation shows an inconsistent process.

The problem is not which way to chart the data in Figure 9.5, but rather one of stopping to think about what those data mean. A process that fails 8 out of 532 times is not the same as one that fails 160 out of 480 times!

Can we place the data of Figure 9.5 on a *p*-chart? Inspection of the running record in Figure 9.4 will reveal that not only is this process changing from day to day, but it is also changing within a day, making the daily percentages merely descriptive rather than analytic. Since the limits on a *p*-chart require a constant percentage within each period, these data are not appropriate for a *p*-chart.

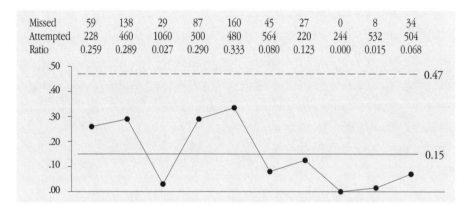

Figure 9.5: Daily Proportion Missed Installations for Panel A

Therefore, when placing data based on counts of items on an *XmR* Chart you should always stop to think about the message contained in the data themselves. With counts of items the contextual interpretation may be sufficient to tell the story, and when this is the case, all further analysis is superfluous.

As a further example, Table 9.4 shows the percentages of neonatal autopsies for one hospital for one ten-year period.

Table 9.4: Neonatal Autopsies

Year	1	2	3	4	5	6	7	8	9	10
Neonatal Fatalities	38	60	67	57	49	46	53	45	32	40
No. Autopsies	35	44	46	32	36	24	30	16	13	26
Autopsy %	92%	73%	69%	56%	73%	52%	57%	36%	41%	65%

If we place the percentages of Table 9.4 on an *XmR* Chart none of the points will fall outside the limits. The central line will be 61.4% with limits at ± 38%. Limits this wide are simply telling you that there are big changes from year to year. Since the percentages of Table 9.4 are based on reasonably large counts we should also look at these values and interpret them in context. When the autopsy rate goes from over 90 percent to under 40 percent something has to be changing! While the *XmR* Chart does not show these changes as signals, contextual interpretation tells us that things are not the same from year to year.

No analysis technique is perfect. You always have to *think* first, and then think statistically.

9.6 Outliers or Signals?

In Figure 9.3 three points fall above the upper limit and are interpreted as evidence of a lack of homogeneity within these data (i.e., signals). To address the question of homogeneity this is all we need do. We have definite evidence that some dominant Assignable Cause is changing the fraction nonconforming, and we need to take action to identify this Assignable Cause. Line One has multiple personalities.

However, if we wish to characterize what Line One has the *potential* to do we might delete the three excessive values and use the remaining 13 values to estimate the *Hypothetical Failure Rate* as:

$$\bar{p} = \frac{23}{5693} = 0.00404$$

In performing this computation we have treated the three exceptional points as *outliers*—points that are not typical of the process. If you are going to work to identify the Assignable Causes for these points and then to take steps to remove the effects of these Assignable Causes from the process, then this computation provides an *approximation* of what Line One *might* be made to do. However, if you are not going to work to operate Line One predictably, then the calculation above represents nothing more than wishful thinking.

Line One has the potential of operating with a Failure Rate of 0.4%. But in order to achieve this potential you will have to remove the effects of the Assignable Causes. All outliers are, *prima facie*, signals of a lack of homogeneity. Simply removing them from the computations in order to polish the statistical inferences will not fix the underlying reality that the process is being operated unpredictably. ***Data manipulation may result in clearer inferences, but it divorces those inferences from the process that is generating the data.*** Removing outliers from the calculations in order to estimate what a predictable process can do only makes sense if you plan to follow through and actually remove the Assignable Causes of the outliers from your process.

9.7 Comparing Two Proportions with Charts

If you have several proportions collected over time for each of two conditions, then you can compare the two conditions by using the proportions to create *XmR* Charts for each condition. If the routine variation of one condition creates points that fall outside the limits of the other condition, then the two conditions are detectably different.

◆ ◆ ◆

Dr. Deming often noted that the outcomes for his Red Bead Experiment depended upon which paddle was used in drawing the beads from the box. Based on this, a statistician who was using a plastic bowl filled with plastic beads in his classes decided to compare two paddles. Paddle A was made of wood and contained 25 holes, while Paddle B was made of plastic and contained 40 holes. A series of 20 drawings was made using each paddle and the counts of red beads shown in Table 9.5 were obtained.

Table 9.5: No. of Red Beads Observed in 40 Drawings from the Same Bead Bowl

Paddle A	3	1	2	0	1		5	3	2	3	2		2	1	1	2	3		5	3	3	3	2
Paddle B	3	4	3	1	1		5	3	4	5	5		1	2	5	3	2		5	8	5	3	4

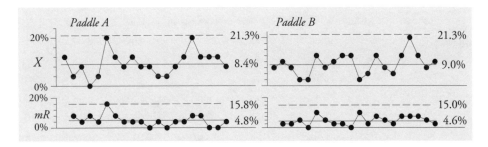

Figure 9.6: *XmR* Charts Comparing Two Paddles

Since the two paddles contain different numbers of holes we need to convert the counts in Table 9.5 into proportions before comparing them. This was done and the proportions were used to create the *XmR* Charts shown in Figure 9.6.

The homogeneity of both series of counts, and the identical Upper Natural Process Limits on the two charts suggest that any difference between these two paddles is too small to detect with this amount of data. They both yield essentially the same proportion of red beads.

Note that the different chunkiness of the two sets of proportions is indicated by the different sets of tick marks for Paddle A and Paddle B. With only five possible values within the limits on the first Moving Range Chart we are approaching the borderline of chunky data. Therefore, I would not interpret the one moving range of 16% as a signal of a lack of homogeneity for Paddle A or as an indication of any difference between the two paddles.

Of course, a lack of homogeneity for either of the two series of proportions will undermine any simple or straightforward comparison between the two conditions. Some limited and conditional comparisons may be attempted, but the presence of a lack of homogeneity is an overwhelming presence that requires explanation before any meaningful comparisons of actual performance can be made. For example, if we wanted to compare the failure rates for Lines One and Two (from Section 9.2) the unpredictable operation of Line One would undermine any comparison we might make. Until we learn how to operate Line One predictably we cannot characterize it as having a single failure rate.

However, there are situations where we might wish to make hypothetical comparisons. As was noted in the previous section, the *XmR* Chart for Line One suggests that it could be operated with a hypothetical failure rate of 0.00404. While this failure rate is subject to learning how to operate the process predictably and, therefore, does not actually characterize our *current* process, we might wish to make a comparison between Lines One and Two under a best case scenario.

The failure rates for Lines One and Two are shown in parts per thousand in Table 9.6. Ignoring the three excessively high failure rates and their associated moving ranges when computing the limits for Line One, we end up with a pair of *XmR* Charts that allow a comparison of Line Two with the best that we can hope to achieve with Line One. These charts are shown in Figure 9.7. (The points shown as white dots were not used in computing the limits for Line One.)

Table 9.6: Parts per Thousand Failing On-Line Test for Lines One and Two

LINE ONE

Period	1	2	3	4	5	6	7	8	9	10	11	12	13	14	15	16
No. Failed	1	0	2	3	1	0	2	3	2	0	4	14	21	2	12	3
No. Made	432	435	427	409	415	433	438	452	457	441	451	402	398	460	412	443
Failure Rate	2.3	0.0	4.7	7.3	2.4	0.0	4.6	6.6	4.4	0.0	8.8	34.8	52.8	4.3	29.1	6.8

LINE TWO

	1	2	3	4	5	6	7	8	9	10	11	12	13	14	15	16
No. Failed	0	0	0	1	2	0	2	1	3	1	1	1	2	0	0	1
No. Made	625	643	616	596	683	611	605	568	665	652	625	621	650	635	628	694
Failure Rate	0	0	0	1.7	2.9	0	3.3	1.8	4.5	1.5	1.6	1.6	3.1	0	0	1.4

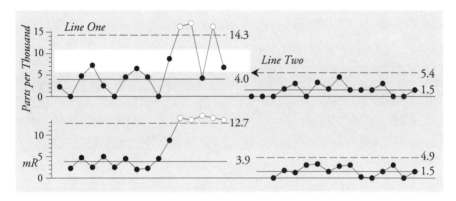

Figure 9.7: *XmR* Charts Comparing Lines One and Two

The disparity between the two sets of limits and the four routine points for Line One (7.3, 6.6, 8.8, & 6.8) that fall outside the limits for Line Two combine to tell the same story. Clearly, even if we learn how to operate Line One predictably, Line One is not likely to have the same low failure rate that Line Two already displays.

The advantage of using *XmR* Charts to make such hypothetical comparisons is that the charts display any lack of homogeneity that may be present in the data, and thereby provide a visual clue that the comparison is merely hypothetical. Formula-based comparisons do not do this.

9.8 Comparing Two Single Proportions

When you have a single proportion for each of the two conditions, *and when you are willing to assume that each of your counts represents a single universe*, you can compare the two conditions by obtaining an interval estimate for the difference of the two proportions.

Say that you want to compare the proportions of items having a given characteristic under two conditions. If n_1 items obtained under Condition One are examined, and y_1 of these items have the characteristic, then the observed proportion having the characteristic for Condition One will be $p_1 = y_1/n_1$. If n_2 items obtained under Condition Two are examined and y_2 of these items have the characteristic, then the observed proportion having the characteristic for Condition Two will be $p_2 = y_2/n_2$.

When the minimum of the set $\{\, y_1\,,\,(n_1 - y_1)\,,\,y_2\,,\,(n_2 - y_2)\,\}$ exceeds 5, an approximate $100(1-\alpha)\%$ Interval Estimate for the difference in the proportions for the two conditions will be:

$$[\, p_1 - p_2 \,] \;\pm\; z_{\alpha/2} \sqrt{\frac{p_1\,(1 - p_1)}{n_1} + \frac{p_2\,(1 - p_2)}{n_2}}$$

- If a 99% Interval Estimate does not contain zero, then the two conditions are detectably different.
- If the 99% Interval Estimate does contain zero but the 90% Interval Estimate does not, then the two proportions may be different but the evidence is not overwhelming.
- If a 90% Interval Estimate contains zero, the two conditions are not detectably different.

Using the data of Table 9.4, Paddle A had a total of 42 Red Beads out of a total of 500 beads examined, giving a binomial point estimate of $p_1 = 42/500 = 0.084$. Paddle B had a total of 72 Red Beads out of a total of 800 beads examined, giving a binomial point estimate of $p_2 = 72/800 = 0.090$. Since it is reasonable to assume that the Bead Bowl did not change during the course of this experiment, we can use the formula above to compare the two observed proportions. A 90% Interval Estimate for the difference between the two paddles is:

$$[\, p_1 - p_2 \,] \;\pm\; z_{\alpha/2} \sqrt{\frac{p_1\,(1 - p_1)}{n_1} + \frac{p_2\,(1 - p_2)}{n_2}}$$

$$= [\, 0.084 - 0.090 \,] \;\pm\; 1.645 \sqrt{\frac{.084(.916)}{500} + \frac{.090(.910)}{800}}$$

$$= -0.006 \;\pm\; 0.026 \;=\; -0.032 \text{ to } 0.020$$

Since this interval estimate contains zero we must conclude that there is no detectable difference between these two paddles.

Returning to the example of Section 9.2, while Line One was operated unpredictably we estimated in Section 9.5 that it had the potential to operate with 0.404% defective. This value was based on the 23 defective units produced in the 13 half-hour periods when 5693 units came off the line.

Line Two produced 10,117 units and had 15 fail the on-line test which gives a sample proportion of $p_2 = 0.0015$ or 0.15%.

A 99% Interval Estimate for the difference between the actual failure rate for Line Two and the hypothetical failure rate for Line One is:

$$[\,p_1 - p_2\,] \ \pm \ z_{\alpha/2} \sqrt{\frac{p_1\,(1-p_1)}{n_1} + \frac{p_2\,(1-p_2)}{n_2}}$$

$$= [\,0.0040 - 0.0015\,] \ \pm \ 2.576 \sqrt{\frac{.004(.996)}{5693} + \frac{.0015(.9985)}{10117}}$$

$$= \ 0.0025 \ \pm \ 0.0024 \ = \ 0.0001 \ \text{to} \ 0.0049$$

Since this interval does not contain zero it is likely that, even when we operate Line One predictably, it will still have a higher failure rate than Line Two. Our simple point estimate of this difference is the difference in the observed proportions, 0.25%.

Unlike the charts in Figure 9.5, the interval estimate above does not make explicit the fact that the comparison between lines is merely hypothetical. This can result in misunderstandings on the part of those with whom you share the results. While there are situations where we might get away with the use of inferential techniques with data that are not homogeneous, you should be very careful that everyone understands the hypothetical nature of such an analysis and the conditional nature of the interpretation of the results.

9.9 Comparing Proportions for Several Conditions

If you have proportions for several conditions, and *if you are willing to assume that each of the areas of opportunity represents a single universe*, then you can compare the conditions by using an approximate procedure known as a Chi-Square Contingency Test.

Assume that, for each of k conditions, we have the count x_i of the number of items, out of $\mathbf{n}_i$ items, that possess a specific attribute. When k is greater than or equal to 3, we can examine the possibility that all k conditions have the same value for $\mathbf{p}$ = the proportion with the attribute being counted. This is done as follows:

Create the 2 by k table of observed counts:

Observed Counts

Condition	1	2	3	...	k
No. With Attribute	x_1	x_2	x_3	...	x_k
No. Without Attribute	$\mathbf{n}_1 - x_1$	$\mathbf{n}_2 - x_2$	$\mathbf{n}_3 - x_3$	...	$\mathbf{n}_k - x_k$

Next we have to obtain the marginal totals for each row and each column of this table of observed counts, and the total count N as well:

Observed Counts with Totals

Condition	1	2	3	...	k	Totals
No. With	x_1	x_2	x_3	...	x_k	R_1
No. Without	$\mathbf{n}_1 - x_1$	$\mathbf{n}_2 - x_2$	$\mathbf{n}_3 - x_3$	...	$\mathbf{n}_k - x_k$	R_2
Totals	C_1	C_2	C_3		C_k	N

While it is true that, in this case $C_1 = \mathbf{n}_1$, $C_2 = \mathbf{n}_2$, etc., we will eventually encounter situations where this is not the case. Therefore, in the interest of generality I will use the notation C_1, C_2, etc. To find the expected counts for each cell we use the column totals, the row totals, and the grand total according to the formulas shown in the following table. These expected counts reflect what should happen, on the average, if every condition has the same value for the proportion with the attribute, $\mathbf{p}$.

Expected Counts

Condition	1	2	3	...	k	
No. With	$C_1 R_1 / N$	$C_2 R_1 / N$	$C_3 R_1 / N$	...	$C_k R_1 / N$	R_1
No. Without	$C_1 R_2 / N$	$C_2 R_2 / N$	$C_3 R_2 / N$	...	$C_k R_2 / N$	R_2
	C_1	C_2	C_3		C_k	N

Usually the expected counts are computed out to at least one decimal place. For simplicity denote the observed counts by the symbol o_j for $j = 1$ to $2k$, and denote the expected counts by the symbol e_j for $j = 1$ to $2k$. We will combine the observed counts and the expected counts cell by cell in the manner defined by the following equations. If every expected count exceeds 10, our chi-square test statistic for this 2 by k table will be:

$$\chi^2 = \sum \frac{(o_j - e_j)^2}{e_j}$$

If this test statistic exceeds a reasonably large critical value from a Chi-Square Distribution having $k{-}1$ degrees of freedom (or if this test statistic corresponds to a reasonably small probability of exceedence) then the k conditions are *not likely* to have the same proportion, **p**.

If every expected count exceeds 5, but some are less than 10, our chi-square test statistic for this 2 by k table will need to incorporate Yates correction into each term:

$$\chi^2\text{(corrected)} = \sum \frac{(\,|o_j - e_j| - 0.5\,)^2}{e_j}$$

If this test statistic exceeds a reasonably large critical value from a Chi-Square Distribution having $k{-}1$ degrees of freedom (or if this test statistic corresponds to a reasonably small probability of exceedence) then the k conditions are *not likely* to have the same proportion, **p**.

If some of the *expected* counts are less than 5, the Chi-Square test will be unsatisfactory and should not be used.

◆ ◆ ◆

The statistician mentioned earlier also had a third paddle. Paddle C was wooden and contained 25 holes. Twenty drawings from the same Bead Bowl resulted in the counts shown in Table 9.6. The question to be answered is whether or not these three paddles yield a different proportion of Red Beads in drawings from this Bead Bowl. To create the contingency table we use the totals for each paddle:

Table 9.7: No. of Red Beads Observed in 60 Drawings from the Same Bead Bowl

Paddle A	3	1	2	0	1	5	3	2	3	2	2	1	1	2	3	5	3	3	3	2
Paddle B	3	4	3	1	1	5	3	4	5	5	1	2	5	3	2	5	8	5	3	4
Paddle C	1	1	3	5	1	2	3	3	2	3	4	1	3	3	4	1	3	3	1	2

The Table of Observed Counts would look like:

Observed Counts

	Paddle A	Paddle B	Paddle C	Totals
Red	42	72	49	163
White	458	728	451	1637
Totals	500	800	500	1800

From the marginal totals we find the table of expected counts:

Expected Counts

	Paddle A	Paddle B	Paddle C	Totals
Red	45.3	72.4	45.3	163
White	454.7	727.6	454.7	1637
Totals	500	800	500	1800

All the expected counts exceed 10, so our Chi-Square test statistic is:

$$\chi^2 = \sum \frac{(o_j - e_j)^2}{e_j}$$

$$= \frac{(42 - 45.3)^2}{45.3} + \frac{(72 - 72.4)^2}{72.4} + \frac{(49 - 45.3)^2}{45.3} +$$

$$\frac{(458 - 454.7)^2}{454.7} + \frac{(728 - 727.6)^2}{727.6} + \frac{(451 - 454.7)^2}{454.7} = 0.60$$

Since the 95th percentile of a Chi-Square Distribution having 2 degrees of freedom is 5.99, the test statistic of 0.60 does not provide any evidence that the three paddles result in different proportions of Red Beads. The differences between the observed counts and the expected counts are small enough to be due to chance.

The degrees of freedom for an *r* by *c* contingency table, consisting of *r* rows and *c* columns, is equal to $(r-1)(c-1)$. For our 2 by 3 table this gives 2 degrees of freedom. The easiest way to understand this number is that, given the marginal totals, you only have to specify the values for two cells in order to obtain the values for all the other cells by subtraction.

Yesterday the Day Shift produced 955 units, 85 of which failed the on-line test. The Swing Shift produced 940 units, 46 of which failed the on-line test. The Night Shift produced 947 units, 39 of which failed the on-line test. Is there a detectable difference in the proportion of units that fail the on-line test between these three shifts?

The Table of Observed Counts would look like:

Observed Counts

Shift	Day	Swing	Night	*Totals*
Failed	**85**	**46**	**39**	*170*
Passed	**870**	**894**	**908**	*2672*
Totals	*955*	*940*	*947*	*2842*

From the marginal totals we find the table of expected counts:

Expected Counts

Shift	Day	Swing	Night	*Totals*
Failed	**57.1**	**56.2**	**56.6**	*170*
Passed	**897.9**	**883.8**	**890.4**	*2672*
Totals	*955*	*940*	*947*	*2842*

The Chi-Square test statistic is therefore:

$$\chi^2 = \sum \frac{(o_j - e_j)^2}{e_j}$$

$$= \frac{(85 - 57.1)^2}{57.1} + \frac{(46 - 56.2)^2}{56.2} + \frac{(39 - 56.6)^2}{56.6} +$$

$$\frac{(870 - 897.9)^2}{897.9} + \frac{(894 - 883.8)^2}{883.8} + \frac{(908 - 890.4)^2}{890.4} = 22.3$$

Since the 95th percentile of a Chi-Square Distribution having 2 degrees of freedom is 5.99, the test statistic of 22.3 provides strong evidence that the three shifts have different proportions of units that fail the on-line test. The differences between the observed counts and the expected counts are greater than can be attributed to chance.

Notice that this analysis does not consider whether or not the failure rates were constant throughout each shift. It merely assumes that they are constant and proceeds to draw conclusion that the shifts are different. Both the nature of the inference and the quality of the information provided by this analysis is fundamentally different from that provided by process behavior charts. On those rare occasions when you can safely assume the data are homogeneous, the traditional inferential approaches make sense. In all other cases let the user beware.

9.10 Summary

Count data can be characterized as either counts of items or counts of events. Counts of items have an area of opportunity defined by the number of items examined, **n**. The number with the attribute or the number without the attribute may be used when counting items. Counts of events will be covered in the next chapter.

If your data have been collected under one condition you will generally be interested in estimating the proportion having the attribute under that one condition. While you may compute descriptive statistics using aggregated counts of items it takes more than simple descriptive statistics to characterize an underlying process. In particular, before you can use counts of items to represent an underlying process you will need to know if the areas of opportunity for those counts can logically be said to represent a single universe. While the assumption of a single universe may be reasonable with small areas of opportunity, it becomes increasingly suspect with large areas of opportunity, and may be checked by placing a series of counts or proportions on an *XmR* Chart.

If your data have been collected under two conditions, you may compare the two conditions using two *XmR* Charts. Under more stringent conditions, where you are willing to assume that each of your areas of opportunity represents a single universe, you can compare proportions using interval estimates.

If your data have been collected under three or more conditions, you could place sequences of counts from each condition on separate *XmR* Charts. *If you are willing to assume that each of the areas of opportunity represents a single universe*, then you can compare the conditions by using an approximate procedure known as a Chi-Square Contingency Test.

Chapter Ten

Counts of Events

The preceding chapter describes ways to analyze data based on counts of items. This chapter will discuss data based on counts of events. Counts of events will always have an area of opportunity that consists of some finite region of a continuum of space and time or production.

10.1 Inference for Counts of Events: One Condition

It is more difficult to work with counts of events than with than counts of items. This is mostly due to the different nature of the areas of opportunity for a count of events. As we saw in the previous chapter, descriptive statistics are easy to obtain, but getting values that we can use to describe the underlying process requires careful thought. While it may be easy to observe the number of events of a given type, and to compute a rate for these events, the question is: When can we use this descriptive rate as an estimate of a process parameter?

Once again, the answer lies in the homogeneity question. If the area of opportunity for the count of events represents one universe, then our statistic will estimate a parameter. If the area of opportunity represents more than one universe, then the descriptive statistic will not estimate any underlying process parameter.

Assume that we have an automated inspection system that reports the number of blemishes per roll of material and that Table 10.1 contains the counts for 50 successive rolls produced on the same line and scanned by the same inspection system.

The average number of blemishes per roll is 29.16. These 50 counts are placed on an *XmR* Chart in Figure 10.1 where the only hint of a problem is one moving range of 16, which is arguably equal to the Upper Range Limit.

Assuming that these counts are homogeneous, we might compute a global standard deviation statistic of $s = 5.808$ (with 49 *d.f.*) and obtain a 90% Interval Estimate

Table 10.1: Number of Blemishes per Roll

Roll	1	2	3	4	5	6	7	8	9	10	11	12	13	14	15	16	17
Count	33	37	24	35	22	23	25	23	32	34	33	37	26	36	35	23	26

Roll	18	19	20	21	22	23	24	25	26	27	28	29	30	31	32	33	34
Count	22	33	36	38	22	21	23	35	26	35	24	33	21	35	27	26	25

Roll	35	36	37	38	39	40	41	42	43	44	45	46	47	48	49	50
Count	24	23	34	35	34	21	23	34	30	22	25	35	36	37	34	25

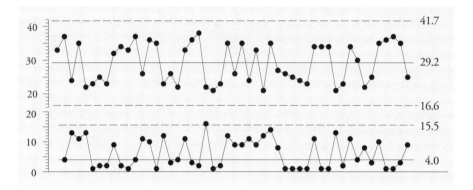

Figure 10.1: *XmR* Chart for Number of Blemishes per Roll

for the mean number of blemishes per roll by using the formula from Chapter Four:

$$\bar{X} \pm t_{.05}\frac{s}{\sqrt{n}} \;=\; 29.16 \pm 1.676\frac{5.808}{\sqrt{50}} \;=\; 27.8 \text{ to } 30.5$$

However, this analysis is flawed and these values are useless because rolls are not the proper area of opportunity for these counts.

In this case they were making two different products: Product 105 and Product 108. Moreover, because of the width of the sheet, the rolls for Product 105 are two-thirds the size of those for Product 108. While Table 10.1 does give the number of blemishes per roll, the fact that blemishes are related to physical area, and that the rolls are different sizes, means that the counts of Table 10.1 are not comparable. Defining the area of opportunity as a "roll" is incorrect. Different rolls represent different universes and this difference undermines all of the computations above.

By the way, the histogram of these data (shown in Figure 10.2) would have provided a clue that something was amiss. Multimodal histograms are, in and of themselves, signals that apples and oranges have probably been mixed together. The context for such histograms should always be carefully investigated.

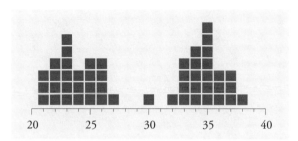

Figure 10.2: Histogram of Number of Blemishes per Roll

One way to remedy the problem of Table 10.1 is to separate the counts according to which product is being inspected, thereby creating two separate charts. Another way to remedy the problem is to change the area of opportunity to reflect the different sizes of the rolls.

Product 105 has an area of 1500 square yards per roll, and Product 108 has a area of 2180 square yards per roll. Therefore, we can make the counts of Table 10.1 comparable by converting them into rates. The blemishes per hundred square yards are shown in Table 10.2.

Now that we have adjusted the counts into rates that represent the underlying process we can use these values for analysis. The *XmR* Chart for the blemish rates in Table 10.2 is given in Figure 10.3. It shows a homogeneous set of rates.

Since these data appear to be reasonably homogeneous we can use them to characterize the underlying process. This process has averaged about 1.58 blemishes per hundred square yards, with Natural Process Limits of 1.31 to 1.86. In addition, the global standard deviation statistic for these 50 rates is $s = 0.1005$ (with 49 degrees of freedom).

Table 10.2: Number of Blemishes per Hundred Square Yards

Roll	1	2	3	4	5	6	7	8	9	10	11	12	13
Rate	1.51	1.70	1.60	1.61	1.47	1.53	1.67	1.53	1.47	1.56	1.51	1.70	1.73

Roll	14	15	16	17	18	19	20	21	22	23	24	25	26
Rate	1.65	1.61	1.53	1.73	1.47	1.51	1.65	1.74	1.47	1.40	1.53	1.61	1.73

Roll	27	28	29	30	31	32	33	34	35	36	37	38	39
Rate	1.61	1.60	1.51	1.40	1.61	1.80	1.73	1.67	1.60	1.53	1.56	1.61	1.56

Roll	40	41	42	43	44	45	46	47	48	49	50
Rate	1.40	1.53	1.56	1.38	1.47	1.67	1.61	1.65	1.70	1.56	1.67

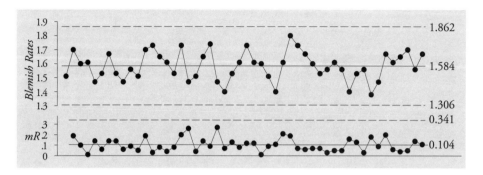

Figure 10.3: *XmR* **Chart for Blemishes per Hundred Square Yards**

Therefore, the basic uncertainty in our estimate of the mean blemish rate is:

$$\bar{X} \pm t_{.05}\frac{s}{\sqrt{n}} \;=\; 1.584 \pm 1.676\,\frac{.1005}{\sqrt{50}} \;=\; 1.56 \text{ to } 1.61$$

So while the individual Blemish Rates for each roll may range from 1.31 to 1.86 per hundred square yards without signifying a change in the process, our best estimate of the Mean Blemish Rate is that it is between 1.56 and 1.61 per hundred square yards.

The 99% Interval Estimate for the Mean Blemish Rate is:

$$\bar{X} \pm t_{.005}\frac{s}{\sqrt{n}} \;=\; 1.584 \pm 2.678\,\frac{.1005}{\sqrt{50}} \;=\; 1.546 \text{ to } 1.622$$

Mean blemish rates below 1.546 are inconsistent with these data. Mean blemish rates above 1.622 are also inconsistent with these data.

- Counts are comparable only when their areas of opportunity are approximately the same size. Converting counts into rates allows comparisons across unequal sized areas of opportunity. Failure to properly define the area of opportunity can undermine your analysis of counts of events.

- When the average *count* falls in the vicinity of 1.0 the *XmR* Chart will begin to display the effects of chunky data, and it will no longer be a satisfactory analysis technique for counts of events or their rates.

• Whenever a collection of counts of events has an *average count* that exceeds 5.0, the traditional formulas for interval estimates of location will provide satisfactory estimates for the mean count or mean rate.

10.2 Using the Poisson Model

If you only have a single count, Y, and the area of opportunity for that count is a, then the ratio Y/a may be used as a point estimate of the rate of occurrence for a Poisson process. This rate is often represented by the symbol λ. A $100(1-\alpha)\%$ Interval Estimate for λ may be obtained from the formula:

$$\frac{A}{2a} < \lambda < \frac{B}{2a}$$

where A is the lower $\alpha/2$ critical value from a Chi-Square distribution having $2Y$ degrees of freedom, and B is the upper $\alpha/2$ critical value from a Chi-Square distribution having $(2Y+2)$ degrees of freedom.

When Y is large (exceeds 30) an approximation for the interval above is:

$$\frac{Y}{a} \pm z_{\alpha/2} \frac{\sqrt{Y}}{a}$$

The two formulas above are built on the assumption that the count of events may be characterized by a Poisson distribution. This may be a reasonably conservative assumption, but it is still an assumption that cannot be verified using a single data point. Here we must recall the Second Axiom of Data Analysis: Probability models do not generate your data. The intervals above are conservative, model-based intervals which assume that the variation is a function of the observed value.

For example, the data of Table 10.1 represent Y = 1458 blemishes found in a total of a = 92000 square yards. Our point estimate of the blemish rate per hundred square yards would be essentially the same as was found earlier: 1458/920 = 1.5848. Since Y exceeds 30, we use the second formula above to get a 99% Interval Estimate of the Poisson parameter λ of:

$$1.5848 \pm 2.576 \frac{\sqrt{1458}}{920} = 1.5848 \pm 0.1069 = 1.478 \text{ to } 1.692$$

About the only thing that this interval has in common with the earlier 99% Interval Estimate of the Mean Blemish Rate is the center point of 1.584. This interval is almost three times wider than the earlier interval. The earlier interval was based on 50 observed blemish rates *and the variation they actually displayed*. This interval is based on the total number of blemishes found and an assumption that the variation can be estimated from the observed rate. The first interval is essentially empirical while the second is essentially theoretical. Moreover, the theoretical assumption used in the second interval is unverifiable.

So while we might use the Poisson-based interval estimate out of necessity when we have a single observed count of events, we should always realize that the results are no better than the assumptions they are built upon.

With a series of observed counts of events you can empirically estimate both the location and the dispersion for your data. This will usually allow you to use large sample techniques and to avoid excessive dependence upon assumed theoretical models.

10.3 Comparing Two Conditions

If you have *multiple* counts of events collected under each of two conditions you can compare the two conditions using the techniques from Chapter Six. In particular, the two conditions may be compared using histograms, *XmR* Charts, or interval estimates for the difference in two means.

A trucking company decided to try to increase productivity by putting their workers on a bonus plan. Being conservative, it was decided to test the bonus plan at selected sites for a year before implementing it company-wide. At the end of the year-long trial the usual measures of activity were collected and reported for two groups: Group A consisted of those sites where all of the workers were on the bonus plan; Group B consisted of those sites that did not have the bonus plan. Among the various measures reported were some accident data. Table 10.3 shows the accident rates for reportable injuries per million man-hours over a twelve-month period for both groups.

Table 10.3: Reportable Injuries per Million Man-Hours

	J	F	M	A	M	J	J	A	S	O	N	D	Aver.
Group A	43	40	37	33	30	33	34	35	29	33	31	39	34.75
Group B	35	37	33	32	27	29	31	22	25	30	24	19	28.67

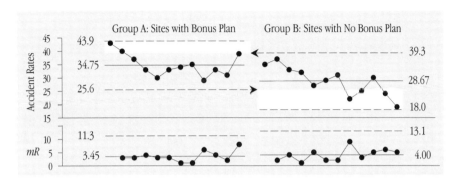

Figure 10.4: *XmR* **Charts for Accident Rates for Groups A and B**

While neither group shows evidence of a lack of homogeneity, these two groups show considerable evidence that they differ. Group A has two points above the upper limit for Group B, while Group B has four points below the lower limit for Group A. The sites with the productivity bonus plan had higher accident rates than the sites without the bonus plan. Why this difference exists is not answered by these data. Baseline data for each of the two groups could help to clarify the situation here, but the difference seen in Figure 10.4 is a real difference.

If we organize the data in Table 10.3 into two subgroups of size 12 we can use the Analysis of Means to compare the overall accident rates between the two groups. The Grand Average is 31.708 while the pooled variance estimate of $SD(X)$ is $s_p = 4.866$. So with $n = 12$, $k = 2$, and an alpha-level of 0.05, Table A.12 gives a quick scaling factor of $H_2 = 0.424$ and the ANOM Chart Detection limits are:

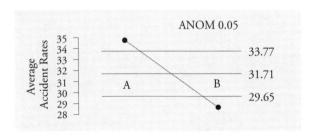

Figure 10.5: *ANOM* **Chart for Average Accident Rates for Groups A and B**

$$\bar{\bar{X}} \pm H_2\ s_p = 31.708 \pm 0.424\ (4.866) = 29.65\ \text{to}\ 33.77$$

Figure 10.5 shows that these two groups have detectably different accident rates.

A third way of comparing the accident rates for the two groups in Table 10.3 would be to use the two-sample *t*-test. The pooled variance of $s_p = 4.866$ has degrees of freedom of $[n_1 + n_2 - 2] = 22$. From Table A.7 our 0.005 *t*-distribution critical value is 2.819. So our 99% Interval Estimate for the difference between the mean accident rates for these two groups is:

$$(\bar{x}_1 - \bar{x}_2)\ \pm\ t_{\alpha/2}\ s_p \sqrt{\ (1/n_1) + (1/n_2)}$$

$$= (34.75 - 28.67) \pm 2.819\ (4.866) \sqrt{(1/12) + (1/12)}$$

$$= 6.08 \pm 5.60 = 0.48\ \text{to}\ 11.68$$

Since this interval does not contain zero it is unlikely that these two groups have the same mean accident rate. Their average accident rates can be said to be detectably different.

If, instead of the data in Table 10.3, you were simply told that the Group A sites worked 3 million man-hours and had 104 reportable injuries during the year, while the Group B sites worked 17 million man-hours and had 487 reportable injuries, you could use the Poisson interval estimates to compare the two groups. For Group A a 90% Interval Estimate of the Mean Accident Rate would be:

$$\frac{Y}{a} \pm z_{\alpha/2}\ \frac{\sqrt{Y}}{a}\ =\ \frac{104}{3} \pm 1.645\ \frac{\sqrt{104}}{3}\ =\ 34.67 \pm 5.59\ =\ 29.06\ \text{to}\ 40.25$$

While the 90% Interval Estimate for Group B would be:

$$\frac{Y}{a} \pm z_{\alpha/2}\ \frac{\sqrt{Y}}{a}\ =\ \frac{487}{17} \pm 1.645\ \frac{\sqrt{487}}{17}\ =\ 28.65 \pm 2.13\ =\ 26.51\ \text{to}\ 30.79$$

Here our results are equivocal, unlike the other analyses. However, the fact that these intervals have so little overlap makes it somewhat unlikely that the two groups have the same Mean Accident Rate.

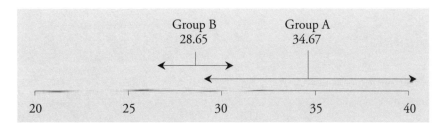

Figure 10.6: 90% Poisson Interval Estimates of Accident Rates

Using the Poisson interval estimate is a shot in the dark. It is essentially a worse-case analysis. If we used the 12 monthly accident rates for each group to create two 90% Interval Estimates, we would end up with intervals that do not overlap. This increase in sensitivity is why it is always preferable to have several counts of events per condition rather than simply obtaining a single count of events for each condition.

10.4 Comparing Several Conditions

If you have *multiple* counts of events collected under each of three or more conditions you can compare the conditions using the techniques from Chapter Seven. In particular, if there are only a few conditions you may use *XmR* Charts for your comparisons. Regardless of the number of conditions, you may use Average and Range Charts, ANOM Charts or the Analysis of Variance to compare the mean rates or mean counts for the various conditions.

The data of Table 7.1 could be considered to be counts of events with equal sized areas of opportunity. Since all the techniques listed above are illustrated using the data of Table 7.1 the reader is referred to Chapter Seven for examples of how to compare several conditions based on multiple counts of events per condition.

If you have only one count of events for each of several conditions you may use techniques developed for performing an Analysis of Variance with subgroups of size one. For more about this topic see *Understanding Industrial Experimentation, Second Edition*, by this author.

10.5 Summary

Counts of events are more like measurements than they are like counts of items. While they quantify discrete events using the counting numbers, they essentially define the rate of occurrence of the events within some continuum. Thus, counts of events consist of two parts: the discrete count and the finite portion of the continuum examined. They have both a discrete and a continuous component. This dual nature of counts of events has been the source of countless headaches.

When you have a single count and the value for its area of opportunity, you can only assume that its behavior might be modeled by some probability model and compute interval estimates accordingly. The traditional, and appropriately conservative, model is the Poisson distribution. While inferences built on this foundation are little more than quantified guesswork, we may use them out of necessity.

Just as it is better to have several measurements rather than just one, it is also better to have several counts of an event than a single count. With several counts of an event we can empirically characterize the behavior of the counts rather than having to assume that a particular model applies. This also allows us to use analysis techniques that are more familiar and easier to explain to our audience. Since analysis consists of both discovery and the communication of those discoveries, this issue of using familiar analysis techniques is very important. People do not often act on what they do not understand, and the most brilliant analysis is worthless if it is not understood by those who need to take action.

Chapter Eleven

Counts for Three or More Categories

In Chapters Five through Eight we considered ways to analyze data that consisted of measurements. In Chapters Nine and Ten we considered ways to analyze data based on counts of items and counts of events. In this chapter we shall look at a generalization of counts of items.

In Chapter Nine the counts of items were based on simple dichotomies. Each item was either a "success" or a "failure." While we could work with either category, the fact that there were only two categories meant that a knowledge of one would immediately tell us about the other category as well. In this chapter techniques for working with counts of items for three or more categories will be presented.

11.1 Categorical Frequencies for One Condition

If we have N items that we can consider to have been obtained under the same condition, and if each one of these N items has been categorized into one of k categories where $k \geq 3$, then our data will consist of k counts. With k categorical counts there is little we can do except present descriptive statistics. However, exactly which descriptive statistics are appropriate will depend upon the degree of ordering among the categories.

COMPLETELY NOMINAL CATEGORIES

When the categories are purely nominal, possessing no particular ordering, about all that we can do is to create a bar graph showing the frequencies for each category. This bar graph may be turned into a Pareto Diagram by placing the categories in order of descending frequencies, if such a presentation makes sense in the context of the data.

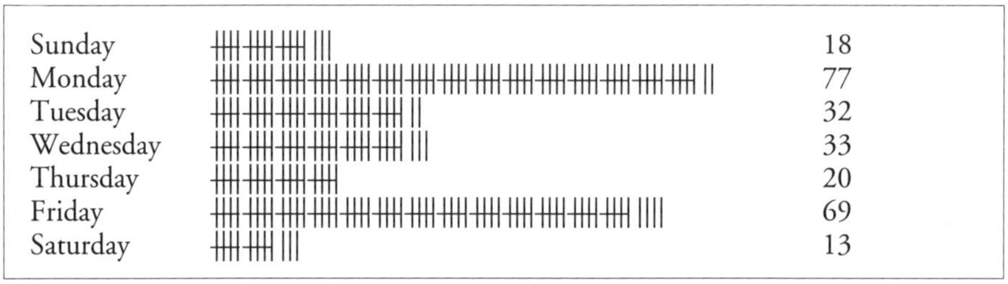

Sunday	‖‖‖ ‖‖‖ ‖‖‖ ‖‖‖ ‖‖	18
Monday	‖‖‖ ‖‖‖ ‖‖‖ ‖‖‖ ‖‖‖ ‖‖‖ ‖‖‖ ‖‖‖ ‖‖‖ ‖‖‖ ‖‖‖ ‖‖‖ ‖‖‖ ‖‖‖ ‖‖‖ ‖‖	77
Tuesday	‖‖‖ ‖‖‖ ‖‖‖ ‖‖‖ ‖‖‖ ‖‖‖ ‖‖	32
Wednesday	‖‖‖ ‖‖‖ ‖‖‖ ‖‖‖ ‖‖‖ ‖‖‖ ‖‖‖	33
Thursday	‖‖‖ ‖‖‖ ‖‖‖ ‖‖‖	20
Friday	‖‖‖ ‖‖‖ ‖‖‖ ‖‖‖ ‖‖‖ ‖‖‖ ‖‖‖ ‖‖‖ ‖‖‖ ‖‖‖ ‖‖‖ ‖‖‖ ‖‖‖ ‖‖‖	69
Saturday	‖‖‖ ‖‖‖ ‖‖‖	13

Figure 11.1: Number of Twenty-Dollar Bills Presented

An example of such purely nominal categorical frequencies is provided by a tally chart created by a cashier at a hotel restaurant. Since she always ran short of change on Mondays and Fridays she decided to collect some data to document her need for more change on those days.

Since there is a natural order to the days of the week, you might think that these categories are not purely nominal. However, in this case there is nothing to be gained by creating a Pareto, or performing any other analysis. The simple tally plot speaks for itself. She needs at least twice as much change on Mondays and Fridays as she needs on the other days.

For an example of a Pareto Diagram, consider the first known bar chart, created by William Playfair in 1786, and shown in Figure 11.2. This bar chart shows the extent of exports and imports for Scotland for 1781 and is already organized in a stairstep manner. However, since there are two sets of categorical frequencies shown (exports and imports) we might extract the export data to create the modern Pareto Diagram in Figure 11.3.

While it is not generally a good thing to show multiple sets of data on a single graph, Playfair's original graph works since it only tries to compare imports and exports. In fact, these comparisons can be quite interesting. Russia can be seen to have been a major supplier to Scotland, but it did not buy much back from Scotland. Ireland on the other hand bought quite a bit more from Scotland than Scotland did from Ireland. But perhaps of greatest interest is the imbalance of trade between Scotland and America. While America bought a lot from Scotland, Scotland did not buy a lot from America. After all, 1781 was the year that Washington accepted Cornwallis' surrender at Yorktown!

With categorical frequencies collected under one condition these simple graphs may be all that is appropriate in the way of analysis.

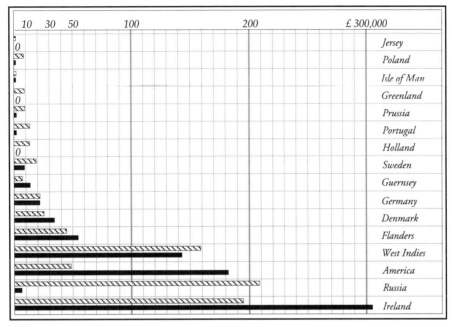

The Black Lines are Exports.   The Ribbed Lines are Imports.

Figure 11.2: William Playfair's Bar Chart

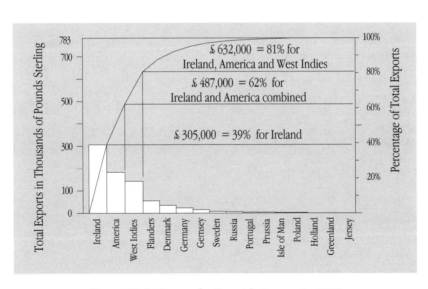

Figure 11.3: Pareto for Scottish Exports in 1781

POSITIVE AND NEGATIVE CATEGORIES

When the categories can be grouped into positive and negative groups it also makes sense to report the proportion of positive responses. Notice that this approach essentially collapses the multiple categories back down to two categories and results in a simple count of items.

Categorical frequencies will often have this positive and negative aspect when they come from rankings and survey responses.

ORDINAL CATEGORIES

Finally, when the categories possess a natural and logical ordering, we will sometimes impose an artificial metric upon the categories by assigning numeric values to the ordered categories (usually 1, 2, 3, etc.) and then computing a pseudo-average for the set of counts. Common examples of such pseudo-averages are grade point averages and average responses for survey questions which use a Likert scale response. For example, one company performed an annual survey of employees. Among the questions on this survey was one about how the employee felt about the company:

	strongly disagree	disagree	neutral	agree	strongly agree
This company is a good place to work.	1	2	3	4	5

Out of 7262 employees who answered this question, 496 strongly disagreed, 232 disagreed, 992 were neutral, 3024 agreed and 2518 strongly agreed. Thus a total of 5542 out of 7262 gave a positive response, which is 76.3 percent. The pseudo-average response is:

$$\frac{496\,(\,1\,) \; + \; 232\,(\,2\,) \; + \; 992\,(\,3\,) \; + \; 3024\,(\,4\,) \; + \; 2518\,(\,5\,)}{7262} = 3.94$$

Both the 76.3 percent positive and the pseudo-average of 3.94 provide a characterization of the bar graph shown in Figure 11.4.

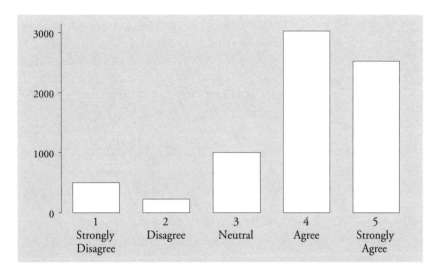

Figure 11.4: Responses to "This Company is a Good Place to Work"

SEQUENCES OF CATEGORICAL FREQUENCIES

While there is little that can be done with a single set of categorical frequencies, there are opportunities to learn from sequences of categorical frequencies. For example, while the company above had a 76.3 percent positive response this year, how does this value compare with the same value from previous years? Table 11.1 shows the responses to this same question over the past eleven years.

Table 11.1: Responses to "This Company Is A Good Place to Work."

Year	1	2	3	4	5	6	7	8	9	10	11
No. Pos.	3861	4018	4162	4221	4253	4282	4422	4596	4942	5235	5542
No. Emp.	5287	5438	5617	5714	5723	5747	5911	6147	6548	6989	7262
Percent	73.03	73.88	74.10	73.87	74.32	74.52	74.82	74.77	75.47	74.90	76.32
mR	—	0.85	0.22	0.23	0.45	0.20	0.30	0.05	0.70	0.57	1.42

Using the values from the first ten years to compute the limits, the Average is 74.37% positive, and the Average Moving Range is 0.40%, resulting in the *XmR* Chart in Figure 11.5.

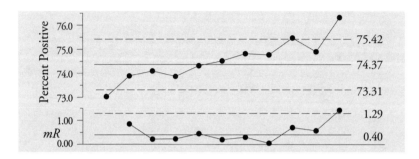

Figure 11.5: *XmR* **Chart for Proportions: "This Company is a Good Place to Work"**

Here we see a definite upward trend, with evidence of a jump in the current year. While this example uses the percentages of positive responses, we could use the same approach with the counts or percentages from each category over time, resulting in a separate *XmR* Chart for each category.

COMPARING PAIRS OF PERCENTAGES

If all we had to use to make a comparison were the counts for a single category for two years, or two surveys, or two periods, we could only compute an interval estimate on the difference of two proportions as was illustrated in Section 9.7. For example, to compare the percent positive for years 10 and 11 we would have $y_1 = 5235$, $n_1 = 6989$, $y_2 = 5542$, and $n_2 = 7262$, and an approximate 90% Interval Estimate for the difference in the percents positive would be:

$$[\, p_1 - p_2 \,] \;\pm\; z_{\alpha/2} \sqrt{\frac{p_1\,(1-p_1)}{n_1} + \frac{p_2\,(1-p_2)}{n_2}}$$

$$= [\, 0.7490 - 0.7632 \,] \;\pm\; 1.645 \sqrt{\frac{0.7490(1-0.7490)}{6989} + \frac{7632(1-0.7632)}{7262}}$$

$$= -0.0142 \;\pm\; 0.0118 \;=\; -0.0260 \text{ to } -0.0024$$

Based on this analysis these two percentages are not likely to be the same. This is in agreement with the last moving range of Figure 11.5, which also suggests that there is a detectable difference between the percents positive for Years 10 and 11.

COMPARING PSEUDO-AVERAGES

While we can get away with the use of the interval estimate above to compare the *percentages* for any one category over two time periods, it would be incorrect to use a two-sample *t*-test to compare the *pseudo-averages* for Years 10 and 11.

While we compute and use pseudo-averages (such as grade-point averages) all the time, it is important to understand that these pseudo-averages are dependent upon an arbitrary metric that we have imposed upon the underlying ordinal data. While this allows a single number summary for location, it is merely a convention, not an actual value—you may have had a GPA of 3.2, but your grades were A, B, C, etc. The convention used to create the pseudo-average does not extend to the direct computation of a meaningful measure of dispersion.

Since traditional interval estimates depend upon an internal measure of dispersion, they all require a minimum of interval-scale data before they can be used appropriately. The interval estimate for the proportions worked because the estimates of dispersion depended upon the proportions themselves. In contrast to this, an interval estimate for the difference of two pseudo-averages would require separate measures of dispersion to be computed from the ordinal-scale data using the imposed metric. Since such measures of dispersion would be meaningless, the interval estimate would also be meaningless.

So how can we compare pseudo-averages over time? Since we cannot obtain a measure of variation from the ordinal data *within* each time period, we will need to use a technique that filters out noise by using the variation in the pseudo-average values *between* the time periods. In short, virtually the only analytic technique that will work with pseudo-averages is the *XmR* Chart. Since the moving ranges are computed between the time periods, they are not dependent upon the metric used to compute the pseudo-averages. As long as the pseudo-averages are computed in the same way each period, the moving ranges will empirically track the inherent routine variation present in the pseudo-average values and, therefore, will allow us to detect any exceptional values present.

To illustrate this, Table 11.2 contains the pseudo-averages and moving ranges for the responses to the item "This company is a good place to work." The corresponding *XmR* Chart is shown in Figure 11.6. The limits are based on the first 10 years and are computed using the Median Moving Range.

Table 11.2: Pseudo Averages for "This Company Is A Good Place to Work."

Year	1	2	3	4	5	6	7	8	9	10	11
Average	3.875	3.893	3.898	3.893	3.903	3.907	3.913	3.912	3.941	3.915	3.946
mR	—	0.018	0.005	0.005	0.010	0.004	0.006	0.001	0.029	0.026	0.031

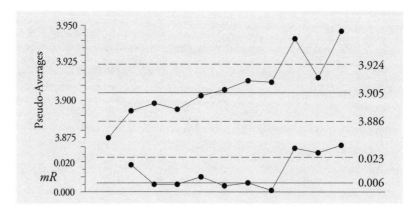

Figure 11.6: *XmR* Chart for Pseudo-Averages

With sequences of categorical frequencies for completely nominal categories you could track the percentage for a given category over time on its own *XmR* Chart.

When the various summary statistics or frequencies are tracked on an *XmR* Chart the question being asked by the chart is "has a change occurred?" Points outside the limits, or sequences of points that satisfy the various run tests, are evidence of a change.

In using the *XmR* Chart to evaluate sequences of values based on categorical frequencies, it is important to remember the basic assumption of the *XmR* Chart: that successive values need to be logically comparable (see Section 3.3). While the use of the *XmR* Chart with sequences of values based on categorical frequencies will usually be very satisfactory, there are occasions when the point-to-point changes are so severe that nothing will ever fall outside the limits. This means that you will have to exercise some judgment about the sequence of values. Return to Section 9.5 for more on this topic.

11.2   Categorical Data for Two or More Conditions

As soon as we have a set of categorical frequencies collected under two or more conditions we will want to make a comparison between the conditions. About the only question that makes sense here is whether the changes in the set of categorical frequencies between the various conditions represent a real change in the underlying system or whether these changes could have occurred by chance.

The simple, traditional, and straightforward way of answering this question is to form a two-way contingency table and use a Chi-Square test. While the mechanics of this test will be identical to those shown in Section 9.8, the application is slightly different. While we will still have two or more conditions, we will now have r different categories. In the format of Section 9.8 we now have r rows with two or more columns. However, we still use the marginal totals to compute expected frequencies for each cell, we compute a Chi-Square statistic in the same manner, and we interpret that statistic in the same way: a large value would indicate a change between the categories, while a small value would indicate no detectable difference.

In practice, since the comparisons made by the Chi-Square statistic are made within each cell, it does not matter what we call the columns and what we call the rows in a contingency table. Thus, a Chi-Square test on a contingency table consisting of r rows and k columns can be said to be testing whether all the columns are the same, or it can be said to be testing whether all the rows are the same.

Say that you have four robots that install pal-nuts on an assembly. Also assume that there are four failure modes that can occur with any robot, namely you could have a missed installation due to 1. upside-down nut; 2. dropped nut; 3. off-location arm; and 4. jammed feed tube. If data were collected for each robot on the number of missed installations due to each problem over a two day period, you might end up with counts such as those shown in Figure 11.7.

Failure Mode	Robot A	Robot B	Robot C	Robot D	Totals
#1	10	14	11	18	53
#2	30	37	37	40	144
#3	67	56	66	63	252
#4	82	94	90	122	388
Totals	189	201	204	243	837

Figure 11.7: 4 by 4 Contingency Table for Missed Installations

By multiplying each row total by each column total and dividing by the grand total we can obtain an expected frequency for each of the sixteen cells. These expected frequencies are shown in parentheses beside the original counts in Figure 11.8. Using the observed counts, o_{ij}, and the expected counts, e_{ij}, we can compute our Chi-Square statistic:

$$\chi^2 = \sum \sum \frac{(o_{ij} - e_{ij})^2}{e_{ij}}$$

Failure Mode	Robot A	Robot B	Robot C	Robot D	Totals
#1	10 (12.0)	14 (12.7)	11 (12.9)	18 (15.4)	53
#2	30 (32.5)	37 (34.6)	37 (35.1)	40 (41.8)	144
#3	67 (56.9)	56 (60.5)	66 (61.4)	63 (73.2)	252
#4	82 (87.6)	94 (93.2)	90 (94.6)	122 (112.6)	388
Totals	189	201	204	243	837

Figure 11.8: Missed Installations and Expected Frequencies

Since every cell has an expected frequency that exceeds 10, we do not need to incorporate Yates correction into each term as outlined in Section 9.8. The counts and expected frequencies of Figure 11.8 result in a Chi-Square statistic of;

$$\chi^2 = \sum \sum \frac{(o_{ij} - e_{ij})^2}{e_{ij}} = 6.99$$

The degrees of freedom for this Chi-Square statistic are $(r-1)(c-1) = 9$ *d.f.*

The Chi-Square distribution with nine degrees of freedom has an upper-tail five percent critical value of 16.92. Therefore, we can say that there is no detectable difference in the incidence of failures between these four robots. They are all performing equivalently.

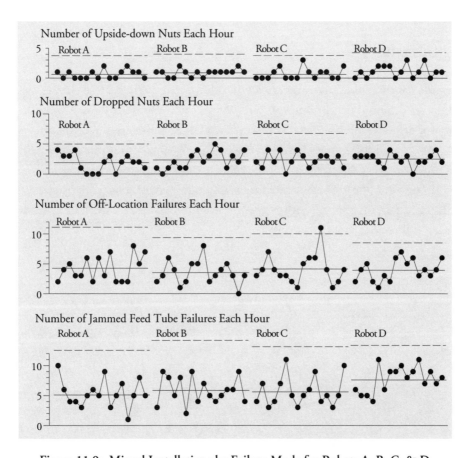

Figure 11.9: Missed Installations by Failure Mode for Robots A, B, C, & D

An alternate approach for these data might be to record the missed installations each hour by failure mode for each robot and to place these counts on four separate charts by failure mode. With separate limits for each robot you would end up with the X-Charts shown in Figure 11.9.

The limits for Failure Mode No. 1, Upside-down Nuts, were based on the Median Moving Ranges because these data are on the borderline of being chunky.

While there was one hour when Robot C had a problem with an exceptional number of off-location failures, there is no detectable difference between robots for any one of the failure modes.

Which of these analyses would you prefer to show, and explain, to your boss? Which of these analyses shows the equivalence of the robots most clearly?

11.3 Summary

Counts for three or more categories will often occur. When these counts are collected under different conditions you will have a fairly complex data structure. The key to properly interpreting such counts is to analyze those counts to discern when they represent real differences between the categories and conditions and when they do not represent real differences.

While this chapter does not introduce any new techniques, it does show how some techniques introduced earlier can be adapted to deal with counts of items occurring in three or more categories.

PART THREE

THE KEYS TO
EFFECTIVE
DATA ANALYSIS

Just as a lever needs a fulcrum in order to work properly, the techniques of data analysis must be used within some conceptual framework. Faulty or incomplete conceptualizations will result in ineffective data analyses. Part Three provides a conceptual framework that will facilitate the use of the techniques of Part Two.

Chapter Twelve outlines a new definition of trouble that is fundamental to any improvement effort. Chapter Thirteen integrates capability and performance indexes with this new definition of trouble.

Chapter Fourteen introduces the concept of the Effective Cost of Production and shows how to use it to choose an improvement strategy. Chapter Fifteen explains the origin of the Effective Cost of Production, while Chapter Sixteen uses the Effective Cost of Production to provide the first technically rigorous explanation of why you need to operate in the Six Sigma Zone.

Chapter Seventeen deals with some problems that have created more confusion than clarity. Chapter Eighteen presents an Improvement Model that outlines a systematic way of putting the techniques of data analysis to work.

Chapter Twelve

The Dual Nature of Trouble

You do not analyze data in a vacuum. Every analysis will have a context, with implicit or explicit objectives, that will guide the analysis. In order to clarify these objectives for yourself and to communicate them to others you will need to be able to characterize both products and processes in meaningful, understandable ways.

Issues concerned with these characterizations and their implications are the subject of this chapter. These characterizations are the building blocks which will allow you to choose which projects to work on and which projects may reasonably be deferred. So we shall begin with the oldest, and most commonly used characterization.

12.1 "We Are In Trouble"

What comes to mind when you hear the phrase above? Virtually everywhere I go, these words bring to mind the image of too much nonconforming product, usually in conjunction with a failure to meet the production schedule. It may be a problem with incoming materials, or the problem may lie within operations, but the image is the same: because of nonconforming product there is the danger of failing to meet the production schedule.

Inevitably, the next thought is "what are we going to do about this problem?" We intervene, and after some amount of effort, we eventually get to a point where we think that we are "out of trouble." Then, if we are lucky, we have a short interval of rest before the next crisis occurs and we have to ride off to deal with trouble elsewhere.

As one engineer expressed it: "We came to work one Tuesday morning and found that we were suddenly in trouble. We went out to the line, got in the way of the operators, and collected some data. After arguing about the data for two weeks, we found we were no longer in trouble. While we took credit for fixing the process, we actually had no idea why we had been in trouble, or how we got out of trouble."

Or in the words of another engineer: "I spend my life working on projects whose average half-life is two weeks, implementing solutions that have an average half-life of two weeks."

This traditional definition of trouble is based upon the acceptability of the process outcomes, and it inevitably results in periods of intense panic alternating with periods of benign neglect. A good process is one with fewer periods of panic.

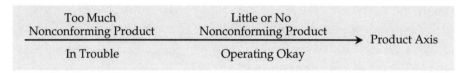

Figure 12.1 The Old Definition of Trouble

With this definition of trouble the focus of every improvement project, whether it is a planned project or a fire fight, will be to reduce the level of nonconforming product. Once this objective has been met the project will be considered successful. If a process has a lot of "trouble" we come to think of that process as a "bad process." Eventually, we will try to fix a bad process, usually by using some new technology, some process upgrade, or by reengineering it in some manner.

On the other hand, a process that has few upsets, or has little or no nonconforming product, will be considered a "good process." Here we generally seek to avoid rocking the boat. Production personnel will generally resist anything more than gently tweaking such a process.

Thus, we have the conventional wisdom regarding process improvement:

> ***Fix the bad processes and ignore the good processes.***

While it is clearly desirable to have a process that produces little or no nonconforming product, the unending rounds of troubleshooting that inevitably accompany the old definition of trouble show that the conventional wisdom is not sufficient to deal with the problems of production. Therefore we will have to look beyond the characterization of the product stream and consider the nature of the underlying process.

12.2 A New Definition of Trouble

When Walter Shewhart created the process behavior chart he gave the world a new definition of trouble.

> *A **process** may be said to be in trouble*
> *when it is **not** operated up to its full potential.*

As we saw in Section 2.4, the limits on a process behavior chart are computed in such a way that they characterize what the process can be made to do. They define the *ideal* of a process that is operating with maximum consistency (which is minimum variation). Thus, as shown in Figure 12.2, the limits define the *process potential*.

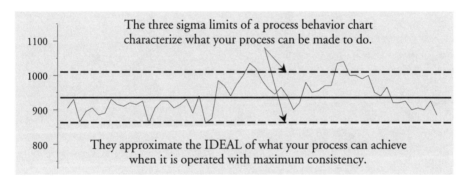

Figure 12.2 What Do You Want to Accomplish?

In contrast to the limits, the points plotted on the process behavior chart represent the actual behavior of the process. They define the *process performance*. Thus a process behavior chart provides a ***procedure*** for comparing the process performance with the process potential. Moreover, by focusing our attention on those points where the performance goes outside the bounds defined by the process potential, the process behavior chart provides a simple mechanism for actually improving the process. See Figure 12.3.

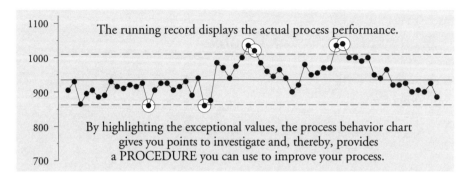

Figure 12.3 By What Method Will You Accomplish It?

Finally, having used the chart to make this comparison, we can make a *judgment* about how close our process performance is coming to the process potential.

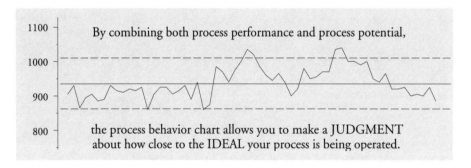

Figure 12.4 How Will You Know When You Have Accomplished It?

These three elements the ideal, the procedure, and the judgment are the three elements of an operational definition. They define what we want to accomplish, a methodology for accomplishing it, and a way to know when we have accomplished it. The process behavior chart provides us with an operational definition of how to get the most out of any process. When a process is operated predictably its actual performance will essentially be the same as its potential. When a process is operated unpredictably its performance will inevitably fall short of the full process potential. Thus, the process behavior chart gives us a new definition of trouble.

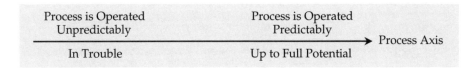

Figure 12.5 The New Definition of Trouble

When your process performance falls short of the process potential you will not be getting what you paid for. This is economic trouble just as surely as are scrap and rework. We will see how to quantify this and other economic problems later.

Now what does this definition of trouble imply about process improvement? When a process is operated predictably it is being operating as consistently as it can be operated in its current configuration. If you want to improve a predictable process, you will have to "change the process in some major way." On the other hand, if a process is operated unpredictably it will *not* be operating up to its full potential. This means that you can improve an unpredictable process by tweaking it. Hence, the new definition of trouble would suggest that we should:

Tweak the Bad Processes and Upgrade the Good Processes.

This differs from the conventional wisdom because it is built upon a different perspective. Instead of using the *Product Axis*, it uses the *Process Axis*. While these two approaches to improvement sound contradictory, they can be reconciled by combining the two perspectives into a unified view.

12.3   The Four Possibilities for Any Process

We can combine the product axis and the process axis to create a simple grid of possibilities that can be used to characterize any process. The horizontal Product Axis separates processes according to whether the product stream is conforming or nonconforming. The vertical Process Axis separates processes according to whether or not they are operated predictably or unpredictably. Thus, when these characterizations of the *product stream* and the *process behavior* are combined we have four distinct categories:

1. Conforming Product & Predictable Process (*No Trouble*),

2. Nonconforming Product & Predictable Process (*Product Trouble*),

3. Conforming Product & Unpredictable Process (*Process Trouble*), and

4. Nonconforming Product & Unpredictable Process (*Double Trouble*).

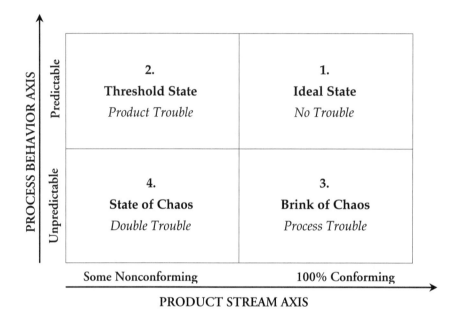

Figure 12.6 **Combining the Two Definitions of Trouble**

These four possibilities can and should be used to characterize every process. Moreover, any attempt to characterize a process using only one definition of trouble or the other will be incomplete and unsatisfactory. As we will see, these four possibilities provide a simple way to determine what type of improvement effort is appropriate. In our discussion of these four states we shall begin with the Ideal State.

THE IDEAL STATE (No Trouble)

For lack of a better name, denote the first of these four categories as the Ideal State. A process in this state is being operated predictably and is producing 100 percent conforming product. The predictability of the process will be the result of deliberate efforts on the part of the producer. A predictable process is an achievement, requiring constancy of purpose and the effective use of process behavior charts. The conformity of the product will be the result of having Natural Process Limits (i.e., limits for individual values) that fall inside the specification limits.

When your process is in the Ideal State, you and your customer can expect the conformity of the product to continue as long as the process is operated predictably. Since the product stream for a predictable process can be thought of as being homogeneous, the measurements taken to maintain the process behavior chart will also serve to characterize the product produced by the predictable process.

How does a process get to be in this Ideal State? Only by satisfying three conditions:

1. The *management* must establish and maintain an *environment* where it is possible to operate the process in a predictable and consistent manner. The operating conditions or target values cannot be selected or changed arbitrarily.

2. The process average must be maintained reasonably close to the appropriate target value.

3. For those characteristics having specifications, the Natural Process Limits must fall inside the specification limits.

Whenever one of these conditions is not satisfied, the possibility of shipping nonconforming product exists. When a process satisfies these three conditions, you can be confident that nothing but conforming product is being shipped. The only way that you can know that these three conditions apply to your process, and the only way that you can both establish and maintain these conditions day after day, is by the use of process behavior charts.

THE THRESHOLD STATE (Product Trouble)

Again, for lack of a better name, denote the second of these four categories as the Threshold State. A process in this state is being operated predictably, but it is producing some nonconforming product. As before, the predictability of the process will be the result of deliberate and persistent efforts on the part of the producer—you cannot accidentally operate a process predictably. Thus, by virtue of the fact that you are operating your process predictably you will know that it is operating as consistently as it currently can operate. Nevertheless, the existence of some nonconforming product will be the result of one or both of the Natural Process Limits falling outside the specification limits.

Thus, in the Threshold State you are getting the most out of your process, yet that is still not good enough to keep you out of product trouble. You cannot simply wait for things to spontaneously improve, so you will have to intervene to either change the process or change the specifications before you can operate in the Ideal State.

If the nonconforming product occurs because the process average is not where it needs to be, then you will need to find some way of adjusting the process aim. Here, the process behavior chart can help to determine when to make adjustments and when to refrain from making adjustments to the process aim.

If the nonconforming product occurs because the process shows too much variation, then you will need to try to reduce the process variation. Since a process that is operated predictably is one that is already being operated with minimum variance (given its current configuration), the only way to reduce the process variation will be to change in the process itself in some major way. As you experiment with major process changes the process behavior chart will allow you to evaluate the effects of your changes. Thus, process behavior charts will not only help you achieve a predictable process, but they also help in moving the process from the Threshold State to the Ideal State.

Since making a major change in the process will often require a lot of work you may, instead, try to get the specifications relaxed. With the process behavior chart to demonstrate and define the consistent *Voice of the Process*, you will at least have a chance to get the customer to agree to a change in the specifications. Without the process behavior chart to demonstrate the predictability of your process you will have no basis for asking for a change in the specifications.

As always, a short-term solution to the existence of nonconforming product is to use 100 percent inspection. However, as has been proven over and over again, 100 percent screening of product is imperfect and expensive. The only way to guarantee that you will not ship any nonconforming product is to avoid making any in the first place. Sorting should be nothing more than a stop-gap measure—not a way of life.

Thus, process behavior charts are not only essential in getting any process into the Threshold State, but they are also critical in any attempt to move from the Threshold State to the Ideal State.

	Some Nonconforming Product	100% Conforming Product

Process Is Predictable	**Threshold State**
	Product Trouble
	
	• PROCESS IS PREDICTABLE
	• SOME NONCONFORMING PRODUCT
	• *Must either…*
	    Change process, or
	    Change specifications
	• Sorting is only a temporary fix
	• *Process Behavior Charts*
	    Maintain process predictability
	    Evaluate efforts at improvement
		Ideal State
		No Trouble
		
		• PROCESS IS PREDICTABLE
		• 100% CONFORMING PRODUCT
		• *Process Behavior Charts*
		    Maintain process predictability
		    Give timely warning
		        of any troubles

Process Is Not Predictable	**State of Chaos** *Double Trouble* • PROCESS IS NOT OPERATED PREDICTABLY • SOME NONCONFORMING PRODUCT • *Assignable Causes* *dominate process* • Random fluctuations due to Assignable Causes will eventually frustrate efforts at process improvement • *The only way out of chaos is to first eliminate the Assignable Causes*	**Brink of Chaos** *Process Trouble* • PROCESS IS NOT OPERATED PREDICTABLY • 100% CONFORMING PRODUCT • All may seem okay, but… • *Assignable Causes determine what is produced by the process!* • Quality and conformance can change in a moment
	Some Nonconforming Product Produced	**100% Conforming Product Produced**

Figure 12.7 The Four Possibilities for Any Process

THE BRINK OF CHAOS (Process Trouble)

The third state could be labeled the Brink of Chaos. Processes in this state are being operated unpredictably even though the product stream currently contains 100 percent conforming product. With the traditional view the fact that you have 100 percent conforming product is considered to be evidence that the process is "operating okay." Unfortunately, this view inevitably leads to benign neglect, which, in conjunction with the unpredictable operation of the process, results in a process whose conformity can disappear at any time. (Have you ever noticed that trouble always appears *suddenly*?)

When a process is operated unpredictably it is subject to the effects of Assignable Causes. These effects can best be thought of as changes in the process that seem to occur at random times. So while the conformity to specifications may lull the producer into thinking all is well, the Assignable Causes will continue to change the process until it will eventually produce some nonconforming product. The producer will *suddenly* discover that he is in product trouble, yet he will have no idea of how he got there, nor any idea of how to get out of trouble. (Of course the sense of being in trouble will cause "solutions" to be tried until, by some means, the conformity improves. However, if the issue of unpredictable operation is not addressed the process will be doomed to recurring bouts of "trouble.") The change from 100 percent conforming product to some nonconforming product can come at any time, without the slightest warning. When this change occurs the process will be in the State of Chaos.

Thus, there is no way to predict what a process in the Brink of Chaos will produce tomorrow, or next week, or even in the next hour. Since the unpredictability of such a process is due to Assignable Causes, and since Assignable Causes are dominant cause-and-effect relationships that are not being controlled by the manufacturer, the only way to move from the Brink of Chaos to the Ideal State is to first eliminate the Assignable Causes. This requires that they be identified, and the operational definition of an Assignable Cause is the process behavior chart.

THE STATE OF CHAOS (Double Trouble)

The State of Chaos exists when an unpredictable process is producing some nonconforming product. The nonconforming product will alert the producer to the fact that there is a problem. The fact that the process is being operated unpredictably means that some of the dominant cause-and-effect relationships that govern the process have not yet been identified. Thus, a manufacturer whose process is in the State of Chaos knows that there is a problem, but he usually does not know what to do to correct it. Moreover, efforts to correct the problem will ultimately be frustrated by the random changes in the process which result from the presence of the Assignable Causes. When a needed modification to the process is made, its effect may well be short-lived because the Assignable Causes continue to change the process. When an unnecessary modification is made, a fortuitous shift by the Assignable Causes may mislead everyone. No matter what is tried, nothing works for long because the process is always changing. As a result, people finally despair of ever operating the process rationally, and they begin to talk in terms of "magic" and "art."

The only way to make any progress in moving a process out of the State of Chaos is to first eliminate the Assignable Causes. This will require the disciplined and effective use of process behavior charts. As long as Assignable Causes are present, you will find your improvement efforts to be like walking in quicksand. The harder you try, the more deeply mired you become.

THE EFFECT OF ENTROPY (The Cause of Much Trouble)

All processes belong to one of these four states. But processes do not always remain in one state. It is possible for a process to move from one state to another. In fact there is a universal force acting on every process that will cause it to move in a certain direction. That force is entropy and it continually acts upon all processes to cause deterioration and decay, wear and tear, breakdowns, and failures.

Entropy is relentless. Because of it every process will naturally and inevitably migrate toward the State of Chaos. The only way this migration can be overcome is by continually repairing the effects of entropy. Of course this means that the effects for a given process must be known before they can be repaired. With such knowledge, the repairs are generally fairly easy to make. On the other hand, it is very difficult to repair something when you are unaware of it. Yet if the effects of entropy are not repaired, they will come to dominate the process and force it inexorably toward the State of Chaos.

THE CYCLE OF DESPAIR (The Result of the Old Definition of Trouble)

Since everybody knows that they are in trouble when their processes are in the State of Chaos, it is inevitable that problem-solvers will be appointed to drag the process out of the State of Chaos. With luck, these problem-solvers can get the process back to the Brink of Chaos—a state which is erroneously considered to be "out-of-trouble" in most operations.

Once they get the process back to the Brink of Chaos the problem-solvers are sent off to work on other problems. As soon as their backs are turned, the process begins to move back down the entropy slide toward the State of Chaos.

New technologies, process upgrades, and all the other "magic bullets" which may be tried can never overcome this Cycle of Despair. You may change technologies—often a case of jumping out of the frying pan and into the fire—but the benign neglect which inevitably occurs when the process is on the Brink of Chaos will allow entropy to drag the process back down to the State of Chaos. Thus, if you focus solely upon conformance to specifications you will be condemned to forever cycle between the State of Chaos and the Brink of Chaos.

No matter how well intentioned your improvement efforts, no matter how knowledgeable you may be about your process, any improvement effort that does not address the issue of operating your process predictably can do no better than to get your process up to the Brink of Chaos.

THE ONLY WAY OUT OF THE CYCLE OF DESPAIR

There is only one way out of this Cycle of Despair. There is only one way to move a process up to the Threshold State, or even to the Ideal State—and that requires the effective use of process behavior charts.

Every producer is confronted with this dual problem. Entropy places a process in the Cycle of Despair. Assignable Causes doom it to stay there. Thus, manufacturers must identify both the effects of entropy and the presence of Assignable Causes. The only way to do this is to use process behavior charts. No other tool will consistently and reliably provide the necessary information in a clear and understandable form on a continuing basis.

The traditional chaos-manager, problem-solving approach is focused upon conformance to specifications. It does not attempt to characterize or understand the behavior of the process. Therefore, about the best that it can achieve is to get the process to operate in the Brink of Chaos some of the time. This is why any process operated without the benefit of process behavior charts is ultimately doomed to operate in the State of Chaos.

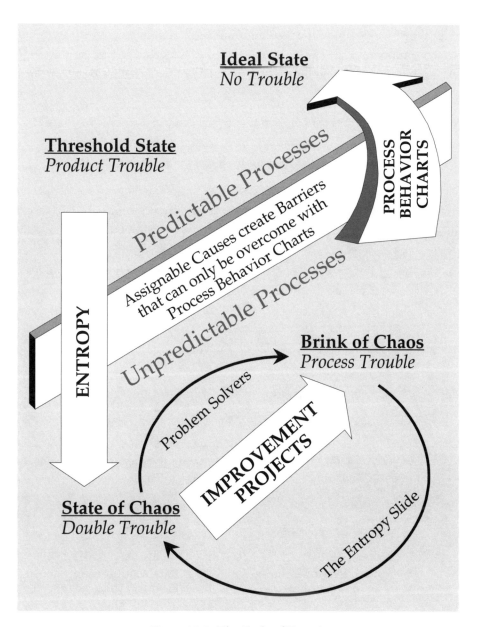

Figure 12.8 The Cycle of Despair

THE NEW MANTRA

Thus, when we combine the two definitions of trouble we end up with a new mantra for improvement. The new mantra may not be as simple as the original mantra, but it does a much better job of reflecting reality and describing appropriate courses of action.

> *Find Assignable Causes for Unpredictable Processes and remove their effects;*
> *Upgrade or adjust Predictable Processes in the Threshold State; and*
> *Ignore or tweak the Predictable Processes in the Ideal State.*

The first line of this new mantra defines how to operate your process with minimum variance. When a process is operated on target with minimum variance it is operating up to its full potential. The second line deals with what you have to do when that is not enough. Thus, this new mantra is one that will guide you through the complexities of improving an existing process. It uses the four possibilities as a matrix to triage your process improvement efforts.

Predictable Process	**Threshold State** *Product Trouble* Adjust Process Aim or Redesign Process	**Ideal State** *No Trouble* Ignore or Gently Tweak Process
Unpredictable Process	**State of Chaos** *Double Trouble* Find Assignable Causes & Remove Their Effects	**Brink of Chaos** *Process Trouble* Find Assignable Causes & Remove Their Effects
	Some Nonconforming **Product Produced**	**100% Conforming** **Product Produced**

Figure 12.9: The Basis for the New Mantra of Process Improvement

12.4 Research and Experimentation Are Not Enough

In addition to Entropy and Assignable Causes you have another adversary. Its name is Complexity, and it is a larger adversary than you may realize. Consider for a moment how many different variables affect any one characteristic of your product. Are there 5, 10, 15 or more? Next, consider how many different levels can be chosen for each one of these variables. Are there 3, 4, 5 or more? If you have ten variables and each variable has four possible levels you will have a total of 4^{10} = 1,048,576 different operating conditions for your process. To begin to understand this number consider changing the operating conditions every hour. If you operated 24 hours a day and 7 days a week it would only take you 120 years to cycle through all of these possible operating conditions.

Thus, waiting for your process to spontaneously begin to operate in a satisfactory manner is like planning to win the lottery. We need a more effective way of finding the right operating conditions than merely performing a random walk. And this is the role of research and planned experimentation.

For any given characteristic there will be dozens, if not hundreds, of cause-and-effect relationships that affect that characteristic. Fortunately, in order to produce a consistent product we do not usually need to control *all* of the cause-and-effect rela-

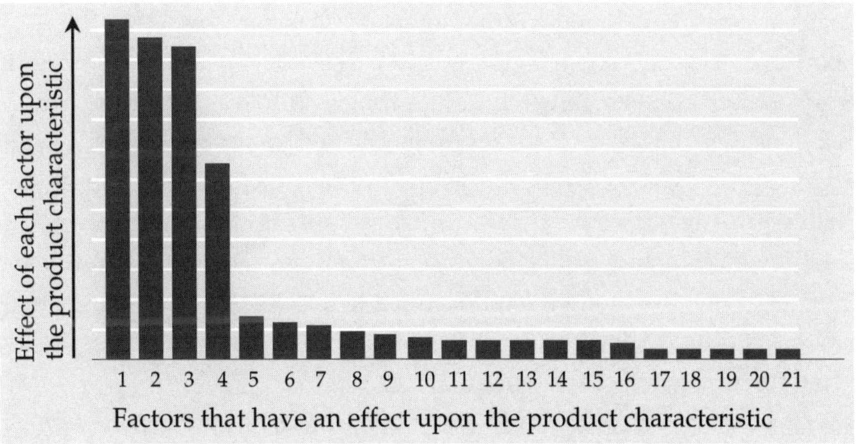

Figure 12.10: Dominant Causes and Lesser Causes

tionships. In most cases, the many different causes will also have different-sized effects. A relatively few causes will have large, dominant effects upon the characteristic, while the remainder will have progressively smaller and less critical effects.

This tendency of cause systems to satisfy the Pareto principle does simplify the complex problems of production. In order to make a product we will need to select and control only those factors having a dominant effect upon a given characteristic. We can then ignore the remaining factors. While these remaining lesser causes will create some small amount of product variation, it will be negligible if we correctly identify the dominant causes. In Figure 12.10 the first four factors account for 78% of the total impact of all 21 factors.

However, once you have taken care of the dominant causes, you will quickly reach a point of diminishing returns. While the remaining causes will have lesser effects, the effort to nullify these lesser causes will usually be on a par with the effort to nullify the dominant causes. Thus, at some point, it is no longer worth the effort to continue to counteract the lesser causes. In Figure 12.10, Factors 5, 6, 7, & 8 account for only 9% of the total impact. Because of these diminishing returns we need to have some way to properly separate the dominant causes from the lesser causes.

For over two hundred years, manufacturers have used experience and guesswork to determine just which factors to control in production. While this has worked in many instances, it has also been responsible for some spectacular failures. And these failures tend to make us painfully aware of the shortcomings of the experience and guesswork approach. As a result, we become interested in new and better ways of separating dominant causes from the lesser causes.

So how do we identify these high-payback causes? It is usually a combination of guesswork, experience, and research. The problem is to identify those cause-and-effect relationships that we need to control in practice, so we begin with a list of the known and expected causes. Since this list will usually include more causes than we can possibly investigate, we will trim this list by ranking these causes according to what we think their impact will be and discarding those causes thought to have the smaller effects. Then we study the reduced list to (a) identify those causes with the dominant effects and (b) determine which levels of these dominant causes will yield a product with the desired characteristic.

The end result of this process is a set of *control factors*—those causes which we think have the greatest impact upon our product characteristic. In production we will control the levels of these control factors. At the same time, we will ignore the remaining cause-and-effect relationships—after all, we did not find them to be part of the dominant causes, so they are relegated to the group of lesser causes.

Figure 12.11 shows a list of 21 factors that were thought to have an impact upon Product Characteristic No. 2. These 21 factors had been arranged in what was thought to be the order of descending impact. Since 21 factors were too many for R&D to consider, they decided to evaluate the top ten factors.

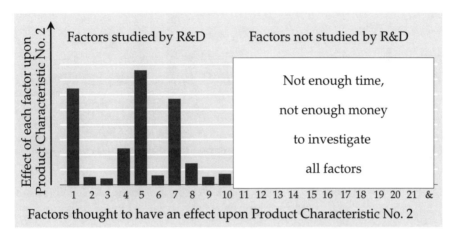

Figure 12.11: Cause and Effect Relationships Studied by R&D

While all 10 factors had an effect upon this characteristic, their effects were not all of the same size. Factors 5, 1, and 7 were found to have the dominant effects. Thus, Engineering told Manufacturing that they would need to carefully control Factors 5, 1, and 7 when they went into production. Except possibly for Factor 4, all other factors were thought to have a minimal impact upon this characteristic and, therefore, could be ignored in production.

The production process was then set up using Factors 5, 1, and 7 as control factors for Product Characteristic No. 2. At the start of production they immediately had problems with too much variation in Product Characteristic No. 2. Because this resulted in a high scrap rate they decided to add Factor 4 to the set of control factors. It didn't help. As they fell further and further behind the production schedule, and as the mountain of scrap increased, they began to talk about the "skill" that it took to make this product. Words like "art" and "magic" were used. Inspection and rework facilities were expanded, and soon the production department had settled down to the all too common routine of "burn the toast and scrape it."

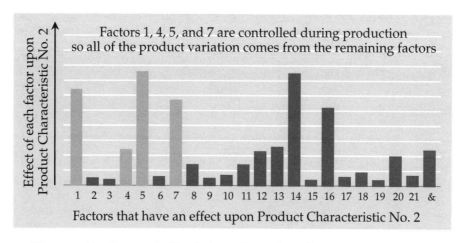

Figure 12.12: Cause and Effect Relationships That Affect Characteristic No. 2

The most common reason for this scenario is seen in Figure 12.12. While some of the dominant factors were properly identified, others were missed. While the manufacturer was unaware of the impact of Factors 14 and 16, the process continued to be under their influence. Since Factors 14 and 16 had not been studied, and were thought to be part of the lesser causes, the manufacturer was not exerting any control over the levels of these factors. Yet, in the course of events, when the levels of either one of these factors changed it would cause a corresponding change in the product characteristic. While the manufacturer remained unaware of Factors 14 and 16, he suffered the consequences of their effects.

This example serves to illustrate that there are three broad categories of cause-and-effect relationships for any process or product characteristic.

The set of dominant causes which the manufacturer chooses to control could be called the control factors. This would be Factors 5, 1, 7, and 4 in the previous example. All remaining cause-and-effect relationships (that are not part of the control factors) could be said to belong to the set of uncontrolled factors.

Of course, the idea is to isolate the dominant causes in the set of control factors. Dominant causes that remain in the set of uncontrolled factors will haunt your process, creating exceptional variation, excess costs, and general grief.

In our example, the problem does not come from an inability to control Factors 5, 1, and 7. It is instead due to the fact that Factors 14 and 16 are not part of the set of control factors. This set of dominant but uncontrolled factors will be called the Assignable Causes.

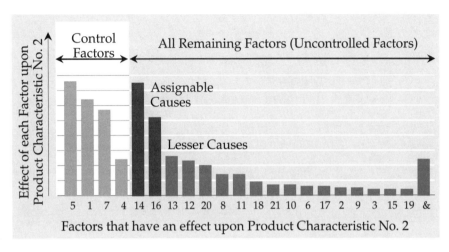

Figure 12.13: Three Types of Cause-and-Effect Relationships

Thus we have Control Factors, Assignable Causes, and Lesser Causes. Since the levels of the control factors are fixed, they contribute little or no variation to the product characteristic. When we place a factor in the control group, we essentially remove it as a source of process variation. *Effort spent trying to fine tune the control factors will be of marginal benefit as long as there are Assignable Causes present.* It does not matter what levels of Factors 5, 1, and 7 we choose as long as we are doing nothing about Factors 14 and 16! ***You cannot optimize any system when some of the dominant cause-and-effect relationships remain unidentified.***

Since the group of Assignable Causes will contain *all* of those dominant causes that are not in the set of Control Factors, this group will be the source of most of the unexplained variation in the product. This is the group of factors that give managers gray hair and ulcers. This group is the major contributor to excess costs of production, low quality, scrap, and rework. Therefore, effort spent in identifying Assignable Causes and making them part of the group of Control Factors will generally have a very high payback.

Finally the group of Lesser Causes will be the source of the run-of-the-mill, routine variation that is always part of the background of all production processes.

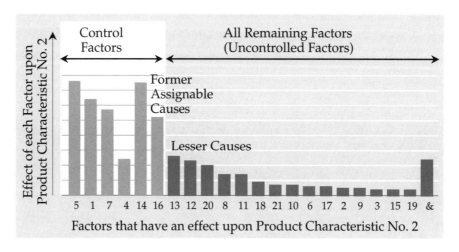

Figure 12.14: The Objective: All Dominant Causes are Control Factors

Effort spent trying to control the Lesser Causes will, at best, yield small returns, and will usually be effort wasted.

It is important to note that whenever we identify a dominant cause-and-effect relationship, and then make that cause a member of the set of Control Factors, we will remove a source of variation from the process. This means that the dominant causes discovered in the R&D phase will result in reduced product variation. However, a partial understanding of which factors are dominant will only result in a partial reduction of variation. And every R&D effort is limited by the ability of the researchers to identify the key factors in advance. Whenever we decide to conduct an experiment there will be some factors that we choose to study, and there will be other factors that we leave out of the study. These excluded factors may be held constant, or randomized, or ignored, but since they are not studied their impact remains unknown. Whenever a dominant cause ends up being held constant, or randomized, or ignored, your experiment can only give you a limited and partial understanding of your process.

However, in spite of your *understanding* of which factors are dominant, your *process* will always be subject to the effects of *all* of the Uncontrolled Factors. When the set of Uncontrolled Factors contains Assignable Causes your process will suffer the consequences. If we listen to, and learn from, the process data, then we can develop a more complete understanding of our process, and as a result we can operate it more profitably.

Therefore, we need to use a technique that will:

- Allow us to learn from our process data;
- Warn us when our process changes;
- Help us to identify the causes of those changes; and
- Enable us to operate our process predictably and on target.

Process behavior charts do all of these things. They complement and complete any R&D program, and they provide an essential foundation for any process improvement effort. The alternative to their use is nothing less than complete and total chaos.

12.5 Operating a Process Predictably

A process is either operated predictably or unpredictably. But does this mean that the *operator* is solely responsible for whether or not the process is operated predictably? By no means! In most cases the Assignable Causes of unpredictable operation are found elsewhere.

For example, an operator may operate a process in an unpredictable manner. This happens when the operator has had inadequate or incorrect training, or when the basis for making process adjustments is itself incorrect (e.g., adjusting the process based on finding an item that is outside the specifications).

The purchasing department may undermine the best of operators by simply providing poor raw materials, or poor equipment.

The maintenance department may cause a process to be operated unpredictably by failing to do required maintenance or by making inadequate repairs.

The supervisor may override the operator and ask for inappropriate process adjustments.

Engineers may provide incorrect guidelines for process operation or they may change guidelines without adequate process understanding.

Managers may foster unpredictable operation by failing to support efforts to fix problems that are identified in the course of production, by setting inappropriate production targets and goals, and by asking the production department to do things that the process is not capable of doing.

In other words, operating a process predictably is an accomplishment that requires the participation of everyone connected with that process. It cannot be done by the operators alone. As was pointed out in Section 12.3, a process can only be operated predictably when *management* establishes and maintains an *environment* where it is possible for a process to be operated predictably. This means that everyone connected with the process will have to be able and willing to respond to signals of process changes presented by the process behavior charts.

Therefore, while a process will either be operated predictably or unpredictably, the intent of using this wording is to emphasize that predictable operation is an achievement requiring the cooperation and understanding of everyone connected with that process.

12.6 Summary

The traditional definition of trouble implicitly assumes that processes are operated predictably. Since this assumption is incorrect, much of the conventional wisdom regarding process improvement is insufficient to deal with the problems of production.

Process behavior charts provide a way of defining the ideal of what a process has the potential to do, a way of moving the process toward that ideal, and a way of judging how close we have come to operating a process predictably. In short, they not only provide an operational definition of when your process is in trouble, but they also provide a way out of that trouble.

When the old and new definitions of trouble are combined we obtain a more realistic model for characterizing our processes and operations. This model provides guidance on which type of improvement effort is needed and a way to understand how good research needs to be integrated with good operational practices in order to get the most out of any process.

Find Assignable Causes for Unpredictable Processes and remove their effects;
Upgrade or adjust Predictable Processes in the Threshold State; and
Ignore or tweak the Predictable Processes in the Ideal State.

You cannot optimize any system
when some of the dominant cause-and-effect relationships
remain unidentified.

Chapter Thirteen

Capability and Performance Indexes

The power of the Four Possibilities as a conceptualization device rests in the fact that it combines the Voice of the Process with the Voice of the Customer and reconciles the actions that are indicated when each voice is considered separately. By combining the behavior of the process with the acceptability of the process outcomes we obtain a realistic assessment of where we are starting from and how to go about making things better.

This chapter presents the traditional indexes used to compare the Voice of the Process with the Voice of the Customer and shows how these traditional indexes are related to the Four Possibilities.

13.1 The Voice(s) of the Process

Many years ago, William Scherkenbach coined the phrase, Voice of the Process, to describe what you could expect to get from a process that was being operated predictably. This voice is given numerical values by the limits for individual values, commonly known as Natural Process Limits. When the data have been obtained in a rational manner, over a reasonable period of time, the Natural Process Limits will define the *actual capability* of a predictable process, and they will also provide a reasonable approximation to the *hypothetical capability* of an unpredictable process. Thus, as Shewhart observed, the limits of a process behavior chart define the ideal of what the process can do or can be made to do.

At the same time, the running record for your process data defines the actual *performance* of your process. Thus, process behavior charts provide a simple, straightforward, and systematic way of comparing the performance of your process with its potential.

When a process is operated predictably its performance will fall within the bounds defined by its potential, and we will end up with a chart like that in Figure 13.1. When this happens we can use the Natural Process Limits to predict the future process performance: While the wire lengths average 109.2 mm, the individual wires are likely to be anywhere between 100.6 mm and 117.7 mm.

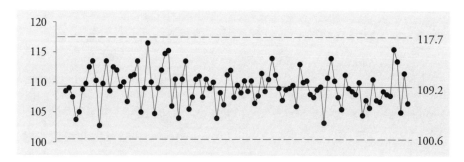

Figure 13.1: The *X* Chart for the Wire Length Data

Thus, a process that is operated predictably is a process that speaks with one voice; its performance is equivalent to its potential and both are characterized by the Natural Process Limits.

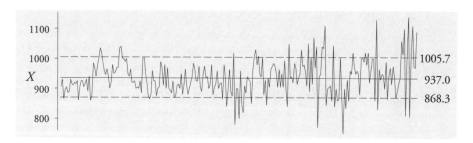

Figure 13.2: The *X* Chart for the Batch Weight Data

On the other hand, the *X*-Chart in Figure 13.2 shows a process that is being operated in an unpredictable manner—the past process performance is not consistent with the process potential. When this happens, the Natural Process Limits will still approximate the process potential, but a different measure will be needed to characterize the past performance of the process.

In Figure 13.2, the Natural Process Limits suggest that this process has the *potential* to produce batches with weights varying between 868 kilograms and 1006 kilograms and averaging 937 kilograms.

The past performance of this process is most easily seen on the histogram in Figure 13.3. As operated, this process actually delivered batches with weights ranging from 750 kg to 1140 kg. Using the global standard deviation statistic of 61.3 kg we might characterize the past performance with the descriptive three standard deviation interval:

$$Average \pm 3s = 937 \pm 3(61.3) = 753\ kg\ to\ 1121\ kg$$

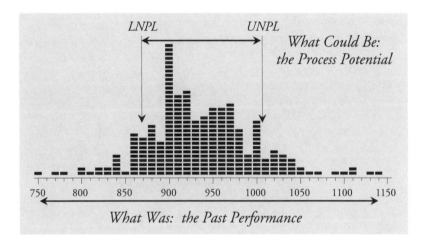

Figure 13.3: The Potential and the Performance of the Batch Weight Process

When a process is operated unpredictably it will have two voices—what it has done in the past and what it has the potential to do in the future. The greater the discrepancy between these two voices the greater the payback from learning how to operate the process up to its full potential.

13.2   The Voice of the Customer

While not every characteristic of a product or a process will have a specification, most of the final product characteristics will have one-sided or two-sided specifications. These specifications are one aspect of the Voice of the Customer. They allow us to sort the good stuff from the bad stuff after the fact. The easiest way to compare the process performance with the specifications is to draw the specifications on the histogram of the process values. (This avoids the problem and confusion of adding specification lines to a process behavior chart, while it also provides a simple and easy way to estimate the fraction of nonconforming product.)

The Wire Length Process has specs of 105 mm ± 8 mm. As can be seen in Figure 13.4, these specifications have resulted in six nonconforming pieces out of 100 pieces. Since this process is being operated predictably we can expect that it will continue to produce about six percent nonconforming in the future. While this process is in the Threshold State, inspection of Figure 13.4 will suggest that we could move this process to the Ideal State by adjusting the process aim.

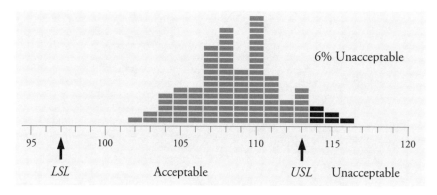

Figure 13.4: The Specifications for Wire Length

The histogram and specifications for the Batch Weight Data are shown in Figure 13.5. There we see a process that has trouble meeting its specifications. Figure 13.2 showed that this process was being operated unpredictably. Moreover, 59 of the 259 values fall outside the specifications of 1000 kg ± 100 kg. During this one week about 23 percent of the batches have been out of specification on weight. An unpredictable process with 23 percent nonconforming product is a process that is deep within the State of Chaos—where it is likely to stay until they learn how to operate it predictably. Work on improving the process aim will not help to any great extent. Work on reducing variation will be premature until the Assignable Causes of exceptional variation have been identified and steps have been taken to remove their effects from this process.

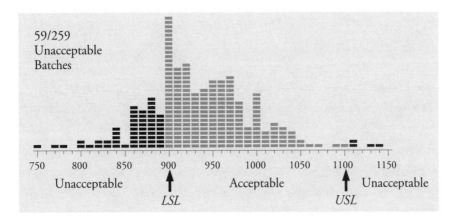

Figure 13.5: The Specifications for Batch Weight

Thus, the process behavior chart will characterize the behavior of the process, while the histogram can display the relationship between the past performance of the process and the specification limits. The fraction nonconforming can be simply obtained from this histogram by counting those items inside and outside the specifications. Since these graphic displays are simple, complete, and assumption-free, they provide effective and powerful ways to compare the Voice of the Process with the Voice of the Customer. They also provide the simplest way to estimate the fraction of nonconforming product (using the binomial point estimate of Section 9.2).

However, since numerical summaries are useful, you will commonly encounter four capability and performance indexes that may be used in conjunction with the process behavior chart and the histogram. These four indexes are the Capability Ratio, C_p, the Centered Capability Ratio, C_{pk}, the Performance Ratio, P_p, and the Centered Performance Ratio, P_{pk}.

Each of these indexes will be discussed and illustrated in the following sections. Later, these indexes will be used to characterize the excess costs associated with a particular process.

13.3 The Capability Ratio, C_p

The first question when comparing the Voice of the Process with the Voice of the Customer is whether or not the process can operate within the specification limits. This question is addressed by the Capability Ratio, C_p.

The Capability Ratio, C_p, compares the *space available within the specifications* with the *space required by the process*. The space available within the specifications is simply the *specified tolerance,* which is the difference between the two specification limits: [*USL – LSL*]. This specified tolerance is simply the elbow room available to the process.

The space required by the process is the *natural tolerance*, which is the difference between the Natural Process Limits: [*UNPL – LNPL*]. Thus, the Capability Ratio is:

$$C_p \; = \; \frac{USL - LSL}{UNPL - LNPL} \; = \; \frac{space\ available\ within\ specifications}{space\ required\ by\ the\ process} \; = \; \frac{USL - LSL}{6\ Sigma(X)}$$

With a predictable process the Capability Ratio defines the *ability* of the process to operate within the specifications. Values greater than 1.00 will be indicative of a process that can be operated in the Ideal State. Values less than 1.00 indicate that some nonconforming product may be unavoidable.

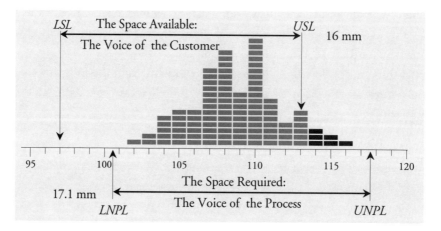

Figure 13.6: The Comparison Made by the Capability Ratio for Wire Lengths

For the Wire Length Data the specifications of 97 mm to 113 mm result in a speci-fied tolerance of 16 mm. The Natural Process Limits of 100.6 mm to 117.7 mm result in a natural tolerance of 17.1 mm. Thus the Capability Ratio for the Wire Length Process is:

$$C_p = \frac{USL - LSL}{UNPL - LNPL} = \frac{16 \text{ mm}}{17.1 \text{ mm}} = 0.936$$

and the space available within the specifications could be said to be 93.6% as large as the space required for this process. This process could almost fit inside the specifica-tions.

With an unpredictable process the Capability Ratio has a more limited mean-ing—it defines whether or not the process has the *potential* to operate within the specifications. Of course, as long as the process is operated in an unpredictable manner this potential will remain unrealized, but the Capability Ratio does at least provide some idea of what can be accomplished.

***The Capability Ratio defines
the elbow room available to a Predictable Process,
and the hypothetical elbow room available to an Unpredictable Process.***

The Capability Ratio expresses the elbow room for the process in terms of the process dispersion, but it does not explicitly consider the process location.

Figure 13.2 shows that the Batch Weight Process has been operated unpre-dictably. The specifications from Figure 13.5 are 900 kg to 1100 kg. Figure 13.2 shows Natural Process Limits of 868.5 kg to 1005.5 kg. Thus, the Capability Ratio for the Batch Weight Data is computed to be:

$$C_p = \frac{USL - LSL}{UNPL - LNPL} = \frac{200 \text{ kg}}{137 \text{ kg}} = 1.46$$

Figure 13.7 shows that this value does not describe what has happened in the past. It does however approximate what this process has the potential to do. Therefore we would interpret this C_p value of 1.46 to mean that this process has the potential to be operated comfortably within the specification limits.

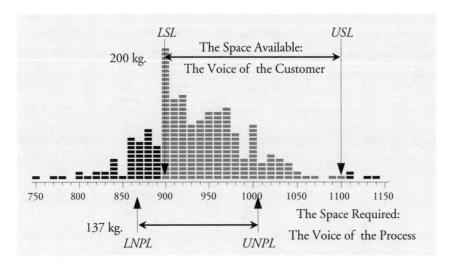

Figure 13.7: The Comparison Made by the Capability Ratio for Batch Weights

In Figures 13.6 and 13.7 there is an offset between the specifications and the Natural Process Limits. This offset is not taken into account when computing the Capability Ratio, C_p. However, it is part of the Centered Capability Ratio, C_{pk}.

13.4 The Centered Capability Ratio, C_{pk}

The second question is whether or not the process is properly centered within the specifications. When we adjust the Capability Ratio so that it takes both the location and the dispersion of the process into account we end up with the Centered Capability Ratio, C_{pk}. This ratio can be described in several different ways. The simplest explanation is that it places the distance from the process average to the nearer specification limit in the numerator and compares that with one-half of the natural tolerance.

If we define the Distance to the Nearer Specification or *DNS* to be:

$$DNS = \text{the smaller of } [\ (Average - LSL) \text{ and } (USL - Average)\ ]$$

then the Centered Capability Ratio could be written as:

$$C_{pk} = \frac{DNS}{(UNPL - LNPL)/2} = \frac{DNS}{3\ Sigma(X)} = \frac{\textit{effective space available}}{\textit{space required}}$$

The numerator will define the effective space available between the process average and the nearer specification. The denominator defines the generic space required by the process on one (either) side of the average. Thus, the Centered Capability Ratio characterizes how close to the nearer specification the process is centered.

If the process is perfectly centered within the specifications C_{pk} will be the same as C_p. As the process moves away from being perfectly centered the value of C_{pk} will be smaller than C_p. Thus, even though we call C_{pk} the Centered Capability Ratio, it is the size of C_{pk}, relative to C_p, that actually characterizes how well centered the process is within the specifications.

Whenever the process average is outside the specification limits the definition of the *DNS* value given above will result in a negative value. Since the denominator will still be a positive number, the Centered Capability Ratio will become negative whenever the process average is on the wrong side of one of the specification limits.

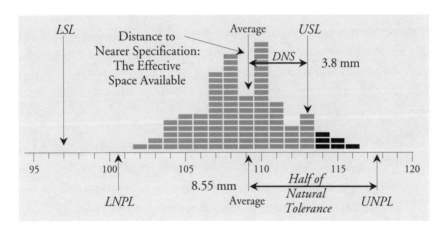

Figure 13.8: The Comparison Made by the Centered Capability Ratio

◆ ◆ ◆

The average for the Wire Length Process is 109.2 mm, so that the nearer specification is the upper specification of 113 mm. This results in a *DNS* value of 3.8 mm. The Natural Process Limits are 100.6 mm to 117.7 mm. Thus, the Centered Capability Ratio for the Wire Length Process is:

$$C_{pk} = \frac{DNS}{(UNPL - LNPL)/2} = \frac{3.8 \text{ mm}}{8.55 \text{ mm}} = 0.444$$

Since this process is not centered the effective space available could be said to be only 44.4% as large as the space required for this process. When this value is compared with the Capability Ratio of 93.6% we get a sense of being considerably off target.

Clearly, it sounds much worse to say that the C_{pk} value is 44 percent than it does to say that we have six percent nonconforming. This is why I prefer to use the histogram and the process behavior chart along with the capability indexes—the numerical summaries may supplement the graphs, but they cannot replace them.

If the Centered Capability Ratio is computed for an unpredictable process the fact that it depends upon the historical average complicates the interpretation of the ratio. In this case the ratio characterizes what would happen if you learned how to operate your process predictably but did not change the process average from its historical value. Since it is likely that in the course of learning how to operate your process predictably you will also discover how to do a better job of getting your process on target, the Centered Capability Ratio, computed for an unpredictable process, is generally a worst case value for what would happen if the process were to be operated predictably. The conditional nature of this interpretation makes this ratio less useful than the Capability Ratio as a characterization of what can be achieved by operating an unpredictable process predictably.

> *The Centered Capability Ratio defines*
> *the effective space available for a predictable process,*
> *and gives a minimum value for the effective space available*
> *when an unpredictable process is operated predictably.*

The nonlinear relationship between the capability indexes and the fraction nonconforming has been a stumbling block with these indices ever since they were first introduced. And yet, since the capability indexes themselves do not mean much to most people, they are invariably converted into fractions nonconforming, even if that number happens to be some small number of parts per million. A way of converting these indexes into *costs* will be provided in the following chapters.

For the Batch Weight Process the historical average was 937 kg. The lower specification is 900 kg. Thus, the *DNS* value is 37 kg. From Figure 13.2 the Natural Process Limits are 868.5 to 1005.5. Therefore the Centered Capability Ratio for the Batch Weight Data is:

$$C_{pk} = \frac{DNS}{(UNPL - LNPL)/2} = \frac{37 \text{ kg}}{68.5 \text{ kg}} = 0.540$$

This C_{pk} value characterizes what would happen if this process was operated predictably with the same process average that it has had in the past. Improving the process aim, relative to the specifications, would result in C_{pk} values that are better than this value of 0.54. At this point this value may not seem very interesting. In the next chapter, however, this value will help us to compute the Effective Cost of Production.

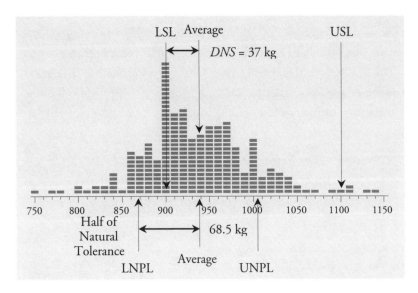

Figure 13.9: The Centered Capability Ratio for the Batch Weight Data

13.5 The Performance Ratio, P_p

In Table 2.7 we saw that the interval defined by [Average ± 3s] will bracket virtually all of the process outcomes regardless of whether or not the process is operated predictably. Here we will use this descriptive interval to characterize the generic past performance of an unpredictable process and to compare that past performance with the specifications. To this end, we will define two performance indexes which will have the same numerators as the capability indexes, but which will have denominators based upon the descriptive statistics.

When a process is operated predictably the following performance indexes will characterize the same things that are characterized by the capability indexes. However, when a process is not operated predictably the performance indexes will merely describe the past.

With an unpredictable process the Capability Ratio, C_p, will characterize the elbow room for the process in terms of the process potential, but the Performance Ratio, P_p, will describe the elbow room in terms of the past performance:

$$P_p = \frac{USL - LSL}{6\,s} = \frac{space\ available}{space\ used\ in\ past}$$

Since the past is past, and since this value does not incorporate the location of the past outcomes, this ratio is of limited interest except in comparison with the Capability Ratio. The greater the degree of predictability with which a process is operated the closer together the Performance Ratio and the Capability Ratio will be. The further apart these two ratios are the greater the degree of unpredictability for the process.

The Performance Ratio characterizes
the elbow room within the specifications
in terms of the space used by the process outcomes in the past.

For the Batch Weight Data the specifications are 900 kg to 1100 kg, while the global standard deviation statistic is $s = 61.3$ kg. These values result in a Performance Ratio of:

$$P_p = \frac{USL - LSL}{6\,s} = \frac{200\ kg}{367.8\ kg} = 0.54$$

The difference between the Performance Ratio of 54% and the Hypothetical Capability Ratio of 146% defines the opportunity for improvement that exists in this process. *Learning how to operate this process predictably will have the same effect as making the specified tolerance three times bigger!* Moreover, while the 146% value is hypothetical, it is not an imaginary number. Since it is based upon the Natural Process Limits, it is based upon the demonstrated process potential.

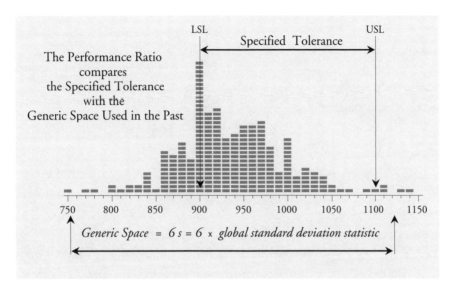

Figure 13.10: The Performance Ratio for the Batch Weight Data

The extent to which the Capability Ratio
exceeds the Performance Ratio
defines the degree of unpredictability for a process
and the opportunity that exists for improving that process.

For the Wire Length Data the global standard deviation statistic was found in Chapter Two to be $s = 2.823$ mm. The specification limits are 105 mm ± 8 mm. Thus the Performance Ratio for the Wire Length Data is:

$$P_p = \frac{USL - LSL}{6\,s} = \frac{16 \text{ mm}}{16.938 \text{ mm}} = 0.945$$

which is very similar to the C_p value of 0.936 found earlier.

13.6 The Centered Performance Ratio, P_{pk}

The Centered Performance Ratio compares the *DNS* with three times the global standard deviation statistic:

$$P_{pk} = \frac{DNS}{3\,s} = \frac{\textit{effective space available}}{\textit{space used in past}}$$

This ratio compares the *DNS* value with a generic characterization of the amount of space on one side of the average where process outcomes are likely to have occurred in the past.

For an unpredictable process, a P_{pk} value greater than 1.0 will mean that you have been in the Brink of Chaos, while a P_{pk} value that is less than 1.0 will probably mean that you have been in the State of Chaos. As with the capability indexes, the value for P_{pk} will always be less than or equal to the value of P_p.

The Centered Performance Ratio
expresses the Distance to the Nearer Specification
in terms of the generic space used by the process outcomes
on one side of the average in the past.

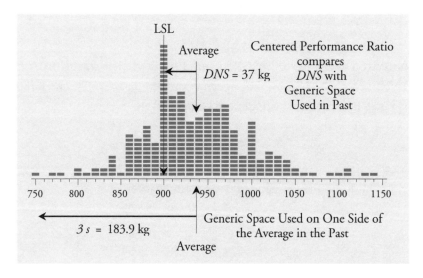

Figure 13.11: The Centered Performance Ratio for the Batch Weight Data

For the Batch Weight Data the specifications are 900 kg to 1100 kg, the global standard deviation statistic is s = 61.3 kg, and the average is 937 kilograms. These values result in a *DNS* value of:

$$DNS = min\left[(Average - LSL) \text{ and } (USL - Average)\right]$$
$$= min\{37\text{ kg and }163\text{ kg}\} = 37\text{ kg}$$

Thus the Centered Performance Ratio for the Batch Weight Data is:

$$P_{pk} = \frac{DNS}{3\,s} = \frac{37\text{ kg}}{183.9\text{ kg}} = 0.20$$

The two performance indexes summarize the past. The values of P_p = 0.54 and P_{pk} = 0.20 for the Batch Weight Data describe a process that has had a lot of nonconforming product in the past, and which has not been centered within the specifications. These two numbers simply quantify the situation shown in Figures 13.10 and 13.11. This process has been deep within the State of Chaos.

For the Wire Length Data the *DNS* value was found in Section 13.4 to be 3.8 mm. The global standard deviation statistic was given in Chapter Two as s = 2.823 mm. Thus, the Centered Performance Ratio for the Wire Length Data is:

$$P_{pk} = \frac{DNS}{3\,s} = \frac{3.8\text{ mm}}{8.469\text{ mm}} = 0.449$$

which is very similar to the C_{pk} value of 0.444 found earlier. When working with a predictable process the corresponding capability indexes and performance indexes will be quite similar in value, differing only in the degrees of freedom used in each computation.

The capability indexes and the performance indexes can be used to quantify what we see on both the process behavior chart and the histogram. Along with the graphs, these index numbers help to define what type of improvement efforts might be needed. The easiest way to see how this is done is to return to the Four Possibilities.

13.7   The Ratios and the Four Possibilities

The capability and performance indexes defined in this chapter are related to the Four Possibilities as shown in Figure 13.12.

Predictable Process	**Threshold State** $C_{pk} < 1$ *Product Trouble* $C_p > 1$ center the process $C_p < 1$ reengineer the process	**Ideal State** $C_{pk} > 1$ *No Trouble*
Unpredictable Process	**State of Chaos** $P_{pk} < 1$ *Double Trouble* $P_p > 1$ Centering may help… but full process potential requires predictable operation.	**Brink of Chaos** $P_{pk} > 1$ *Process Trouble* Full process potential requires predictable operation.
	Some Nonconforming Product Produced	**100% Conforming Product Produced**

Figure 13.12: Capability, Performance, and The Four Possibilities

- Predictable processes with $C_{pk} > 1$ will be in the Ideal State.

- Predictable processes with $C_{pk} < 1$ will usually fall in the Threshold State.

- Unpredictable processes with $P_{pk} > 1$ will have been in the Brink of Chaos.

- Unpredictable processes with $P_{pk} < 1$ will usually have been in the State of Chaos, where they are likely to remain without some intervention.

If your process is in the Threshold State and $C_p > 1$, you can probably move your process to the Ideal State by simply improving the process aim. However, if your process is in the Threshold State and $C_p < 1$, then your process will need to be changed in some fundamental way to get to the Ideal State.

If your process has been in the State of Chaos and yet $P_p > 1$, you may be able to temporarily move your process to the Brink of Chaos by improving the process aim. However, if $P_p < 1$, then your process is likely to remain in the State of Chaos until you learn how to operate it predictably.

13.8   Operational Improvement

The difference between operating a process predictably and operating a process unpredictably is not a matter of having the right process, or having the right process settings, or even having the right product design. While all these can have an impact upon the ability to operate a process predictably, the ultimate issue in operating a process predictably is an operational one. Does everyone involved with operating a process understand what it takes to operate it predictably and do they have the operational discipline to do so over the long haul? The operating environment has to be one that will facilitate predictable operation.

Techniques that improve the process aim will move you from the left to the right in Figure 13.13. Techniques that reduce the process variation will move you from the left to the right in Figure 13.13. Changes in technology, process upgrades, and the reengineering of the process are all intended to move you to the right in Figure 13.13. However, the confusion engendered when such major process changes are imposed upon a process will often result in a process that is in the State of Chaos.

The only way to move from the bottom of Figure 13.13 to the top is to learn how to operate your process predictably, and then to practice the operational discipline needed to maintain your process in a predictable state.

When you identify a dominant cause-and-effect relationship and remove its effects from your process you will be reducing the variation of the process outcomes, and as a result, will move to the right in Figure 13.13. This is true regardless of how you identify the dominant factor.

However, it is a mistake to think that such improvements are permanent. Entropy is relentless. Therefore, without a continuing program for identifying and removing the effects of Assignable Causes, your process will be doomed to operate in the bottom two boxes.

Of all the improvement techniques, only the process behavior chart will let you develop and maintain the discipline required to operate your processes up to their full potential. Designed experiments may help you to define the product design or

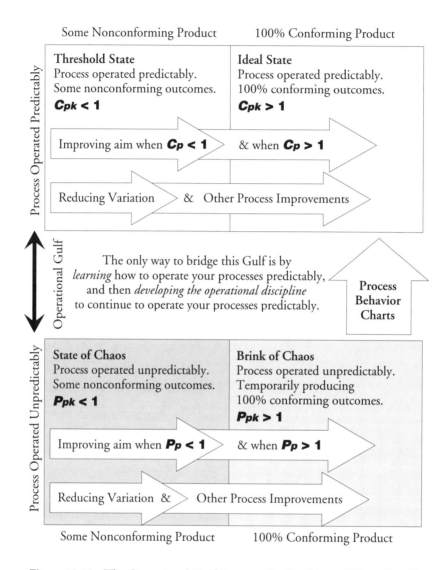

Figure 13.13: The Operational Gulf Between Predictable and Unpredictable

refine the process settings. Automatic process-controllers may help you to maintain the status quo. But only the process behavior chart provides the real-time process feedback needed to allow you to improve your process and achieve that consistency of operation that will allow you to get the most out of your process over the long haul.

13.9   Short-Term and Long-Term Capability

The capability and performance indexes can be used to summarize the relationship between process performance, process potential, and the specifications. While they need to be used in conjunction with the histogram and the process behavior chart, they make useful comparisons. When properly understood these comparisons provide clues to the type of process improvements needed.

However, like all numerical summaries, these capability and performance indexes can be misinterpreted and misconstrued. An example of this is the practice of referring to the capability indexes as "short-term" capabilities and referring to the performance indexes as "long-term" capabilities.

This nomenclature obscures the fact that some processes are operated predictably while others are operated unpredictably. By failing to call attention to this fundamental distinction, this misnomer ignores both the cause of much trouble and the path to avoiding that trouble in the future. It essentially condemns those who use this language to continue to operate in the cycle of despair. These inappropriate labels of short-term and long-term capability result in confusion in both thought and action. Careful definitions and precise terminology are required to achieve clarity in thought and effectiveness in action.

Capability indexes define the actual capability of a predictable process and the hypothetical capability of an unpredictable process. Performance indexes characterize the past performance of an unpredictable process and duplicate the information contained in the capability indexes for a predictable process. Using different language does not change these facts.

13.10   Interpreting and Using Capability Indexes

Capability and performance indexes are being commonly used in commerce today—frequently as targets or objectives for suppliers to meet. In this game of capability roulette it is important to understand the limitations of the capability and performance indexes you compute.

To begin with, as statistics, all capability indexes are biased estimators—on the average the computed statistic will be larger than the actual process capability. While this positive bias declines as the number of degrees of freedom in the estimate of dispersion increases, it never fully disappears.

Interval estimates can help you to understand the limitations of any capability index. We begin with the case in which the process has been operated predictably and we compute the P_p index. Here, *both* P_p and C_p are biased estimates of the actual process capability, and a 90% Interval Estimate for this process capability may be obtained from:

$$P_p \sqrt{\frac{\chi^2_{.05}}{v}} < \text{Process Capability} < P_p \sqrt{\frac{\chi^2_{.95}}{v}}$$

$$P_p \; \textbf{LB} < \text{Process Capability} < P_p \; \textbf{UB}$$

where v is the degrees of freedom for the global standard deviation statistic used in the denominator of P_p.

The same approach may be used to obtain an *approximate* 90% Interval Estimate for the process capability using C_p:

$$C_p \sqrt{\frac{\chi^2_{.05}}{v}} < \text{Process Capability} < C_p \sqrt{\frac{\chi^2_{.95}}{v}}$$

$$C_p \; \textbf{LB} < \text{Process Capability} < C_p \; \textbf{UB}$$

where v is the degrees of freedom used to compute the Natural Process Limits used in the denominator of C_p.

Table 13.1 contains **LB** and **UB**, the square roots of the Chi-Square percentiles divided by their degrees of freedom.

For example, the computed Capability Ratio for the Wire Length Process was C_p = 0.936. The Natural Process Limits used to find this value were based on 100 observations and had 60 degrees of freedom. An approximate 90% Interval Estimate for the capability of this process from Table 13.1 would be:

$$0.936 \, (0.848) = 0.79 \quad \text{to} \quad 0.936 \, (1.148) = 1.07$$

Since the Wire Length Data displayed the homogeneity that we expect from a predictable process both C_p and P_p are estimates of the process capability. When we computed a P_p value for the Wire Length Data we used the descriptive global stan-

Table 13.1: Factors for Approximate 90% Interval Estimates for C_p and P_p

d.f.	LB	UB	d.f.	LB	UB	d.f.	LB	UB	d.f.	LB	UB
5	.479	1.488	20	.736	1.253	55	.842	1.155	250	.926	1.073
6	.522	1.449	21	.743	1.247	60	.848	1.148	300	.933	1.067
7	.556	1.418	22	.749	1.242	65	.854	1.142	350	.938	1.062
8	.584	1.392	23	.754	1.236	70	.860	1.137	400	.942	1.058
9	.608	1.371	24	.760	1.232	75	.865	1.133	450	.945	1.055
10	.628	1.353	25	.764	1.227	80	.869	1.128	500	.948	1.052
11	.645	1.338	26	.769	1.223	85	.873	1.125	550	.950	1.049
12	.660	1.323	27	.773	1.219	90	.876	1.121	600	.952	1.047
13	.673	1.311	28	.777	1.215	100	.883	1.115	650	.954	1.045
14	.685	1.300	29	.781	1.211	110	.888	1.110	700	.956	1.044
15	.696	1.291	30	.785	1.208	120	.893	1.105	750	.957	1.042
16	.705	1.282	35	.801	1.193	140	.901	1.097	800	.959	1.041
17	.714	1.274	40	.814	1.181	160	.907	1.091	850	.960	1.040
18	.722	1.266	45	.825	1.170	180	.913	1.086	900	.961	1.039
19	.730	1.259	50	.834	1.162	200	.917	1.082	1000	.963	1.037

dard deviation statistic, $s = 2.823$, having 99 degrees of freedom. This Performance Ratio was $P_p = 0.945$, which results in a 90% Interval Estimate for the process capability of:

$$0.945\,(0.882) \;=\; 0.83 \quad \text{to} \quad 0.945\,(1.116) \;=\; 1.05$$

As we would expect, the larger degrees of freedom for P_p results in a slightly tighter interval estimate than the one based on C_p.

Inspection of Table 13.1 will show that C_p and P_p are not known to within 20 percent until they are based on at least 35 degrees of freedom. They are not known to within 10 percent until they are based on 140 degrees of freedom. And they are not known to within plus or minus 5 percent until they are based on 550 degrees of freedom.

The centered capability indexes, C_{pk} and P_{pk}, have an estimate of the process dispersion in the denominator, just like the capability indexes C_p and P_p. However, in addition, the centered capability indexes also have an estimate of the distance to the nearer specification in the numerator. This introduces an additional bit of uncertainty into the computed values for C_{pk} and P_{pk}. To deal with this additional uncertainty we have to use the factors in Table 13.2 to obtain *approximate* 90% Interval Estimates for the centered capability indexes.

Since the Wire Length Data display the homogeneity we expect from a predictable process, both C_{pk} and P_{pk} are estimates of the centered process capability.

263

Table 13.2: Factors for Approximate 90% Interval Estimates for C_{pk} and P_{pk}

d.f.	LB	UB	d.f.	LB	UB	d.f.	LB	UB	d.f.	LB	UB
5	.340	2.096	20	.665	1.386	55	.803	1.211	250	.910	1.092
6	.384	1.971	21	.673	1.376	60	.812	1.200	300	.920	1.082
7	.423	1.866	22	.680	1.368	65	.821	1.188	350	.927	1.075
8	.458	1.773	23	.686	1.358	70	.828	1.181	400	.933	1.069
9	.492	1.693	24	.693	1.351	75	.835	1.174	450	.936	1.066
10	.525	1.618	25	.698	1.342	80	.839	1.168	500	.939	1.063
11	.544	1.587	26	.704	1.335	85	.844	1.163	550	.941	1.060
12	.561	1.556	27	.710	1.328	90	.848	1.158	600	.942	1.058
13	.577	1.530	28	.715	1.320	100	.857	1.149	650	.944	1.056
14	.592	1.505	29	.720	1.313	110	.862	1.143	700	.946	1.055
15	.606	1.482	30	.725	1.309	120	.868	1.137	750	.947	1.053
16	.619	1.460	35	.746	1.281	140	.878	1.126	800	.949	1.052
17	.632	1.440	40	.764	1.259	160	.885	1.118	850	.950	1.051
18	.644	1.419	45	.780	1.238	180	.893	1.110	900	.951	1.049
19	.656	1.402	50	.793	1.222	200	.899	1.104	1000	.953	1.047

For these data our estimated *DNS* was 3.8 mm and the global standard deviation statistic was $s = 2.823$. Thus, the P_{pk} value for the Wire Length Data was found to be:

$$P_{pk} = \frac{3.8 \text{ mm}}{3\,(2.823)} = 0.449$$

Since the global standard deviation statistic has 99 degrees of freedom we say that this capability index also has 99 degrees of freedom. Interpolating in Table 13.2, therefore, we obtain an approximate 90% Interval Estimate of the centered process capability to be:

$$0.449\,(0.856) = 0.38 \quad \text{to} \quad 0.449\,(1.150) = 0.52$$

Earlier we computed the Centered Capability Ratio for the Wire Length Data and found $C_{pk} = 0.444$. This estimate had 60 *d.f.* giving an approximate 90% Interval Estimate of:

$$0.444\,(0.812) = 0.36 \quad \text{to} \quad 0.444\,(1.200) = 0.53$$

Inspection of Table 13.2 will show that C_{pk} and P_{pk} values based on the "magic number" of 30 degrees of freedom will have an approximate uncertainty of ±30 percent! Centered indexes based on 60 degrees of freedom will still have an uncertainty of ±20 percent. In order to know the value of a centered index to within ±10 percent you will need to have 200 degrees of freedom, and to know the value to within ±5 percent you will need to have 900 degrees of freedom.

◆ ◆ ◆

For the Batch Weight Data the Capability Ratio was C_p = 1.46. Since the process was operated unpredictably, this value only approximates the hypothetical capability of this process. This value was based on Natural Process Limits that were computed using the first 61 observations (see Section 3.2) and so both they and the Capability Ratio have 36 degrees of freedom. Using Table 13.1, this gives an approximate 90% Interval Estimate for the *hypothetical capability* of:

$$1.46 \, (0.804) \; = \; 1.17 \quad \text{to} \quad 1.46 \, (1.191) \; = \; 1.74$$

We also computed a Centered Capability Ratio of C_{pk} = 0.54 for the Batch Weight Data. Like C_p, this C_{pk} value has 36 degrees of freedom. Using Table 13.2 we can find an approximate 90% Interval Estimate for the *minimum hypothetical Centered Capability Ratio* of:

$$0.54 \, (0.750) \; = \; 0.41 \quad \text{to} \quad 0.54 \, (1.303) \; = \; 0.70$$

The performance indexes for the Batch Weight Data were P_p = 0.54 and P_{pk} = 0.20. (The fact that P_p is numerically the same as C_{pk} is just a coincidence.) Each of these performance indexes was computed using the global standard deviation statistic of s = 61.3 kg. Since this s statistic has 258 degrees of freedom each of these performance indexes is also said to have 258 degrees of freedom. However, since both P_p and P_{pk} were computed using all of the values (there were only 259 batches made last week) it does not make sense to compute Interval Estimates based on P_p and P_{pk}. Neither the Performance Ratio P_p nor the Centered Performance Ratio P_{pk} contain any uncertainty. They fully and completely *describe the past.* There is no sampling uncertainty in either number., Since the process is operated unpredictably, these descriptive statistics do not characterize the underlying process in any meaningful manner.

In each case the hypothetical capability index values are two to three times larger than the performance indexes, suggesting substantial improvements may be had by operating this process predictably.

This author has encountered many instances where C_{pk} values are computed using 5 to 10 degrees of freedom. When this is done, the resulting values will have so much uncertainty as to be of no practical utility. Because of their nature, capability and performance indexes will always need substantial degrees of freedom before they are known with any real precision.

(This section is based upon the material and derivations given in Chou, Owen, and Borrego, *Journal of Quality Technology, Vol. 22,* pp. 223-229, July 1990.)

13.11 Summary

Process behavior charts and histograms with specification limits allow you to compare the Voice of the Process with the Voice of the Customer. Numerical summaries complement these graphic comparisons. The main problem with numerical summaries is not their computation but rather their interpretation, since their meaning changes with the status of the process.

When the Process is Operated Predictably:

- C_p and P_p both characterize the same thing—the elbow room for the process. They both express the specified tolerance as a percentage of the space consumed by the natural process variation.
  Interval Estimates make sense.

- C_{pk} and P_{pk} both characterize the same thing—the Distance to the Nearer Specification. They both express this *DNS* value as a percentage of the generic space required by natural process variation on one side of the process average.
  Interval Estimates make sense.

- P_p and P_{pk} will have greater degrees of freedom than C_p and C_{pk}.

When the Process is Operated Unpredictably:

- C_p and P_p will estimate *different* things.

- C_p characterizes the *hypothetical* elbow room that is likely to exist when this process is operated predictably. This ratio expresses the specified tolerance as a percentage of the hypothetical space required by this process when it is operated with maximum consistency.
  Interval Estimates make hypothetical sense.

- P_p describes the past performance of the process. It expresses the specified tolerance as a percentage of the generic space used by the past process outcomes. With an unpredictable process P_p will always be smaller than C_p because it is estimating a smaller quantity. Interval Estimates do not make sense here since there is not one underlying process, but many.

When the Process is Operated Unpredictably:

- C_{pk} and P_{pk} will characterize *different* things.

- C_{pk} will express the historical *DNS* value as a percentage of the hypothetical space required on one side of the average when this process is operated with maximum consistency. This value is effectively a minimum hypothetical C_{pk} that can be achieved with predictable operation of the process. Interval Estimates rarely make sense here since this value is itself a lower bound.

- P_{pk} will express the historical *DNS* value as a percentage of the generic space used on one side of the average by the past process outcomes. With an unpredictable process P_{pk} will always be estimating a smaller quantity than C_{pk} will be estimating.
  Interval Estimates do not make sense here since there is not one underlying process, but many.

Because of the shifting meanings for these commonly computed indexes it is impossible to ever have a meaningful discussion using the capability or performance indexes alone. You will always have to know whether or not the underlying process is being operated predictably.

However, with an unpredictable process, it is possible to capitalize on the differences between the performance indexes and the capability indexes by converting these indexes into Effective Costs of Production. This conversion is the topic of the next two chapters.

Chapter Fourteen

Using the Effective Cost of Production

Since capability indexes and performance indexes are not always easy to interpret they are frequently converted into other measures of performance such as the fraction of nonconforming product, a defects per million rate, or an esoteric "sigma level" for the process.

Rather than these traditional, and occasionally questionable, conversions, this chapter will outline how the indexes of the previous chapter can be directly converted into the metric that managers prefer—dollars. While the details of this conversion will be given in the next chapter, this chapter will focus on how the Effective Cost of Production can be used to determine the potential returns for different improvement strategies.

14.1 The Effective Cost of Production

Let us begin by thinking about an idealized situation where all incoming material is right on target and delivered right on time, all machines run at full efficiency with no down time, and everybody does their job exactly the right way every time. In this scenario you should have maximum productivity and maximum efficiency. Since your output volume would be maximized you would have the lowest unit cost of production possible for your operation. Call this unit cost the *nominal cost of production*. (In practice you may not actually know this value, but it is still a useful concept.)

Next think about your *actual cost of production*. How many units were produced and what were your operational expenses to produce them? In practice your incoming material will not always be there on time. Nor will these materials always be exactly on target. Your machines will have down time, and will not always be operated efficiently. Your employees will not always operate your processes consistently. And then there are the costs of rework, the costs of scrap, and other types of costs associated with routine production. When all of these are taken into account it is inevitable that the actual cost of using your incoming materials and producing a finished product will be higher than the nominal cost of production defined above.

If you knew both the actual cost of production and the nominal cost of production you could form their ratio and use this ratio as a way to characterize the efficiency of an operation. However, unlike many of the other numerical summaries of efficiency, this measure of efficiency would be proportional to actual costs. This ratio is known as the *Effective Cost of Production* and is defined as:

$$\textit{Effective Cost of Production} = \frac{\textit{Actual Cost of Production}}{\textit{Nominal Cost of Production}}$$

Every bit by which the Effective Cost of Production exceeds 1.00 (or 100%) represents waste, inefficiency, and excess costs built into your operations. Processes with Effective Costs of Production between 1.00 and 1.10 will be fairly efficient. These processes can be said to be in the economic zone. Processes with larger Effective Costs of Production will be less efficient and less economically viable than those with smaller values for the Effective Cost of Production.

In practice, you may not know the nominal cost of production. It is, after all, rather an idealized value where everything works as it is supposed to work. Moreover, uncertainty about how to allocate overhead charges can present a roadblock to actually computing a nominal cost of production.

Likewise, there will often be several different ways of computing a value for the actual cost of production, making even this real number elusive. So how can we ever find the Effective Cost of Production?

It turns out that once the specifics of a situation have been defined, an appropriate value for the Effective Cost of Production can be determined directly from the two capability indexes (or the two performance indexes). Tables of these Effective Costs of Production as a function of the two capability indexes are provided in the Appendix, and the basis for these tables is given in the next chapter.

The four tables in the Appendix, Tables A.17 to A.20, were selected from 37 such tables given in *The Process Evaluation Handbook* by this author. Table A.17 covers the situation where all nonconforming product is scrapped. Table A.18 covers the situation where all nonconforming product is reworked. Tables A.19 and A.20 are for the situations where nonconforming product on one side is scrapped while that on the other side is reworked at a cost that is one-half the cost of scrapping the item.

These tables can be used with the capability and performance indexes to characterize an Effective Cost of Production for different scenarios as outlined in the following sections.

14.2 The Benchmark Cost of Production

Before you can determine the potential savings to be obtained by various improvement efforts you will need a benchmark value to use for comparison. A benchmark value for the Effective Cost of Production can be obtained using the performance indexes. Since the performance indexes describe the past they will provide an Effective Cost of Production value that characterizes the past efficiency of a process. Moreover, as a historical value, this *Benchmark Cost of Production* (or *Benchmark ECP*) will also provide a reasonable approximation to what you might expect in the future until things take a turn for the worse. Certainly, since spontaneous improvement is rare, you should not expect to do substantially better than the *Benchmark ECP* until you improve the process in some way.

If you do not have a reasonable estimate of the nominal cost of production then you may use the *Benchmark ECP* to express directly the degree of inefficiency in your process. An estimate of the percentage by which you can reduce your actual costs of production by improving your process can be obtained by computing the simple ratio:

$$Potential\ Savings \ = \ \frac{Benchmark\ ECP - 1.00}{Benchmark\ ECP}$$

If you are fortunate enough to have a reasonable estimate of the nominal cost of production you can use the *Benchmark ECP* along with the nominal cost and the annual volume to obtain an estimate of the excess costs associated with the inefficiencies in your process. In order to do this we recall that the amount by which the Effective Cost of Production exceeds 1.00 is the excess cost for your process. Therefore, we estimate the excess cost according to the formula:

$$Excess\ Cost \ = \ [Benchmark\ ECP - 1.00] \ \times \ Nominal\ Cost \ \times \ Annual\ Volume$$

For the Batch Weight Data all nonconforming batches were scrapped. In the last chapter we saw that this process was deep inside the State of Chaos, having a Performance Ratio of $P_p = 0.54$ and a Centered Performance Ratio of $P_{pk} = 0.20$.

Table A.17 covers the situation in which all nonconforming product is scrapped. In the column that corresponds to $P_p = 0.50$ and in the row that corresponds to $P_{pk} = 0.20$ we find a *Benchmark ECP* value of 1.69. This value means that the actual cost of producing these batches has been 69% greater than it should be! If you could remove all of the inefficiencies from this process you could reduce your actual cost of production by as much as:

$$Potential\ Savings\ =\ \frac{Benchmark\ ECP - 1.00}{Benchmark\ ECP}\ =\ \frac{0.69}{1.69}\ =\ 0.408\ \ or\ 41\%$$

In this case the nominal cost of production was \$500 per batch. The annual volume was about 13,000 batches per year. Combining these values with the *Benchmark ECP* provides an estimate of the excess costs associated with this process:

$$Excess\ Costs\ =\ 0.69 \times \$500 \times 13,000\ =\ \$4.5\ million\ per\ year$$

This \$4.5 million is the opportunity pool (or entitlement) for this process.

14.3 The Centered Cost of Production

In most instances, the simplest form of process improvement consists of improving the process aim. Therefore it is appropriate to begin by assessing the benefits to be gained by operating the process on target.

The amount by which a process has been operated off target in the past will be reflected in the difference between the two performance indexes, P_p and P_{pk}. The extent to which the Centered Performance Ratio, P_{pk}, falls short of the value of the Performance Ratio, P_p, is a direct measure of how far off target the process has been in the past. Therefore, to estimate the benefits of operating your process on target, set the value of P_{pk} to be equal to the value computed for P_p and find the corresponding Effective Cost of Production. This value will be known as the *Centered Cost of Production* (or *Centered ECP*).

The difference between the *Benchmark ECP* and the *Centered ECP* provides an estimate of the amount by which the *excess costs* can be reduced by learning how to operate your process consistently on target. The amount by which you can reduce your *actual cost* of production by operating consistently on target would be approximated by:

272

$$\textit{Savings from Centered Operation} \ = \ \frac{\textit{Benchmark ECP} - \textit{Centered ECP}}{\textit{Benchmark ECP}}$$

If you happen to have a nominal cost of production you can extend the numerator above to approximate the annual savings from operating your process consistently on target:

Amount Saved by Centered Operation =
      [Benchmark ECP – Centered ECP] × *Nominal Cost* × *Annual Volume*

If the Batch Weights could be centered at the target value of 1000 kg the P_{pk} value would increase to be the same as the P_p value. Rounding off both P_{pk} and P_p to the value of 0.50 results in a *Centered ECP* of 1.40.

With a *Benchmark ECP* of 1.69, this *Centered ECP* value corresponds to a reduction in the actual cost of production of:

$$\textit{Savings from Centered Operation} \ = \ \frac{1.69 - 1.40}{1.69} \ = \ 0.171 \ \text{ or } 17\%$$

With a nominal cost of \$500 per batch the annual amount saved by consistently operating this process on target is estimated to be:

$$0.29 \times \$500 \times 13{,}000 \ = \ \$1.885 \text{ million per year}$$

14.4 The Predictable Cost of Production

If your process is already being operated predictably, and the base line data do not display any evidence of unpredictable operation, then about all that can be done without changing the process in some major way is to operate on target. In this case the calculations above will have already defined the potential savings and the following calculations will simply be replowing the same field.

However, if your process has not been operated predictably in the past, there are two legitimate questions to be answered: How much can we save by operating this process predictably? and How much can we save by operating this process predictably and on target? This section and the next will show how to use the Effective Cost of Production to answer these two important question.

Just as the performance indexes characterize the past performance of the process relative to the specifications, the two capability indexes characterize the process potential relative to the specifications. Thus, once we have computed values for C_p and C_{pk} we can use these values with the tables to find a *Predictable Cost of Production* (or *Predictable ECP*). This *Predictable ECP* will approximate what would happen if you learned how to operate your process predictably *while the process average remained at its historical value*. Since, in most cases, the discoveries that are part of learning how to operate a process predictably will also allow you to adjust the process aim, the *Predictable ECP* is essentially a worst-case value.

When compared to the *Benchmark ECP* the *Predictable ECP* will provide an estimate of the savings to be obtained by predictable operation at the historic process average. Both theory and experience have shown that you will almost certainly do better than is indicated by the *Predictable ECP*.

If you do not have a value for the nominal cost of production you can estimate the savings from predictable operation to be at least:

$$Savings\ from\ Predictable\ Operation\ =\ \frac{Benchmark\ ECP - Predictable\ ECP}{Benchmark\ ECP}$$

If you have a value for the nominal cost of production then the numerator of the ratio above can be multiplied by the nominal cost and the annual volume to obtain an estimate of the minimum annual amount to be saved by predictable operation to be:

Annual Amount Saved by Predictable Operation =
        [Benchmark ECP – Predictable ECP] × *Nominal Cost* × *Annual Volume*

If the process that produced the Batch Weight Data could be operated predictably with an average of 937 kg we would have a C_{pk} value 0.54 and a C_p value of 1.46. Rounding these values to 0.5 and 1.5 we find a *Predictable ECP* value of 1.51 from Table A.17.

With a *Benchmark ECP* of 1.69 this *Predictable ECP* value corresponds to a reduction in the actual cost of production of:

$$\text{Savings from Centered Operation } = \frac{1.69 - 1.51}{1.69} = 0.107 \text{ or } 11\%$$

With a nominal cost of \$500 per batch the annual amount saved by operating this process predictably with an average of 937 kg is estimated to be at least:

$$0.18 \times \$500 \times 13{,}000 = \$1.17 \text{ million per year}$$

14.5 The Minimum Cost of Production

For any process, the minimum value of the Effective Cost of Production will occur when that process is operated predictably and on target. When a predictable process is on target the Centered Capability Ratio will be the same as the Capability Ratio. Therefore, to approximate what might happen to your excess costs of production when you learn how to operate your process predictably and on target you will let both C_{pk} and C_p have the value computed for C_p and find the corresponding Effective Cost of Production. Denote this *ECP* value as the *Minimum Cost of Production* (or *Minimum ECP*).

If you do not have a value for the nominal cost of production you can estimate the savings from operating predictably and on target to be at least:

$$\text{Potential Savings } = \frac{\text{Benchmark ECP} - \text{Minimum ECP}}{\text{Benchmark ECP}}$$

If you have a value for the nominal cost of production then the numerator of the ratio above can be multiplied by the nominal cost and the annual volume to obtain an estimate of the annual amount to be saved by operating predictably and on target to be:

Annual Amount Saved by Operating Predictably and On Target =
    [Benchmark ECP – Minimum ECP] × *Nominal Cost* × *Annual Volume*

If the Batch Weights could be centered at the target value of 1000 kg while the process was operated predictably, the C_{pk} value would increase to be the same as the

C_p value. Rounding off both C_{pk} and C_p to the value of 1.50 results in a *Minimum ECP* of 1.05.

With a *Benchmark ECP* of 1.69 this *Minimum ECP* value corresponds to a reduction in the actual cost of production of:

$$\textit{Savings from Operating Predictably and On Target} = \frac{1.69 - 1.05}{1.69} = 0.379 \text{ or } 38\%$$

With a nominal cost of $500 per batch the annual amount saved by consistently operating this process predictably and on target is estimated to be:

$$0.64 \times \$500 \times 13{,}000 = \$4.16 \text{ million per year}$$

In Section 14.2 we estimated that the opportunity pool for this process was $4.5 million. Here we see that they can capture 92 percent of this entitlement by simply learning how to operate their current process predictably and on target. No major process upgrade is needed. No redesign of the product or process is required. No capital expenditures needed. By simply learning how to get the most out of their current process they can move from the State of Chaos to the Ideal State and have a process that is operating in the economic zone with an *ECP* of 1.05.

14.6 Using the Effective Cost of Production

This section will use the Wire Length Data for another illustration of the use of the Effective Costs of Production. The Wire Length Data were given in Chapter Two. They consist of 100 values which display the homogeneity that is characteristic of a process that is operated predictably. The performance indexes are $P_p = 0.945$ and $P_{pk} = 0.449$, while the capability indexes are $C_p = 0.936$ and $C_{pk} = 0.444$. Nonconforming items are scrapped.

Step One: Find the *Benchmark ECP*:

From Table A.17, with $P_p = 0.9$ and $P_{pk} = 0.4$ we find a *Benchmark ECP* of 1.45. Thus, we estimate that the excess costs for this process amount to almost one-third of the actual production costs.

Step Two: Find the *Benchmark ECP – Centered ECP*:

Centering this process would bring the P_{pk} value up to match the P_p value of 0.9. This would result in a *Centered ECP* value of 1.14. Thus, centering this process would reduce the excess costs from 0.45 to 0.14 resulting in savings of:

$$Savings\ from\ Centered\ Operation\ =$$
$$\frac{Benchmark\ ECP - Centered\ ECP}{Benchmark\ ECP} = \frac{1.45 - 1.14}{1.45} = 0.214\ \ or\ \ 21\%$$

Since this process is already being operated predictably the following computations will mimic those given above. They are not needed in practice, but will be covered here as an illustration of why they are not needed in practice.

Step Three: Find *Benchmark ECP – Predictable ECP*:

From Table A.17, with $C_p = 0.9$ and $C_{pk} = 0.4$ we find a *Predictable ECP* of 1.45, which is exactly the same as the *Benchmark ECP*. (Recall that when a process is operated predictably the two performance indexes estimate the same things that the two capability indexes estimate.) Thus, there are no additional savings to be had from predictable operation since they are already operating this process predictably!

Step Four: Find *Benchmark ECP – Minimum ECP*:

The *Minimum ECP* will occur when the process is operated predictably and on target. When C_{pk} is equal to $C_p = 0.9$ we find a *Minimum ECP* value of 1.14. Thus the potential savings from operating predictably and on target are:

$$Potential\ Savings\ = \frac{Benchmark\ ECP - Minimum\ ECP}{Benchmark\ ECP} = \frac{1.45 - 1.14}{1.45} = 0.214$$

which is exactly the same as found in Step Two above.

Notice that in this example the only improvement needed was to operate the process on target, and so the analysis using the *ECP* values points to this fact and estimates the savings to be had by making this improvement.

In obtaining estimates of entitlement values for a process we do not have to have high precision. Ballpark values are generally sufficient to determine if a project is appropriate or not. In the Wire Length Data, if the long wires were reworked instead of being scrapped, the initial *ECP* would have been 1.40 instead of 1.45. Since the final *ECP* would remain the same, the savings would only be 18 percent of actual, rather than 21 percent. In either case, the decision on the project is likely to remain the same. This ability to use reasonable approximations frees us from having to specifically compute *ECP* with high precision for each situation.

As will be shown, the *ECP* value is dependent upon the probability model used to represent the process outcomes. However, in practice, the number that we actually use is the *difference* between two *ECP* values computed under the same probability model. Since these differences are less sensitive to the model than the *ECP* values themselves, we end up with a reasonably robust procedure regardless of the model we use. The tables were prepared using the ubiquitous model of maximum entropy—a generic normal distribution—since it is sufficiently conservative to provide satisfactory *ECP* values.

The four Effective Costs of Production are listed in Table 14.1.

Table 14.1: Effective Costs of Production

Indexes Used	Effective Cost of Production	Interpretation
P_p & P_{pk}	*Benchmark ECP*	What Was
P_{pk} set equal to P_p	*Centered ECP*	On Target Operation
C_p & C_{pk}	*Predictable ECP*	Predictable with Historical Average
C_{pk} set equal to C_p	*Minimum ECP*	Predictable and On Target

Working with the four Effective Costs of Production in Table 14.1 will allow you to characterize how much the excess costs can be reduced by different improvement strategies. If you have a nominal cost of production and an annual volume you can extend these savings over a year's time to estimate the savings in dollar amounts. If you do not have a nominal cost of production you can still make rational decisions using the *ECP* values themselves.

Table 14.2 shows the four Effective Costs of Production for the Batch Weight Data while Table 14.3 shows those for the Wire Length Data.

Table 14.2 shows that while there are substantial savings to be had by operating on target, those savings can be doubled by learning to operate this process predictably and on target. When this process is operated predictably and on target it has a *Minimum ECP* of 1.05, meaning that it can operate in the economic zone and making major process upgrades unnecessary.

Table 14.2: Effective Costs of Production for the Batch Weight Data

Indexes Used	Effective Cost of Production	Est. Savings
$P_p = 0.54$ & $P_{pk} = 0.20$	Benchmark ECP = 1.69	—
$P_{pk} = P_p = 0.50$	Centered ECP = 1.40	17% of actual
$C_p = 1.46$ & $C_{pk} = 0.54$	Predictable ECP = 1.51	11% of actual
$C_{pk} = C_p = 1.50$	Minimum ECP = 1.05	38% of actual

Table 14.3 shows that the only improvement strategy needed to get the most out of the Wire Length Process is to operate this process on target. Moreover, when operated predictably and on target, this process will still have excess costs that amount to 14% of nominal. Since the economic zone is defined to be that region where the *ECP* is below 1.10, we can say that this process is not currently capable of operating in the economic zone.

Table 14.3: Effective Costs of Production for the Wire Length Data

Indexes Used	Effective Cost of Production	Est. Savings
$P_p = 0.945$ & $P_{pk} = 0.449$	Benchmark ECP = 1.45	—
$P_{pk} = P_p = 0..945$	Centered ECP = 1.14	21% of actual
$C_p = 0.936$ & $C_{pk} = 0.444$	Predictable ECP = 1.45	0% of actual
$C_{pk} = C_p = 0.936$	Minimum ECP = 1.14	21% of actual

The Creel Yield Data given in Table 2.6 revealed an unpredictable process. The average is 3492.1 and the global standard deviation statistic is 38.3 units. The Upper Specification Limit is 3550, and the Lower Specification Limit is 3410. Thus P_p is 0.61 and P_{pk} is 0.50.

The Natural Process Limits in Figure 2.16 are 3479.5 to 3504.7. These values result in a C_p of 5.6 and a C_{pk} value of 4.6. Assuming that all nonconforming product is reworked, Table A.18 gives the Effective Costs of Production shown in Table 14.4.

Table 14.4: Effective Costs of Production for the Creel Yield Data

Indexes Used	Effective Cost of Production	Est. Savings
$P_p = 0.61$ & $P_{pk} = 0.50$	Benchmark ECP = 1.29	—
$P_{pk} = P_p = 0.60$	Centered ECP = 1.27	1.5% of actual
$C_p = 5.6$ & $C_{pk} = 4.6$	Predictable ECP = 1.03	20% of actual
$C_{pk} = C_p = 5.0$	Minimum ECP = 1.00	22% of actual

Here we see that the major savings will occur when this process is operated predictably. Centering this process will have little impact. Moreover, this process has the potential of operating with zero excess costs. Reengineering is not required.

14.7 Summary

By computing these four Effective Costs of Production you can evaluate the potential savings to be obtained from various improvement efforts. These Effective Costs of Production are not arbitrary since they are founded on the information contained in the process data. They can be used in their raw form, or they can be converted into monetary values whenever you can determine a reasonable value for either the nominal cost of production or the actual cost of production.

Regardless of the form in which you use these Effective Costs of Production, their simplicity and ease of use will help you to identify those projects that are worth the effort and those that are not worth doing. Moreover, they will help you choose the improvement strategy that will result in the greatest gain for the least cost.

The relationship between the performance and capability indexes and the Effective Cost of Production will be defined in detail in the next chapter.

Chapter Fifteen

The Basis for the
Effective Cost of Production

The uses of the Effective Costs of Production were illustrated in the previous chapter. This chapter will outline how the Effective Costs of Production are connected to the capability indexes and describe how to compute them. Additionally, formulas for determining the Effective Cost of Production for data based on counts will be given.

15.1 The Structure of the Effective Cost of Production

Let us return to the definition of the Effective Cost of Production as the actual cost of producing and using an item, divided by the nominal cost of production and use for that item:

$$\textit{Effective Cost of Production} = \frac{\textit{Actual Cost of Production \& Use}}{\textit{Nominal Cost of Production \& Use}}$$

To understand this ratio we will have to examine its components.

The actual costs of production will have to include all the costs associated with all the items produced. These costs will include the costs of producing an item, plus the costs of rework, plus the costs of scrap. While these are the only costs considered by most producers, there is one more cost category that needs to be included as well, and that is the cost of using conforming product.

The easiest way to understand the costs associated with using conforming product is to think about your own suppliers and consider all of the time and effort expended in order to get your supplier's material to work in your process. What would your operations be like if all of your incoming material was always exactly on target? What would your operations be like if your equipment always worked the same? The actions taken because your incoming materials are not always the same and your equipment does not always work the same way will inevitably result in costs. These are costs associated with the use of the materials and equipment. While these costs do not show up at production, any realistic assessment of the costs of production should include them.

Thus, the actual cost of producing and using an item will consist of the nominal cost of production plus the average excess costs per unit associated with producing and using such items.

Actual Cost of Production & Use = Nominal Cost + Average Excess Costs

Based on the two expressions above, it appears that we can obtain a value for the Effective Cost of Production if we can characterize the Average Excess Costs.

15.2 The Average Excess Costs

Since, in the end, we always have to pay for our supplier's excess costs we adopt the perspective of the customer and define the excess costs to consist of three components.

1. The cost of scraping nonconforming items. Since the producer will have to incorporate the cost of scrap into his overhead costs, and since the customer has to pay for the producer's overhead, the customer will indirectly end up paying for the scrap that is produced.

2. The cost of reworking nonconforming items. Once more, the excess costs associated with rework will have to be buried in the producer's overhead, so while the customer will pay for the reworked item, he will also have to pay for the excess costs of reworking it as well.

3. The cost of using conforming product. This is a direct cost to the customer. It consists of all of those actions taken by the customer to get his equipment and the supplier's materials to work properly together.

Thus, the job of characterizing the Average Excess Costs consists of determining each of these three components.

Since scrapping an item is a cut-your-losses action, ideally taken only when it is cheaper to scrap the item than to use it, we can think of the cost of scrap to be a fixed cost. That is, let C_S denote the cost of scrapping an item. This cost will have to equal the cost of the raw materials plus the cost of all processing done to the item, the cost of inspection, and perhaps the cost of disposal as well.

The average cost of scrap will be the cost of scrapping an item multiplied by the proportion of the items that are scrapped. If we let the probability model shown in Figure 15.1 represent the distribution of process outcomes, and if items below the lower specification limit are to be scrapped, then the proportion scrapped will be defined by the area under the curve to the left of the *LSL*.

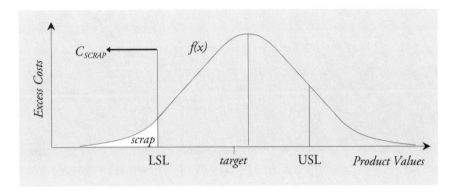

Figure 15.1: Scrap and the Cost of Scrap

If we let the vertical axis denote excess costs associated with the production of an item, we can see that there would be a fixed excess cost, C_S, for those items that are scrapped. As a result, the Average Cost of Scrap would be:

$$\textit{Average Cost of Scrap} \ = \ C_S \times \textit{Proportion Scrapped} \ = \ C_S \int_{-\infty}^{\text{LSL}} f(x)\,dx$$

The average cost of rework will be the cost of reworking an item multiplied by the proportion of the items that are reworked. If items above the upper specification limit are to be reworked, then the proportion reworked will be defined by the area under the curve to the right of the *USL*.

While different items may require different amounts of rework, in our attempt to obtain an average cost of rework we shall, for simplicity, use an average cost of reworking an item, C_R. This single value will result in a fixed excess cost for those items that are reworked. As a result, the Average Cost of Rework would be:

$$\textit{Average Cost of Rework} = \ C_R \times \textit{Proportion Reworked} \ = \ C_R \int_{\text{USL}}^{\infty} f(x)\,dx$$

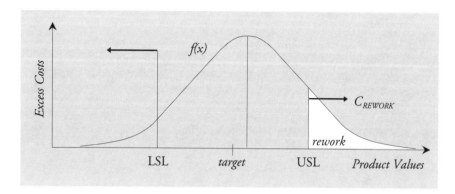

Figure 15.2: Rework and the Cost of Rework

Thus, we know the excess cost function in two regions—scrap and rework. To fill in the rest of the curve we need to think about the nature of excess costs. Excess costs are the result of variation. They are costs incurred because everything is not right at the target value. If we could make everything right at the target value, there would be no excess costs of production. Therefore, we define the excess cost function to be zero at the target value, as shown in Figure 15.3.

In most cases the cost of scrapping an item and the average cost of reworking an item can be determined. This means that the three portions of the Excess Cost Function shown in Figure 15.3 will generally be known.

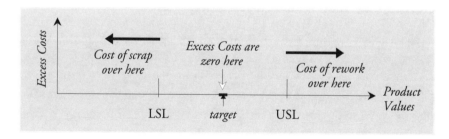

Figure 15.3: The Three Known Portions of the Excess Cost Function

But how do we fill in the gaps? Since we know that small deviations from the target can be tolerated, we prefer to use quadratic curves to connect the three known portions of the Excess Cost Function. These quadratic curves will have their minimum at the target value, and will connect with the fixed portions of the Excess Cost

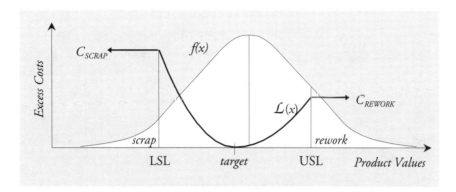

Figure 15.4: A Realistic Excess Cost Function

Function to give the piecewise continuous curve shown as $\mathcal{L}(x)$ in Figure 15.4.

This Excess Cost Function suggests that when an item falls near the target there will be few excess costs associated with its use. However, as an item falls further and further away from the target the costs of using the item will increase. Moreover, these costs will increase up to that point where it will be cheaper to scrap, or to rework, the item, than it will be to try to use it. Since this is consistent with reality, the curve in Figure 15.4 is a realistic Excess Cost Function. This Excess Cost Function will be symmetric when all nonconforming product is treated alike (either scrapped or reworked). When nonconforming product on one side is scrapped, while that on the other side is reworked, we will have an asymmetric Excess Cost Function as shown in Figures 15.4 and 15.5.

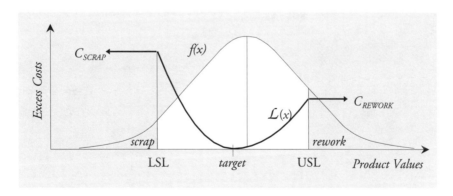

Figure 15.5: Conforming Product and the Cost of Use Curve

Using the Excess Cost Function, $\mathcal{L}(x)$, in Figure 15.5, the excess costs associated with using conforming parts may be found by multiplying $\mathcal{L}(x)$ by the model for the process outcomes, $f(x)$, and integrating between the specification limits:

$$Average\ Cost\ of\ Use\ =\ \int_{LSL}^{USL} \mathcal{L}(x)\,f(x)\,dx$$

Combining the Average Cost of Scrap, the Average Cost of Use, and the Average Cost of Rework, we have the Average Excess Costs to be:

$$Average\ Excess\ Costs\ =\ \int_{-\infty}^{\infty} \mathcal{L}(x)\,f(x)\,dx$$

To actually evaluate this integral we will have to break it down into four parts: the region below *LSL*, the region between *LSL* and the target, the region between the target and *USL*, and the region above *USL*. By plugging in the equations for the quadratic curves we end up with a generic, four term expression for the Average Excess Costs, which can be evaluated for any particular probability model, $f(x)$, that seems appropriate:

$$Average\ Excess\ Costs\ =\ C_S \int_{-\infty}^{LSL} f(x)\,dx \qquad \text{excess costs due to scrap}$$

$$+\ C_S \int_{LSL}^{target} \frac{(x-target)^2}{(LSL-target)^2}\,f(x)\,dx \qquad \text{due to deviations below target}$$

$$+\ C_R \int_{target}^{USL} \frac{(x-target)^2}{(USL-target)^2}\,f(x)\,dx \qquad \text{due to deviations above target}$$

$$+\ C_R \int_{USL}^{\infty} f(x)\,dx \qquad \text{excess costs due to rework}$$

If we replace the four integrals with the following symbols:

$$\mathbf{ISP} = \int_{-\infty}^{LSL} f(x)\, dx \qquad \text{Integral for Scrap Proportion}$$

$$\mathbf{IBT} = \int_{LSL}^{target} \frac{(x - target)^2}{(LSL - target)^2}\, f(x)\, dx \qquad \text{Integral Below Target}$$

$$\mathbf{IAT} = \int_{target}^{USL} \frac{(x - target)^2}{(USL - target)^2}\, f(x)\, dx \qquad \text{Integral Above Target}$$

$$\mathbf{IRP} = \int_{USL}^{\infty} f(x)\, dx \qquad \text{Integral for Rework Proportion}$$

we can simplify the Average Excess Costs expression to become:

$$Average\ Excess\ Costs = C_S\,\mathbf{ISP} + C_S\,\mathbf{IBT} + C_R\,\mathbf{IAT} + C_R\,\mathbf{IRP}$$

$$= C_S \left\{ \mathbf{ISP} + \mathbf{IBT} + \frac{C_R}{C_S} \left[\mathbf{IAT} + \mathbf{IRP} \right] \right\}$$

$$= C_S \times Curly\ Brackets$$

To evaluate the *Curly Brackets* expression you will need the following:

1. the ratio of the average cost of reworking an item to the cost of scrapping an item;

2. the target and specification limits; and

3. an appropriate probability model to use in characterizing the process outcomes.

Since the normal distribution is the distribution of maximum entropy, its use in evaluating the *Curly Brackets* expression will provide a generic, worst-case value which will generally be sufficient to provide reasonable approximations to the Effective Cost of Production.

15.3   Finding The Effective Cost of Production

In order to evaluate the Effective Cost of Production we will need to rewrite the original equation in terms of quantities that we can compute. In Section 15.1 we wrote:

$$\text{Effective Cost of Production} \;=\; \frac{\text{Actual Cost of Production \& Use}}{\text{Nominal Cost of Production \& Use}}$$

Careful thought about this expression will reveal that the numerator will have to encompass all of the product produced while the denominator can only refer to the product that was actually shipped. Thus, if we let NC represent the nominal cost to produce each unit, and recalling that **ISP** is the proportion scrapped, we can write the denominator as:

$$\text{Nominal Cost of Production \& Use} \;=\; NC\,[\,1.0 - \textbf{ISP}\,]$$

At the same time, to avoid double accounting for the units that are scrapped, the numerator of the ratio above can be written as:

$$\text{Actual Cost of Production \& Use} = \text{Nominal Cost of Units Shipped}$$
$$+ \text{Average Excess Costs}$$

$$= NC\,[\,1.0 - \textbf{ISP}\,] + C_S\,[\,\text{Curly Brackets}\,]$$

$$= NC\left[\,1.0 - \textbf{ISP} + \frac{C_S}{NC}\,\text{Curly Brackets}\,\right]$$

By combining these new expressions for the numerator and denominator, we can write the Effective Cost of Production as:

$$\text{Effective Cost of Production} \;=\; \frac{1.0 - \textbf{ISP} + \dfrac{C_S}{NC}\,\text{Curly Brackets}}{1.0 - \textbf{ISP}}$$

For those situations where C_S is essentially the same as the nominal cost, NC, the Effective Cost of Production can be simplified to be:

$$\text{Effective Cost of Production} \;=\; \frac{1.0 - \text{proportion scrapped} + \text{Curly Brackets}}{1.0 - \text{proportion scrapped}}$$

The previous expression does not depend upon the nominal cost to produce a unit, which means that it can be evaluated for general situations and expressed as a function of the capability indexes. Tables of the Effective Cost of Production defined by the expression above are provided for 37 different process situations in *The Process Evaluation Handbook* by this author. Four of these tables are included in the Appendix.

Tables A.19 and A.20 cover the situation in which material beyond one of the specification limits is scrapped while material beyond the other specification is reworked at a cost that is one-half the cost of scrap.

Table A.17 is for the situation in which all nonconforming product is scrapped. The values in this table were obtained under the assumption that $C_S \approx NC$. Since C_S is frequently larger than NC, the values in Table A.17 are actually lower bounds on the Effective Cost of Production.

Table A.18 is for the situation in which all nonconforming product is reworked. Here the calculations were made under the assumption that $C_R \approx NC$. When C_R is less than NC, the values in Table A.18 will be upper bounds on the Effective Cost of Production. However, since we primarily work with the differences between Effective Costs of Production, these upper bounds and lower bounds will still provide a reasonable guide to the savings to be obtained from different improvement projects.

15.4 Summary of *ECP* for Measurements

Since the Effective Cost of Production is determined by the process data, it provides a reasonable way to characterize the efficiency of a production operation. Since it is proportional to dollars, it places the proper emphasis upon the effects of different shifts and changes in the process. Since it combines the costs of scrap, rework, and using the conforming product, it is a complete measure that provides a macro-economic perspective.

So how can you make use of this measure? Perhaps the most powerful way to use the Effective Cost of Production is to evaluate the potential savings to be obtained from various improvement projects. By comparing two Effective Cost of Production values you can easily and directly compute the potential savings that can be realized by various improvement strategies. Furthermore, since the published tables link the capability indexes to the Effective Costs of Production, you will not usually need to actually compute your Effective Costs of Production, but can simply look them up once you have your performance indexes or your capability indexes.

However, for those who wish to do so, the integrals can be evaluated for your specific situation and you can directly compute your own Effective Cost of Production using the formulas given in this chapter.

15.5 Effective Costs of Production for Counts of Items

There is a fundamental difference between count data and measurement data, and this difference simplifies the job of finding the Effective Cost of Production for count data. While measurements quantify some characteristic of an item, counts will either classify the item or enumerate events.

When counts classify an item as unacceptable it will be subject to two actions—scrap or rework. When the item is scrapped the cost of producing that item is lost. When the item is reworked the cost of the materials is salvaged while the value added is lost. Thus, the Average Excess Costs for counts which classify the items can be written as:

$$Average\ Excess\ Costs\ =\ C_S\ \textbf{ISP}\ +\ C_R\ \textbf{IRP}$$

where C_S is the cost of scrapping an item, **ISP** is the proportion scrapped, C_R is the cost of reworking an item, and **IRP** is the proportion reworked. If we let NC be the nominal cost of producing an item, and assume that $NC \approx C_S$, then we can rewrite the expression above as:

$$Average\ Excess\ Costs\ =\ NC\ \left[\ \textbf{ISP}\ +\ \frac{C_R}{NC}\ \textbf{IRP}\ \right]$$

In this expression the cost of rework divided by the nominal cost can be thought of as the complement of the cost of the materials salvaged by the rework divided by the nominal cost:

$$\frac{C_R}{NC}\ =\ 1\ -\ \frac{Cost\ of\ Materials\ Salvaged}{Nominal\ Cost}$$

When rework consists of doing a job over, and there are no materials salvaged, then we assume that $C_R \approx NC$. We combine these expressions using the first three equations of the preceding section. There we defined the Effective Cost of Production as:

$$Effective\ Cost\ of\ Production\ =\ \frac{Actual\ Cost\ of\ Production\ \&\ Use}{Nominal\ Cost\ of\ Production\ \&\ Use}$$

The Denominator of this ratio was defined to be:

$$Nominal\ Cost\ of\ Production\ \&\ Use\ -\ NC\,[\,1.0\ \ \mathbf{ISP}\,]$$

And the numerator of the Effective Cost of Production was defined as being the sum of the cost of units shipped and the average excess costs:

$$Actual\ Cost\ of\ Production\ \&\ Use\ =\ Nominal\ Cost\ of\ Units\ Shipped$$
$$+\ Average\ Excess\ Costs$$

When we use the expression for the Average Excess Costs associated with counts of items from the preceding page we get a numerator of:

$$Actual\ Cost\ of\ Production\ \&\ Use\ =\ NC\,[\,1.0 - \mathbf{ISP}\,] + NC\left[\,\mathbf{ISP} + \frac{C_R}{NC}\,\mathbf{IRP}\,\right]$$

When divided by the Nominal Cost of Production & Use this gives:

$$Effective\ Cost\ of\ Production\ =\ \frac{1 + \dfrac{C_R}{NC}\,\mathbf{IRP}}{1 - \mathbf{ISP}}$$

This equation provides a simple way to compute the Effective Cost of Production from counts of items. This value depends upon the proportion reworked, the proportion scrapped, and the cost of the material salvaged by rework as a proportion of the nominal cost of the item. While this formula is easy to use, brief tables of these Effective Costs of Production are provided in the Appendix as Tables A.21 to A.24.

15.6 Effective Costs of Production for Counts of Events

Counts that enumerate discrete events, such as blemishes or discrepancies, are commonly used to determine the grade, or quality, of the product. (When the count or the rate exceeds certain threshold values the product is downgraded by various amounts, or even scrapped.) In one plant, this resulted in product classified as Firsts, Irregulars, Seconds, and Rags. For simplicity I will use these labels in the following discussion and will assume that rags are disposed of as scrap.

For the product classified as Irregulars the difference between the selling price of the Firsts and that of the Irregulars is a cost of production. Denote this difference as D_1. This difference is like the cost of rework since you have given up this amount of income in order to avoid scrapping the product. Likewise, for the product classified as Seconds the difference between the selling price of the Firsts and that of the Seconds is another cost of production. Denote this difference as D_2. If we denote the proportion of product that is classified as Irregulars as p_1, the proportion of product classified as Seconds as p_2, and if we let p_S denote the proportion classified as rags, we will end up with the following equation for the Effective Cost of Production:

$$\textit{Effective Cost of Production} = \frac{1 + \dfrac{D_1}{NC}\, p_1 + \dfrac{D_2}{NC}\, p_2}{1 - p_S}$$

For the case with more than two downgraded categories additional terms would be added in the numerator. For the case with no scrap the denominator would become 1.0. It should be noted that the differences D_1 and D_2 are differences between selling prices while NC is still the nominal cost of producing the product. This means that the ratios in the terms in the numerator can exceed 1.0.

Because the equation above depends upon the specifics of a particular situation it is not feasible to try to construct tables for these values.

Chapter Sixteen

The Six Sigma Zone

Having developed a more realistic model for the excess costs of production, and having followed the implications of that model to their logical conclusion we obtained the Effective Cost of Production. In this chapter the Effective Cost of Production will be used to develop a rigorous, sound, and easily understood economic justification for operating your processes in the Six Sigma Zone.

The argument presented here is more rigorous, more comprehensible, and more useful than the common arguments involving parts-per-million nonconforming. As a result, this chapter will free you from having to use the traditional arguments which, mathematically, are nothing more than statistical snake oil—a blend of tortured computations and incompatible, highly questionable assumptions, having a hypnotic effect and often resulting in a suspension of critical thinking. (In the interests of exorcism, the next chapter will give an explanation of the fallacies contained in the common parts-per-million arguments.)

16.1 The Effective Cost of Production Curves

In the previous chapter, we established that the Effective Cost of Production could, for a given situation, be considered to be a function of the capability indexes. In the interest of simplicity, consider the case in which all nonconforming product is reworked, and assume that the cost of rework is similar to the nominal cost of production. In this case, the excess cost function will be symmetric and the Effective Cost of Production will depend solely upon the capability indexes and the probability model used. Table A.18 was computed using the distribution of maximum entropy—a normal probability model. If we assume that the process is perfectly centered within the specifications, then the Centered Capability Ratio, C_{pk}, will be equal to the Capability Ratio, C_p, and we can plot the Effective Cost of Production on the vertical axis versus the Capability Ratio on the horizontal axis to obtain Figure 16.1.

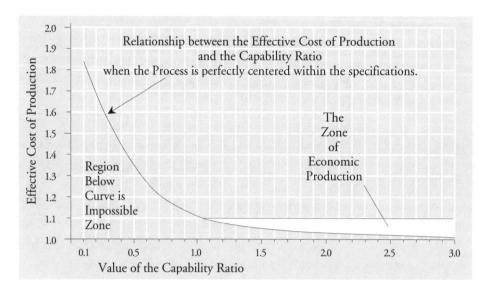

**Figure 16.1: The Effective Cost of Production for a Centered Process
When All Nonconforming Product is Reworked**

THE ZONE OF ECONOMIC PRODUCTION

Given the way the curve in Figure 16.1 flattens out on the right it seems reasonable to define the *Zone of Economic Production* to be that region where your Effective Cost of Production is 1.10 or less. When a process is perfectly centered you will enter this Zone of Economic Production *only* when you have a C_p value greater than 1.05.

The curve in Figure 16.1 is the best you can do. It represents the case where the process is perfectly centered within the specifications. When the process is less than perfectly centered it will be represented by a curve that will be above the curve in Figure 16.1. One such curve is shown in Figure 16.2.

Figure 16.2 shows the curve that corresponds to having a process average that is off target by 0.9 *Sigma(X)*. This curve can be found from Table A.18 by finding the *ECP* values for combinations of C_p and C_{pk}, where $C_{pk} = [\,C_p - 0.3\,]$.

For any given value of the Capability Ratio, C_p, the effect of being 0.9 *Sigma(X)* off target is represented by the vertical displacement between the two curves in Figure 16.2. There we see that when your process average is 0.9 *Sigma(X)* off target you will have to have a Capability Ratio in excess of 1.42 in order to operate in the Zone of Economic Production.

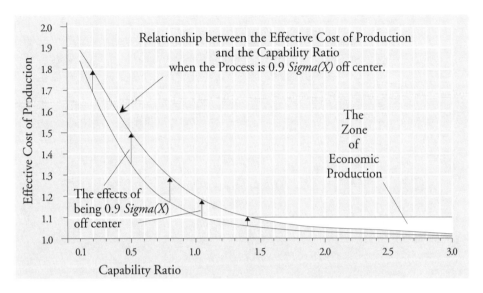

Figure 16.2: The Zone of Economic Production
When All Nonconforming Product is Reworked
and the Process is 0.9 *Sigma(X)* Off Center

Since *no* technique for analyzing *small* amounts of data will be very sensitive to shifts in the process average that amount to 0.9 *Sigma(X)* or less, the curves in Figure 16.2 have serious implications for production. In particular, for you and your suppliers to achieve the desirable goal of economic production, your suppliers will need to have a capability index in the neighborhood of 1.5 or larger, and they will also need to have a way to monitor their processes to keep them operating on or near their target values.

When the Centered Capability Ratio C_{pk} is 0.5 units smaller than C_p the process average will be 1.5 *Sigma(X)* off target. The Effective Cost of Production Curve for this situation is shown in Figure 16.3. There we see that the effect of being up to 1.5 *Sigma(X)* off target will move the zone of economic production out to those values of C_p in excess of 1.87.

Techniques for analyzing small amounts of data will tend to be slow to detect shifts in the process average that amount to less than 1.5 *Sigma(X)*. As a result, even when your suppliers are monitoring their processes to keep them centered, there may be periods of time when they operate in the zone between the top two curves in Figure 16.3.

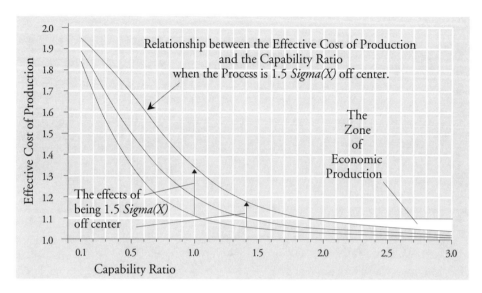

**Figure 16.3: The Zone of Economic Production
When All Nonconforming Product is Reworked
and the Process is 1.5 *Sigma(X)* Off Center**

Continuing in the manner above, we could look at the curves for processes that are off center by 3.0, 4.5, and 6.0 *Sigma(X)*. These curves are shown in Figure 16.4. Fortunately it is easy to detect when a process is this far off target. Any reasonable monitoring procedure will quickly let your supplier know when the process average has drifted by this amount. Therefore, while the Zone of Economic Production for these last three curves is completely off the graph, it is of little interest to those who have an effective mechanism for maintaining a process on target.

Of course, if your supplier does not have an effective mechanism for maintaining a process on target, then you will suffer the consequence of having an Effective Cost of Production that is much larger than it needs to be.

Shifts of 3.0, 4.5, and 6.0 *Sigma(X)* were used in Figure 16.4 simply because shifts of this size are quite common in virtually all production processes that are not operated predictably. Moreover, as was shown in Chapter Two, even larger process shifts are not unusual. Thus, the consequences shown in Figure 16.4 do not exaggerate or overstate the situation in the least.

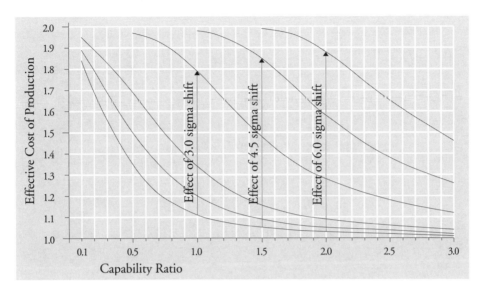

**Figure 16.4: The Effective Costs of Production Curves
When All Nonconforming Product is Reworked
and the Process is More Than 3 *Sigma(X)* Off Center**

Now what do these Effective Cost of Production Curves tell us about economic production? By taking into account the fact that small shifts (one sigma or less) are hard to detect, and shifts of up to 1.5 *Sigma(X)* will not always be detected quickly, we can use Figure 16.5 to make some statements about the relationship between the Capability Ratio and the Effective Costs of Production that we will actually experience in practice.

In Figure 16.5 the vertical arrows represent the range of values for the Effective Cost of Production that are likely to occur when your supplier operates at various capabilities. There we see that with a C_p value of 1.05 we could experience any *ECP* value from 1.10 up to 2.00, depending upon how far off target our process was operating. With a C_p value of 1.42 we could experience any *ECP* value from 1.06 up to 2.0, depending upon how far off target our process was operating. With a C_p value of 1.87 we could experience any *ECP* value from 1.04 up to 2.0, depending upon how far off target our process was operating. (The upper limit of 2.0 seen here is created by the simplifying assumption that all rework results in conforming product. When the nonconforming product is scrapped the curves have no upper bound on the *ECP* value, as is shown in Figure 16.8.)

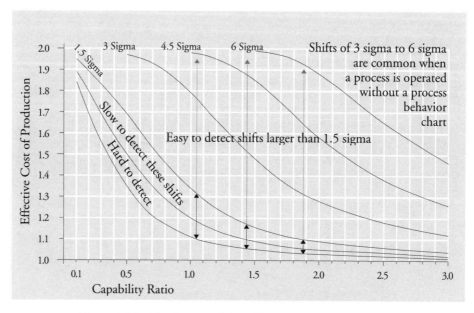

Figure 16.5: The Ranges of the Effective Costs of Production
You Can Expect at Different Capabilities
When All Nonconforming Product is Reworked

All three vertical lines in Figure 16.5 show that, in the absence of an effective mechanism for detecting shifts in the process average, NO value for the Capability Ratio can guarantee that you will operate in the Zone of Economic Production.

The only way to realize the benefits of having a comfortably large Capability Ratio is to have an effective mechanism for detecting shifts in the process average. If you do not have a mechanism for detecting process changes there is no value for the Capability Ratio that is large enough to guarantee that you will always operate in the economic zone.

Thus, while it is desirable to have a capability index of 1.5 to 2.0, there is more to economic operation than achieving a good capability number. You will have to be able to detect changes in the process, and keep the process centered within the specifications, even when the capability is 2.0 or larger!

16.2 An Illustration

The Creel Yield Data introduced in Chapter Two have the X Chart and histogram shown in Figure 16.6. One hundred percent of the product values fall within the specifications of 3410 to 3550.

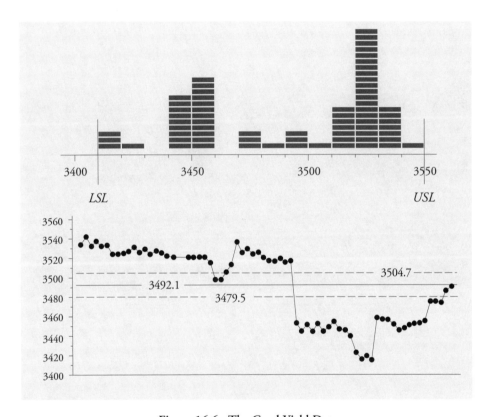

Figure 16.6: The Creel Yield Data

The Average is 3492.1 and the global standard deviation statistic is 38.3. Thus, the Performance Ratio is 0.61 while the Centered Performance Ratio is 0.50. Assuming all nonconforming product will be scrapped, these values result in a *Benchmark ECP* of 1.32 or 132%.

The X Chart shows the Natural Process Limits to be 3479.5 to 3504.7, with a *Sigma(X)* of 4.2. Thus, the hypothetical Capability Ratio is 5.56, and the hypothetical

Centered Capability Ratio is 4.60. These values correspond to an *Predictable ECP* of approximately *ECP* = 1.03 or 103%.

Thus, while this process is capable of being operated in the economic zone, it has not been in the economic zone in the past. This is because no effort was being made to operate on target. As a result, while all the values were within the specifications, the inspection costs associated with the use of this material were so great that the customer could not afford to use this material in a high volume application. While he could justify the expense for a specialty product with a high profit margin, he could not operate economically enough to use this material in mass production.

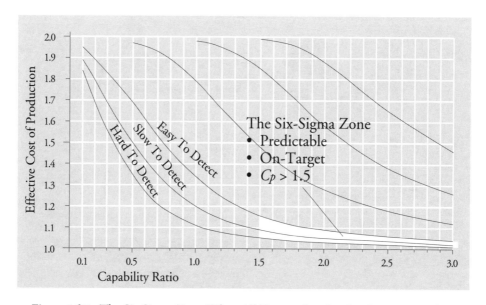

Figure 16.7: The Six Sigma Zone When All Nonconforming Product is Reworked

Would you like to have capability indexes of 5.5 and 4.6?

Does having a good Capability Ratio guarantee that you will operate in the economic zone? It was not enough in the situation just discussed.

16.3 The Six Sigma Zone

So how can you and your suppliers operate in the economic zone? Making allowance for those process changes that are hard to detect or slow to be detected, we can say that a process that is operated predictably and on target will spend most of its time between the bottom two curves of Figures 16.7 and 16.8, with only occasional periods of operation between the second and third curves. This means that if you want to operate with an Effective Cost of Production that is below 110% you will need to operate your processes predictably and on target, and you will need to have a Capability Ratio that is in the vicinity or 1.5 to 2.0.

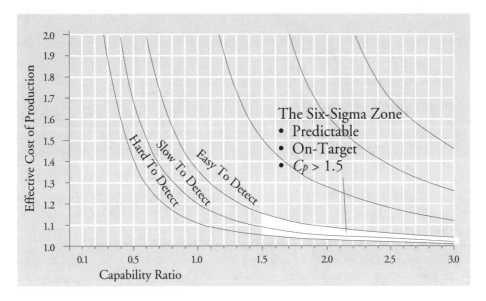

Figure 16.8: The Six Sigma Zone When All Nonconforming Product is Scrapped

Thus, the Six Sigma Zone is that region where a predictable and capable process will operate with an Effective Cost of Production that is less than 110% of nominal most of the time.

Without the use of an effective process monitor there is no capability value that can guarantee that you will operate in the Economic Zone.

Therefore, an essential part of operating within the Six Sigma Zone is the discipline and constancy of purpose that is required in order to operate a process predictably. This is why methodologies for creating "six sigma processes" which do not emphasize the issue of predictable operation are incomplete, naive, and doomed to ultimately fail when the process goes on walkabout.

Figure 16.9 shows how the Six Sigma Zone is a subset of the Ideal State. It can only be attained when a process with a Capability Ratio in excess of 1.5 is operated predictably and on target.

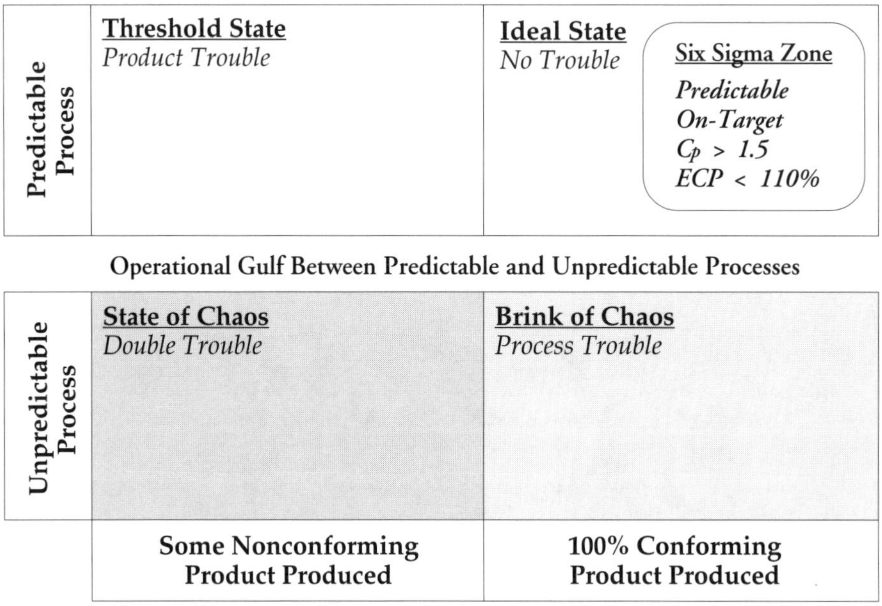

Predictable Process	**Threshold State** *Product Trouble*	**Ideal State** *No Trouble* **Six Sigma Zone** *Predictable* *On-Target* *C_p > 1.5* *ECP < 110%*

Operational Gulf Between Predictable and Unpredictable Processes

Unpredictable Process	**State of Chaos** *Double Trouble*	**Brink of Chaos** *Process Trouble*
	Some Nonconforming Product Produced	**100% Conforming Product Produced**

Figure 16.9: The Six Sigma Zone is a Subset of the Ideal State

16.4 Summary

While Figures 16.1 to 16.3 showed that it can be economical to have capability indexes in the range of 1.5 to 2.0, Figure 16.4 and Section 16.2 should have completely destroyed the myth that there is some magical value for the Capability Ratio that will result in economic production. A Capability Ratio of 1.5 or greater may open the door to economic production, but it does not guarantee that you will achieve and maintain economic production.

To realize the full benefits of having a Capability Ratio of 1.5 or larger you will need to have an effective mechanism for operating your process on target and for detecting unplanned changes in the process. *Moreover, you will need the operational discipline to use that mechanism consistently over time.* The simplest such mechanism is a process behavior chart.

The Six Sigma Zone is, therefore, a subset of the Ideal State in which your process will consistently operate with an Effective Cost of Production that is less than 110 percent of nominal.

Chapter Seventeen

Some Problems

As shown in the previous chapters, there is a rigorous, economically sound, and easily determined justification for operating in the Six Sigma Zone. The methodology for operating in the region of economic production is proven and well-known. And the way to determine just what aspect of the process needs attention is part of this proven and known approach.

However, the fact that a sound approach is available does not prevent people from reinventing the wheel, and the Six Sigma movement has been no exception. This chapter will look at some of the aspects of various Six Sigma programs that are problematic.

17.1 Problems with Defects Per Million

In the past, in an attempt to explain the economics of operating with capabilities of 1.5 to 2.0, capability indexes have been converted into specialized parts-per-million nonconforming values, sometimes referred to as defects per million (*DPM*). While you may have used these *DPM* values, there are several problems with this approach. Fortunately, with the ability to use the Effective Cost of Production outlined in the preceding chapters you no longer need to use *DPM* values.

The first problem with the defects per million approach is that it is incomplete. Unlike the Effective Cost of Production, the parts-per-million nonconforming argument focuses only upon the scrap and rework rate and ignores the excess costs experienced by the customer.

The second problem has to do with the way the defects per million values are computed. In most cases the conversion of capability indexes into a fraction nonconforming is fairly straightforward: you choose some probability model to use, determine the relationship between the model and the specification limits using the capability indexes, and compute the area under the model outside the specifications. The result is your fraction nonconforming. While there is nothing inherently wrong with this conversion, there are situations where the results lack credibility.

Conversions of capability ratios into fractions nonconforming are reasonable when the capability ratios are less than 1.0. This is because capabilities that are less than 1.0 will generally correspond to a situation where a substantial portion of the outcomes are outside the specifications and the fraction nonconforming will be some parts-per-hundred value.

However, as the capability indexes get close to 1.0 the fraction nonconforming will drop below one percent. When this happens the computed value becomes more dependent upon the *probability model* used than the *process*. When we are working in the extreme tails of a probability model our results become highly dependent upon our choice of model. As the capability indexes become substantially larger than 1.0 we end up computing the *infinitesimal* areas under the *extreme* tails of a probability model that we have *assumed* will characterize our process outcomes.

Here it is important to recall Axiom 4 from Chapter One: No histogram can be said to follow a particular probability model. Regardless of the probability model we may pick, there will always be a discrepancy in the extreme tails between the model and our data. This discrepancy is unavoidable. Consequently, any conversion of large capability indexes into parts-per-million nonconforming values has always been questionable. Using the infinitesimal areas under the extreme tails of a probability model that you have assumed will characterize your process outcomes is equivalent to raising an assumption to the third or fourth power—the result simply has no credibility. Yet it is exactly these parts-per-million values that are used to obtain the Six Sigma *DPM* values. So the second problem with the Six Sigma parts-per-million nonconforming values is that they take a straightforward conversion that is only appropriate for parts-per-hundred computations and use it in an inappropriate manner.

Then we have the problem of processes not being operated predictably. The use of a probability model in the conversion outlined in the previous paragraphs implicitly assumes that your underlying process is being operated predictably. So how can the parts-per-million values be adjusted to reflect the demonstrable reality that most processes are not operated predictably?

When a process is operated unpredictably there is not one universe but many universes—not one model but many different models. While we might select a generic normal probability model for a predictable process, the problem of selecting a collection of probability models to characterize an unpredictable process quickly becomes intractable. At this point the usual Six Sigma sales pitch engages in a bit of pure rationalization—*it assumes that an unpredictable process will not shift more than 1.5 standard deviations in either direction.*

Originally this assumption of a 1.5 standard deviation shift was justified by a vague allusion to a "research study." However, no citation was ever given. More recently even this vague allusion is missing and the assumption is merely taken as an axiom. Based on this marvelous, but unfounded, result, the capability indexes were then adjusted to reflect a shift in location of 1.5 standard deviations in one direction and the corresponding, incredibly small parts-per-million values were computed. The common practice of listing these recomputed values along with the original, unshifted capability indexes has generated many questions about the origin of the "goofy" *DPM* numbers found in the Six Sigma literature. Thus the third problem with the Six Sigma parts-per-million values is their dependence upon the assumption that a 1.5 standard deviation shift in location is a *worst-case* scenario. Not only is this incorrect, but it is actually the opposite of the truth.

In Section 16.3 we saw that a 1.5 standard deviation shift was actually a *best case* number. A process operated with the benefit of an efficient mechanism for monitoring the process location will occasionally drift off center. Small shifts will be hard to detect and slightly larger shifts will only be detected slowly, meaning that the process will operate off-center some of the time.

> *However, in the absence of an efficient mechanism*
> *for monitoring the process location,*
> *there is no limit on the size of the shifts that can occur.*

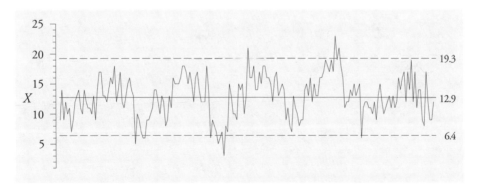

Figure 17.1: *X* Chart for Process Shifting ±3.0 *Sigma(X)*

Charts from earlier examples illustrate this point. Figure 17.1 shows the *X* Chart from Figure 3.3. This process is shifting around by ±3.0 *Sigma(X)*, which is twice as much shifting as is assumed to be the "worst case" by the parts per million arguments. While some points fall outside the limits, none fall very far outside those limits. Anyone who has created even a few process behavior charts will have encountered points further outside the limits than those seen in Figure 17.1.

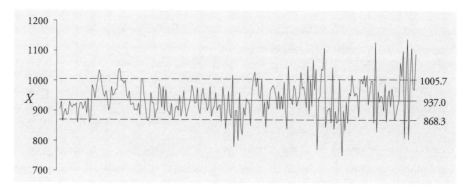

Figure 17.2: *X* **Chart for Process Having Points at +9** *Sigma(X)* **and –8** *Sigma(X)*

Figure 17.2 shows the *X* Chart from Figure 3.4. There we see excursions with points that are up to 9 *Sigma(X)* above the central line and up to 8 *Sigma(X)* below the central line. Excursions like these are quite common in practice.

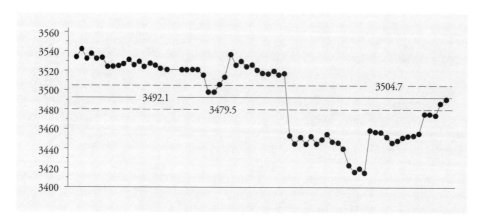

Figure 17.3: *X* **Chart for Creel Yield Data**

And then there is the *X* Chart for the Creel Yield Data shown in Figure 17.3. There the process location changes by an amount equal to 25 *Sigma(X)* during the two week period covered by the chart.

In the light of these examples of how real data from actual processes behave, the assumption that an unpredictable process will not shift location more than 1.5 *Sigma(X)* is completely indefensible. It is simply not true. It never was true, nor will it ever be true. Any argument built on the assumption that an unpredictable process is not going to shift by more than ±1.5 *Sigma(X)* is completely undermined by examples such as those above.

> *The assumption that we can make an allowance*
> *for the effects of an unpredictable process*
> *using a 1.5 Sigma(X) shift, or any other size of shift,*
> *is complete nonsense.*

Finally, the fourth problem with the Six Sigma parts-per-million nonconforming values is the way they are used in reverse to define a "sigma-level" for a process. Based on the parts-per-million numbers obtained with the 1.5 sigma shifts, the actual defect rate observed during a period of production is used in reverse to create what is, in effect, a pseudo-capability index for a process. There are so many problems with this tortured computation that it is difficult to know where to start. The first problem with this reverse use of the actual defect rate is the fact that it uses a descriptive statistic to make an analytic statement about the underlying process without the benefit of performing any analysis. Moreover the most fundamental flaw of this conversion is that it completely ignores the demonstrated fact that some processes are operated predictably while others are not operated predictably. While this conversion claims to deal with this issue based on the 1.5 sigma shift, the mythological nature of the 1.5 sigma shift undermines this claim. Finally, the pseudo capability index obtained from this conversion (usually expressed as a sigma-level for the process) is grossly incorrect for a predictable process and hopelessly optimistic for an unpredictable one. For example, recall the example of Line One from Chapter Nine where we had 1.01 percent defective on one shift. When we charted the values for this shift in Figure 9.1 we found that the process was operated for 5.5 hours with 0.4 percent defective, and operated for 2.5 hours with 2.4 percent defective. What *ppm* value should we use in characterizing the "sigma-level" for this process? What *ppm* value will characterize the next shift?

Thus, there are four problems with the defects per million numbers commonly used in Six Sigma programs.

- They are incomplete, ignoring the excess costs experienced by the customer.
- They apply a standard conversion in a non-standard way to obtain values that have no credibility.
- They treat a best-case adjustment as a worst-case bound.
- And they are then used in reverse to convert an observed level of nonconforming product into a pseudo-capability index for a process without any consideration of process predictability or the lack thereof.

As a result of these four problems any use of the *DPM* values can only be characterized as a triumph of computation over common sense.

17.2 Problems with Defects Per Million Opportunities

A second, flawed parts-per-million number commonly found in the Six Sigma literature is defects per million opportunities (*DPMO*). As soon as *DPM* was used in reverse to define a "sigma level" for a process it was inevitable that someone would want to do the same with data based on the counts of blemishes or defects. Of course the problem with counts of blemishes or defects is that they have an area of opportunity that is defined as a finite portion of some underlying continuum. This means that, unlike parts-per-million values which are dimensionless, defect rates will inevitably have units attached (e.g. 2.5 blemishes per hundred yards in a bolt of cloth). These units get in the way when defining a "sigma level." Therefore, defect rates like the 2.5 blemishes per hundred yards value were simply converted into Defects Per Million Opportunities values by dividing by "opportunity ratios" such as "the number of opportunities per hundred yards." Of course, if we had "one opportunity per foot" we would get:

$$DPMO = \frac{2.5 \text{ blemishes per hundred yards}}{300 \text{ opportunities per hundred yards}} \times 1{,}000{,}000 = 8333 \ DPMO$$

However, if we thought we had "one opportunity per inch" we would get:

$$DPMO = \frac{2.5 \text{ blemishes per hundred yards}}{3600 \text{ opportunities per hundred yards}} \times 1{,}000{,}000 = 694 \ DPMO$$

But, if we have "one opportunity per thread" with 200 threads per inch:

$$DPMO = \frac{2.5}{720000} \times 1{,}000{,}000 = 3.5 \; DPMO$$

Thus, the *DPMO* is a totally subjective value that depends upon how you subdivide the continuum into potential opportunities. It is nothing more than data divided by an assumption.

Ultimately, these illogical attempts to define the "sigma-level" for a process are merely trying to do that which is already done by capability indexes or by direct computations of losses. Since we can now convert capability indexes or counts directly into Effective Costs of Production, these flawed and nonsensical *DPM* and *DPMO* values need to be scrapped.

17.3 Problems with FMEA Risk Priority Numbers

Failure Mode Effect Analysis (FMEA) is an engineering tool that has been heavily adapted for use in Six Sigma programs. It is commonly used to decide what problem to attack. Typically a list of several candidate problems will be rated on three scales, usually Severity of Failure (S), Likelihood of Occurrence (O), and Difficulty of Detection in Advance (D), with possible ratings being any whole number between 1 and 10, with 10 being severe, likely to occur, and impossible to detect. These three ratings are then multiplied together to obtain a value known as a Risk Priority Number (*RPN*) and these *RPN* values are then used to rank the problems. The idea being that the problem with the highest *RPN* value is the one that needs to be worked on. This approach has been the subject of textbooks and has been used as the basis for several different types of voting and ranking schemes. However, there are several problems with the use of Risk Priority Numbers.

While the *RPN* values are spread out from 1 to 1000, they only take on 120 values within this range. Moreover, these 120 *RPN* values are not uniformly spread out between 1 and 1000. Thus, the *RPN* values map 1000 different situations onto 120 values in a nonlinear manner as shown in Figure 17.4.

By mapping 1000 situations onto 120 values these *RPN* values automatically create equivalence classes between the various situations. Consider the equivalence class represented by the *RPN* value of 360. While 360 does not sound like a very large value, only 123 of the 1000 possible combinations will have a larger *RPN* and

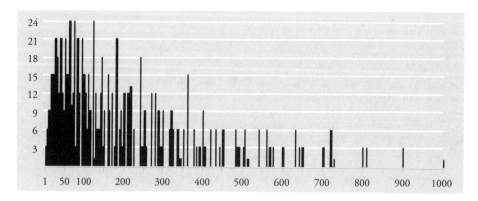

Figure 17.4: Risk Priority Numbers Map 1000 Situations Onto 120 Values

would be ranked above the 15 situations shown in Table 17.1. The labels used come from the auto industry *FMEA Manual*.

Using the criteria given in the auto industry *FMEA Manual* the problem in Row 1 below involves a hazardous failure mode that would affect the safe operation of the vehicle and that would occur without warning. This problem would have a very high incidence of occurrence, affecting approximately one vehicle in three. And this problem would have a moderately high chance of being detected in the design phase and eliminated from the vehicle before production begins.

Table 17.1: Fifteen "Equivalent" Situations With *RPN* = 360

	Severity of Problem		Likelihood of Occurrence		Likelihood of Detection	
1	Hazardous	10	Very High	9	Mod. High	4
2	Hazardous	10	Moderate	6	Low	6
3	Hazardous	10	Moderate	4	Very Remote	9
4	Hazardous	9	Very High	10	Mod. High	4
5	Hazardous	9	High	8	Moderate	5
6	Hazardous	9	Moderate	5	Remote	8
7	Hazardous	9	Moderate	4	Impossible	10
8	Hazardous	8	Very High	9	Moderate	5
9	Hazardous	8	Moderate	5	Very Remote	9
10	Moderate	6	Very High	10	Low	6
11	Moderate	6	Moderate	6	Impossible	10
12	Low	5	Very High	9	Remote	8
13	Low	5	High	8	Very Remote	9
14	Very Low	4	Very High	10	Very Remote	9
15	Very Low	4	Very High	9	Impossible	10

In the same way the problem in Row 15 (of Table 17.1) corresponds to a failure mode that would affect fit and finish. This failure mode would affect approximately one vehicle in three, and cannot be detected in the design phase.

Does it seem reasonable to you that the two problems above should be equivalent? Is a hazardous problem affecting one vehicle in three that might be caught before production of equal importance with an appearance problem affecting one vehicle in three that cannot be caught at the design phase? According to the Risk Priority Numbers they are the same!

The problem with FMEA is not the subjective ordering of the three different aspects of a problem. It is not even a problem to have more levels than adjectives. The problem is with the Risk Priority Numbers and their use to create a ranking between the problems.

One company used only four levels for each aspect of a problem. Severity, Occurrence and Detectability were each ranked using the values 1, 3, 6, and 9, and then these numbers were multiplied together to create an *RPN* value. This reduced version will have only 16 unique *RPN* values spread out in a non-uniform manner on the number line from 1 to 729. This approach maps 64 different situations into 16 "equivalence" classes. Unfortunately, as noted above, situations with the same *RPN* are not at all similar in importance (to see this consider the six cases with *RPN* = 81).

When we place a series of categories in order in some continuum such as Severity, Occurrence, or Detectability, we may represent this ordering with numbers. Such numbers are rankings. If we assign the value of 1 to the lowest ranked category in the continuum, then 1 is below 2, 2 is below 3, 3 is below 4, and so on. Values with this property of order are called ordinal-scale data. The rankings on Severity, Occurrence, and Detectability are intended to be ordinal-scale data.

However, before the operations of addition and subtraction are meaningful you *must* have interval-scale data. Interval-scale data are data which possess both ordering and distance—not only is 1 less than 2, and 2 is less than 3, but also the distance from 1 to 2 is exactly the same as the distance from 2 to 3. It is this notion of distance which gives meaning to addition and subtraction, and without the metric imposed by distance you are operating in Wonderland where 1 + 2 is equal to whatever the Red Queen wants it to be today.

Before the operations of multiplication and division can be meaningful you must have ratio-scale data. Ratio-scale data are data which posses ordering, distance, and an absolute zero point. A classic example of data that are interval-scale but not ratio-scale are temperatures in degrees Fahrenheit or Celsius. Since neither of these scales has an absolute zero, multiplication and division do not make sense. However, addition and subtraction do result in meaningful numbers. For example, in either system

$$60° + 10° = 70°$$

is a true statement. But in either system the equation

$$\frac{60°}{80°} = 0.75$$

is nonsense. Before we can multiply or divide temperatures we must convert them into ratio-scale data by converting them into the Absolute or Kelvin scales, both of which measure temperature relative to an absolute zero point. In the Kelvin scale, 60°C = 333°K while 80°C = 353°K, so that

$$\frac{60°C}{80°C} = \frac{333°K}{353°K} = 0.943$$

This means that 60°C is 94.3% as hot as 80°C, which is a true statement.

In the Absolute scale, 60°F = 519°A, while 80°F = 539°A, so that:

$$\frac{60°F}{80°F} = \frac{519°A}{539°A} = 0.963$$

which means that 60°F is 96.3% as hot as 80°F.

Clearly, using the operation of division with interval-scale values will result in nonsense. Since division and multiplication are two facets of the same operation, neither of these operations make sense with interval-scale data.

Thus, with ordinal-scale data we can use numbers to define an ordering among

Ordinal Scale Data	Interval Scale Data	Ratio Scale Data
Rankings & Groupings of Adjacent Rankings	*Addition & Subtraction Make Sense*	*Multiplication & Division Make Sense*

Figure 17.5: Data Classifications and Arithmetic Operations

categories. With interval-scale data we can use the operations of addition and subtraction to obtain meaningful values. With ratio-scale data we can use the operations of multiplication and division to obtain meaningful values.

All Risk Priority Numbers are the products of three ordinal-scale values!

Because of the properties of ordinal-scale values we cannot obtain meaningful results when we multiply such values together. The lack of a distance function and the lack of an absolute zero will combine to result in inconsistencies where both serious and trivial problems have the same *RPN* value and where some trivial problems end up with larger *RPN* values than other, more serious, problems. This is why any attempt to use *RPN* values is an exercise in absurdity. Their use in the same room with a mathematician will tend to produce a spontaneous explosion. They are utter and complete nonsense raised to the third power.

If you feel that you have successfully used *RPN* values to identify problems to work on, you have been deluding yourself with the elaborate mumbo-jumbo that surrounds the calculation of the *RPN* values. While you may have been successful, that success did not come from the use of the *RPN* values.

When working at the *design phase* there is a rationale to doing an FMEA. In this case you may use the three scales, and use the rankings, *but you should not use the RPN values*. If you feel that you absolutely must have a systematic overall ranking of *all* the failure modes, then use 0 through 9 instead of 1 to 10 for the rankings of each aspect, and then create a three digit code for each failure mode, where the first digit is Severity, the second digit is Occurrence, and the third digit is Detectability. To signify the ordering of these three aspects designate this three digit code as the *SOD* code. This code will result in 1000 values for 1000 situations, leaving you to determine your own equivalence classes. When these *SOD* codes are placed in numerical order they will prioritize the situations first by severity, second by occurrence within each level of severity, and lastly by detectability within each combination of severity and occurrence. These codes can be rearranged in various ways to reflect different priorities. They use the original rankings without distorting them.

When working with an *existing process* there is no need for the elaborate exercise of an FMEA since the process behavior charts can spotlight the problems that need to be addressed in spite of all the fog and confusion associated with production.

17.4 Problems with Special Causes

Walter Shewhart described the routine variation that characterizes a process that is operated predictably as being the result of many cause-and-effect relationships *where no one cause has a dominant effect*. He called such causes of routine variation *Chance Causes* since the resulting routine variation was indistinguishable from random phenomena like radioactive decay and Brownian motion. However, when a single cause-and-effect relationship began to have a dominant effect over the other causes it would become an *Assignable Cause*. Thus, in Shewhart's view, the only difference between a Chance Cause and an Assignable Cause was the magnitude of their effects, and the process behavior chart was the tool Shewhart created for separating the Assignable Causes from the Chance Causes.

Moreover, in Shewhart's work it was clear that some Assignable Causes would be outside the realm of those things that could be controlled by the manufacturer, while other Assignable Causes would be within the sphere of things that the manufacturer could control. Effort expended to remove the effects of an Assignable Cause that is outside the system will not improve the system itself, but it can prevent excessive variation in the process outcomes. However, effort expended to remove the effects of an Assignable Cause that is inside the system will improve both the system and the consistency of the process outcomes. This leverage for process improvement provided by the process behavior chart is clearly demonstrated throughout Shewhart's *Economic Control of Quality of Manufactured Product*, and it has been verified countless times since then.

However, since few manufacturers want to leave things to chance, the use of the term "Chance Causes" to refer to the sources of routine variation was rather unfortunate. To remedy this W. Edwards Deming talked about *Common Causes* and *Special Causes*. His stated intention was simply to change the names. In Dr. Deming's words, "A Special Cause is an Assignable Cause and an Assignable Cause is a Special Cause." Moreover, in *Out of the Crisis* Deming wrote: "It is a hazard to use judgment to distinguish between special causes and common causes."

Nevertheless, as a result of Dr. Deming's discussion about who is responsible for dealing with Special Causes and Common Causes, many have come to believe four misconceptions regarding Special Causes:

Myth 1.   Special Causes are always external to the system.

Myth 2.   Special Causes always have a marginal impact.

Myth 3.   The removal of Special Causes will only restore the status quo.

Myth 4.   Because of Myth 1, you can tell the difference between a Special Cause and a Common Cause by whether or not it is part of the system. (Which is precisely the type of judgment call that Deming was warning against.)

Example after example has been provided in both Shewhart's books and in the various books by this author of how some Assignable Causes are within the manufacturer's sphere of control. Deming even states that "Some Special Causes can be removed only by management." [*Out of the Crisis*, p.320.] Thus any argument that Special Causes are always external to the system is in conflict with both Shewhart and Deming.

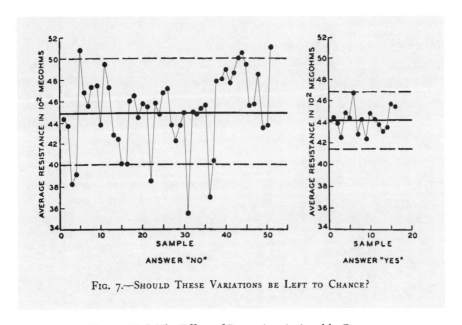

Fig. 7.—Should These Variations be Left to Chance?

Figure 17.6: The Effect of Removing Assignable Causes

Time after time those who have used process behavior charts have reported dramatic reductions in the variation of the process outcomes. Reductions of 50% are common while three-, four-, and five-fold reductions in process variation are not at all unusual. One client reported a 67% reduction while he still had signals of exceptional variation present! Anyone who considers such reductions in variation as "marginal" has never worked in production.

On page 21 of *Economic Control of Quality* Shewhart shows the two Average Charts that are reproduced in Figure 17.6. These two charts reveal the impact of the removal of Assignable Causes. The removal of the Assignable Causes did not simply remove the points outside the limits, but it also resulted in limits that were *half* as wide as the initial limits. Thus, the removal of Assignable Causes does not merely restore the status quo, but can take your process to new levels of consistency.

Thus, the four myths about Special Causes listed above are patently not true. They are inconsistent with the concepts behind the process behavior chart and they are in conflict with over seventy years of experience. If any of these four myths summarize your understanding of Deming's teaching, then you need to read Deming again, and possibly Shewhart as well.

The process behavior chart is the operational definition of a Special, or Assignable, Cause. There is *no other* definition. Special Causes are those cause-and-effect relationships that dominate the routine variation. As a result, it will be economical to seek to identify and exert control over any Special Cause identified by a process behavior chart. On the other hand, seeking to exert control over Common Causes of routine variation will always be a low payback strategy.

Any discussion of whether or not a Special Cause is inside or outside of the system is irrelevant. Moreover, any discussion of *who* is responsible for dealing with Special Causes is irrelevant—a Special Cause is the responsibility of whoever is in a position to do something about it. Special causes represent opportunities for improvement. Common Causes do not.

17.5   Problems with DMAIC Models

An integral part of every Six Sigma program is a DMAIC model (Define, Measure, Analyze, Improve, & Control). These models provide frameworks for Six Sigma improvement projects. While different books have different DMAIC models, these models all have one thing in common—whatever the problem, the answer is assumed to consist of changing the process in some fundamental way. No DMAIC model that this author has seen considers what can be done by operating the current process up to its full potential. In fact, most Six Sigma models do not make any distinction between processes that are operated predictably and processes that are operated unpredictably. They usually just assume that the mythical 1.5 standard deviation shift will make the problem of unpredictable processes go away. As a result these models perform all their computations under the assumption that processes are magically going to operate predictably.

Thus the first major flaw in DMAIC models is the failure to investigate what can be accomplished by operating the current process up to its full potential. Since operating predictably and on target will generally cost nothing, this is the cheapest type of improvement possible. Even when there are associated costs they are usually well within the operating budget and capital expenditures are not required. Moreover, as shown in Section 14.6, operating predictably and on target will frequently allow you to operate in the economic zone, making further improvements unnecessary. However, the published DMAIC models all seem to miss this particular piece of low-hanging fruit.

Since reengineering a process is never cheap, it should be undertaken only when it is needed. If you do not know what can be accomplished by operating the current process predictably and on target, how can you know if you need to reengineer the process? The assumption that every project will need to change something in some major way is the second major flaw in the DMAIC models—they automatically choose a path toward improvement that should only be taken when there is a proven need.

The third problem lies with the assumption that you can identify the appropriate inputs to study. Returning to the argument outlined in Section 12.4, it is very difficult to conduct experiments when we have yet to identify all of the dominant factors. When a process is operated unpredictably it is subject to the effects of unknown, dominant Assignable Causes. If you try to conduct experiments without identifying the Assignable Causes your results will be of limited validity and dubious utility.

Moreover, in the absence of a systematic way of learning from the existing process, many of the machinations of the DMAIC model exist solely in order to identify which inputs to study. These steps add complexity in order to achieve that which can be more easily done using process behavior charts.

Finally the DMAIC models assume that, even though you have given no thought to the support and operational discipline required to operate your current process predictably, you will be able to magically operate the new, upgraded process predictably. Unfortunately, all of our experience with process upgrades tells us otherwise. If you cannot operate your current process, whose idiosyncrasies you know, up to its full potential, then how will you learn how to operate a new process, with new idiosyncrasies, up to its full potential? Operating a process predictably requires a learning organization—one where knowledge is both gained and shared. It is more a matter of practicing a way of thinking than it is a matter of having the right technique. Without the practice in the way of thinking, simply sticking a control chart on a new process and throwing it over the wall to production will not result in predictable operation.

Every time I read a description of a DMAIC model I cannot help but recall the "Thought Method" used by Professor Harold Hill to teach music in *The Music Man*—"if you just think of the notes you want to hear, you will be able to play them." In a similar manner DMAIC models require a lot of steps up front to help you to *think* of those factors you need to study. *You* have to make the effort to *figure out* what your process needs. In contrast to all this elaborate warm-up and mental effort, process behavior charts let the process itself identify those things that need to be investigated.

In short, there is nothing wrong with a DMAIC model that cannot be remedied by using process behavior charts. When these charts are used at the start as the major technique for Measuring, Analyzing, Improving and Controlling your process outcomes they can transform the complexity of the DMAIC model into a very simple and straightforward process of continual improvement.

"But wait," you might say, "what about all the progress that has been made using DMAIC models?" The fact that so much progress has been reported is either a tribute to the ability of the Six Sigma practitioners to identify things that have escaped the notice of previous generations of process engineers, or else it is a commentary on how completely disorganized everyone was to begin with. Since the statistical and organizational tools of Six Sigma do not bring new subject matter knowledge to the table, I will let the reader decide which of these two alternatives is the most likely explanation.

17.6 Do We Need a Gauge R&R Study?

In the Measure phase of most DMAIC models there is a requirement that before you get started on improving your process you use some precious time and energy to verify that you have good measurements. This seems reasonable because, like apple pie and motherhood, no one can be against having good measurements. But before answering the question of whether you need to do a Gauge R&R Study it will be helpful to distinguish between four distinct ways that measurements are used.

DESCRIPTION

One use of data is to describe the item measured. The motivation for this description might be idle curiosity, or a need to stay in touch, or a desire to have the data for future use, but whatever the motivation, this basic use of measurements is to answer the questions of how many or how much. When data are used for description it is important to understand the limitations of the value used—the uncertainty attached to the value itself. The source of this uncertainty will primarily be the uncertainty in the measurement process. Thus, in order to use data to describe the item measured we will need to have a way to define the uncertainty that should be attached to a measurement.

CHARACTERIZATION

A second use of data, closely related to the first, is to characterize the item measured relative to specifications. Here the measurement is used not only to quantify how many or how much, but also to take action on the item measured—to characterize the item measured as being either within or outside specifications. Once again the major source of uncertainty will be the uncertainty introduced by the measurement process. However, instead of attaching our uncertainty to the measurement, we will now need to make adjustments in the specifications in order to make allowances for this uncertainty when we make our decision.

REPRESENTATION

A third use of data is to represent the product that was *not* measured. Here the objective is to characterize *a lot, batch, or product stream* with regard to specifications. In order to do this we have to extrapolate from the product that was measured to the product that was not measured. Of course the basis for such an extrapolation will be the selection procedure used to obtain the product that we did measure. When data are used to represent something that was not measured there are several sources of uncertainty. The uncertainty in the measurement process is still present, but now we also have the additional uncertainties of the representation. The first of these uncertainties comes from the product variation: since the product not measured will differ from the product measured we have an additional source of uncertainty not present in the Description and Characterization uses of data. Additional uncertainties of representation will come from the selection procedure (or the lack thereof in some cases). We will need to have a way of making allowances for all of these uncertainties before we can effectively use data to represent the product not measured.

PREDICTION

A fourth use of data is to predict. Here the objective is to characterize *future process outcomes*. The mechanism used is the characterization of the past behavior of the process. Here we are no longer concerned with classifying some batch of product as conforming or not, but rather with understanding what to expect in the future. When data are used to predict we must be concerned with measurement error, the predictability of the production process, and the combined variation from both sources. Thus, in addition to the sources of variation identified above, there is also the uncertainty associated with the continuation over time. We will need a way of making allowances for these uncertainties so that we can know when the past can be used as a guide for the future.

Since the way you intend to use a measurement will have an impact upon how much you need to know about the sources of uncertainty in that measurement, ***it is impossible to define a single, simple index for the quality of a measurement system***. There are many different aspects of any measurement system. Some of these will affect some uses of data and will have little impact on other uses. While a complete treatment of this subject requires a book, some guidelines are possible here.

In the cases of **Description** and **Characterization** a simple measure of the essential uncertainty of the measurement system, known as the Probable Error, will define how closely to interpret a descriptive measurement and how much to fuzz the specifications to take action on the item measured. (For example, 99% Manufacturing Specifications consist of the Watershed Specifications tightened by three Probable Errors.)

In the cases of **Representation** and **Prediction**, where our interest lies outside the actual items measured, the direct estimation of the various components of uncertainty becomes exceedingly complex. Here it is preferable to take an empirical approach by capturing and summarizing all the sources of uncertainty together, rather than to try to estimate them separately. This collective approach can be taken using process behavior charts, which allow both the Representative and Predictive uses of data when a reasonable degree of predictability is present.

But what about the **traditional Gauge R&R Studies**? These studies collect good data which could be used to answer the questions for cases of Description and Characterization. However, traditional Gauge R&R Studies compute the wrong summary statistics, and then they compound this mistake by completely misinterpreting those misbegotten ratios. Finally, in an effort to escape the unintelligible tangle created by the faulty analysis, these incorrect ratios are compared to an arbitrary and excessively conservative guideline that has not one ounce of rationality to support it. In the end, traditional Gauge R&R Studies have but one objective, and that is to condemn your measurement process whenever measurement error amounts to more than one percent (yes, 1%) of the total variation.

When data are used for **Representation** and **Prediction** the process behavior chart has proven itself to be remarkably forgiving when used with soft and uncertain data. Useful results can still be obtained even when the measurements are considerably less than perfect. Therefore, unless you are a masochist, you do not need to perform a traditional Gauge R&R Study before you start your improvement project.

17.7 Problems with Narrowly Defined Projects

The objective of all Six Sigma projects should be to improve the effectiveness, or the efficiency, of the core processes. Everything else should be secondary to this objective. If you improve the efficiency of a subprocess, but at the same time lower the efficiency of the core process, what have you gained?

At one time a Compounding Department, known as Department 13, had material costs which amounted to 75 percent of their production costs. During what we shall call Year One, a project team was formed and given the job of reducing the material costs in Department 13. During August of Year One, a process change was made which was designed to reduce the material utilization. Following this change the average material cost per 100 pounds of material dropped from $215.22 to $208.20. During March of Year Two, another process modification was implemented. During the next four months the material cost dropped to an average of $205.37 per 100 pounds produced. In July of Year Two a change was made in the formulation of the material used in Department 13. This change resulted in an average material cost of $201.22 per 100 pounds produced. One month later the project team and Department 13 got an award for these successful cost reductions. Finally, in January of Year Three, Department 13 changed suppliers for some of their raw materials. This resulted in an average material cost of $198.46 per 100 pounds produced.

Against this background, the monthly report for July of Year Three showed the following values for Department 13: Production volumes were down four percent from the monthly target. They were also down two percent from last year. The year-to-date value was pretty much in line with the yearly plan value, but it was eight percent below the previous year.

Year-to-date material costs were down almost four percent from a year ago, which was good. For Year Three as a whole, man-hours were up nine percent from last year, which was bad. Energy and fixed costs were up, which surprised no one. Total production costs were essentially unchanged from last year, which was good, especially in light of the *increases* in manhours, energy, and fixed costs.

In all, it was a rather mixed bag of results—some good news, some bad news, some neutral results. Each of the five categories used in the management report will be considered as a separate time series on the following pages. Of course, the complete story is a composite of all of these time series, but we have to assemble the big picture one piece at a time.

We shall begin with the material cost values. The material costs are shown in Figure 17.7. The gaps in the record correspond to the changes made by the project team. The effectiveness of these changes can clearly and easily be seen on this graph. Each of the changes made by the project team did result in definite and real reductions in the material costs.

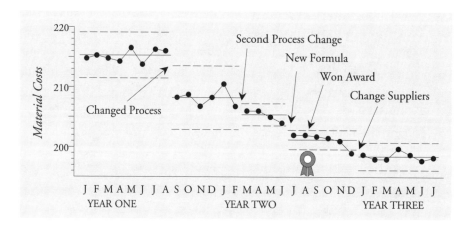

Figure 17.7: *X*-Charts for Material Costs

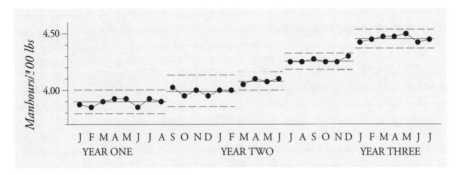

Figure 17.8: *X*-Charts for Man-hours per 100 Pounds

The man-hours per 100 pounds of product are shown in Figure 17.8. The gaps in the record correspond to the changes made by the project team. Clearly there have been increases in the number of man-hours per 100 pounds of product. *Each and every change made by the project team had the effect of increasing the actual labor content of the product.*

The production volumes are shown in Figure 17.9. The gaps in the record correspond to the changes made by the project team. The limits were computed from the first eight values and their moving ranges.

The first eight values suggest an upward trend for the production volumes. However, following the first process change, and continuing through the subsequent changes, there is a downward trend in the production volume. In addition to the two large transition ranges, the moving range chart shows three other points above

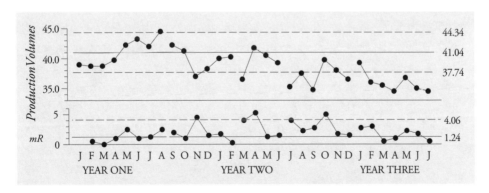

Figure 17.9: *XmR* Chart for Production Volumes

the limit. These three values suggest three additional changes in the level of production in Department 13. If these were deliberate changes made by management, then there is no need to look for Assignable Causes. If these changes were surprises, then there is something to be gained by looking for the Assignable Causes behind these shifts.

Thus, the production volumes are down while the man-hours per 100 pounds are up—*a classic description of declining productivity*—*totally buried in the figures in the Monthly Report.*

The energy and fixed costs are shown in Figure 17.10. They have risen as expected. In fact, the running record shows a fairly straight line sloping upward.

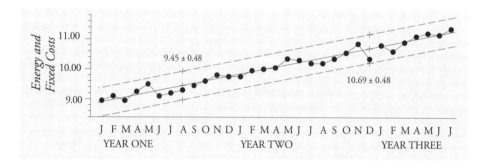

Figure 17.10: Trended *XmR* Chart for Energy and Fixed Costs

The total production costs are shown in Figure 17.11. The gaps in the record correspond to the changes made by the project team. The limits shown were based upon each segment, ignoring the moving ranges shown in white (which represent the four known changes).

The first process change resulted in a definite drop in the total production cost, although inflation of other costs had eroded these gains by the first two months of Year Two. The second process change caused a slight drop in the total production cost. Finally, even though the final change at the beginning of Year Three did reduce the material cost, the increases in the other costs have offset this gain. Still, all in all, they are doing better than they were at the beginning of Year One, or at least it would appear that way from these data.

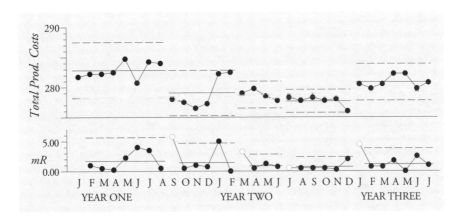

Figure 17.11: *XmR* **Charts for Total Production Costs per 100 Pounds**

While the total cost data and the material cost data look good, and the energy costs look pretty much like they should, there are some indications of trouble in the time series for man-hours and production volumes. Unfortunately, Department 13 does not use its own stuff, and therefore it has no way of assessing the quality of its product.

The figures developed from the records in Department 13 cannot take the quality of the product into account. This makes all of the cost figures suspect, because they are based on pounds shipped, not pounds converted into usable product in Department 14.

Department 14, on the other hand, keeps careful track of their successful conversion rate. Among the problems that can occur in Department 14, the major cause of scrap is "will not mould." The category has been shown to be most directly affected by the quality of the component supplied by Department 13. The percentages of scrap (by weight) due to "will not mould" are shown in Figure 17.12.

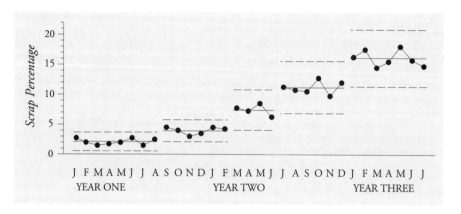

Figure 17.12: *X*-Charts for Scrap Percentages in Department 14

While each segment stays within its own set of limits, each segment, beginning with September of Year One, has points that fall outside the preceding set of limits. This means that each and every signal in these data correspond to one of the changes made by the project team in Department 13.

This negative impact of the project team's efforts was not seen because of the artificial boundary created by the "departments" and the subsequent partitioning of the management data. While everyone was minding their own department, no one was minding the store.

If we delete the pounds of scrap produced in Department 14 from the total amount of product produced in Department 13, then the data for Department 13 will tell a different story. We begin by taking the total production costs and scaling them to reflect the scrap rate due to "will not mould."

Figure 17.13 shows the net value to the company of the changes made by the project team in Department 13. They effectively increased the total cost of the finished product every time they made a change, and they got an award for doing it! One cannot help but recall Dr. Deming's first theorem:

> *"No one gives a hoot about profits—*
> *if they did they would be interested*
> *in learning better ways to make them."*

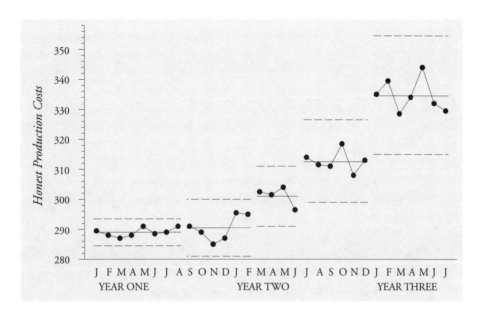

Figure 17.13: *X*-**Charts for the Honest Production Costs in Department 13**

What if the changes had not been made? What if Department 13 had done noth-ing? The total cost per 100 pounds of usable product may be estimated as follows. Assume that Department 13 continued to use the same process, with the same sup-plier, and without the modifications in material usage or formulation. Assume material costs go up five percent each year. Allow for the increases in wages and the increases in energy costs which are known to have occurred. Assume that the scrap rate in Department 14 averages the 2.1 percent shown by the first eight months of Year One, and assume that the labor content of the product stays the same as it was at the beginning of Year One. These conditions will result in the estimated total pro-duction costs shown on the next page in Figure 17.14.

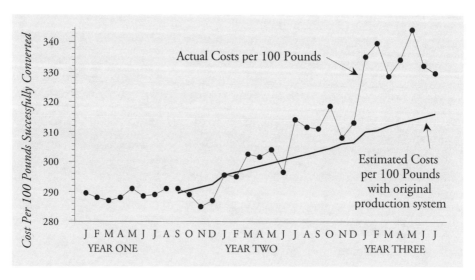

Figure 17.14: Actual Costs versus Estimated Costs

The company would have come out ahead if they had kept the production system which was in place at the beginning of Year One and sent the project team for a two-year, expense-paid vacation in Cuba.

The second tragedy of this story is that the managers had too much invested in the "improvement" effort to admit that it had been a failure. Therefore, the messenger who revealed the effect of all these "process improvements" soon took a job at another company. (The data for this example are contained in Chapter Five of *Understanding Variation, Second Edition*, by this author.)

This is a classic example of the optimization of a subprocess that resulted in a decrease in efficiency for the core process as a whole. Managers must look at the whole picture, not just the narrow slices provided by the departmental figures. The artificial boundaries created by departments can distort both the data and the system.

> *The optimization of each department*
> *will always result in a plant which is suboptimal.*

> *The optimization of the whole system*
> *will require that some departments be operated suboptimally.*

However, by encouraging competition between managers, most organizations make it impossible for departments to cooperate for the good of the company.

In addition, this is an example of a project that had the wrong objective. Rather than being given the job of identifying ways of increasing productivity, this team was told to implement a specific solution—"Reduce material costs in Department 13." Implementing solutions before we identify the problems is a guaranteed short-cut to chaos. Moreover, the managers here confused change with improvement. By changing things without respect to the consequences of those changes they created chaos. Improvement often consists of doing the same things with greater consistency, rather than finding new things to do.

17.8 Summary

Learn how to avoid the logical traps represented by these various problems by learning how to use the process behavior chart as it was intended to be used, as a tool for continual improvement.

The objective of data analysis is understanding and insight. And the best analysis is the simplest analysis that provides that insight and allows you to communicate it to others. While many different techniques have been presented in this book, the primary technique of data analysis is still the process behavior chart. With its simplicity and clarity, it is unsurpassed at providing the maximum insight with the least effort.

Chapter Eighteen

Two Models for Process Improvement

There are five ways to improve an existing process. In order of increasing difficulty these five options are as follows:

- You may operate the existing process on target.
- You may operate the existing process predictably.
- You may operate the existing process predictably and on target.
- You may try to optimize the existing process by changing the target values for the various process inputs.
- You may take the existing process out and shoot it, and start all over again with a new process or a technological upgrade.

The best improvement strategy is the one that delivers the greatest return for the least effort. Realistic models for process improvement will allow you to take advantage of the easier improvements when they are sufficient to meet your needs. In addition, these models should establish, encourage, and reinforce the operational discipline needed to operate every process up to its full potential. This chapter will describe such a model. This model is more sophisticated than the traditional DMAIC models, and yet it is easier to put into practice.

In addition to the improvement model, this chapter will also include a model which executives may use to guide the improvement process toward strategic objectives.

18.1 Getting Started

If you are going to have a formal improvement project then you will need to form a team and plan your project. While this may be necessary when dealing with a specific problem at a high level, involving different departments or even different plants, there are many projects that can be carried out in a more informal manner at a local level using the personnel directly involved within a department. Regardless of the level of structure involved, the key elements of getting started are the following.

- Every team should have a statement of the problem to be addressed (not a pre-determined solution to be implemented).

- Every team should have an appropriately detailed Process Map—a simple block diagram of the process going down the middle of the page with input variables for each block on one side and outcome variables for each block on the other side.

- Once you have a Process Map the simplest thing to do is to use process behavior charts with each of the outcome variables for each block on the Process Map. This will allow you to quickly identify those variables that indicate unpredictable operation of the process. These are the opportunities for quick improvement. By addressing these problems, starting as far upstream as possible and then working downstream, you can bring about dramatic improvements with minimum effort.

This may sound rather minimalist compared with some of the more complex models that have recently been published, but it has the virtue of quickly getting you to the point of collecting and analyzing data in an understandable and usable format.

18.2   Characterize the Status of the Process Outcomes

Use the Four Possibilities to characterize each process outcome as being either in the Ideal State, the Threshold State, the Brink of Chaos, or the State of Chaos. As long as any one step in your process is operated unpredictably you will find it impossible to fully realize what your process can consistently deliver. The reason for this is the often observed fact that reducing the variation in one step will usually reduce the variation in *all* the subsequent process steps. This multiplicative effect means that as you work upstream to reduce variation you will often see improvements downstream. As a result, you cannot fully realize the benefits of improving one step in your process if earlier process steps are operated unpredictably. However, as you make progress towards operating all the process steps predictably you will often find a synergistic reduction of variation occurring in the process outcomes.

Using the Four Possibilities you can identify the process steps needing the greatest attention—those that are operated unpredictably. Whenever a process outcome shows evidence of unpredictable operation the exceptional variation present will generally affect subsequent steps unfavorably. Therefore, those process steps whose outcome variables are either in the Brink of Chaos or the State of Chaos are the logical places to start your improvement project.

Process steps whose outcomes are in the Threshold State may be candidates for improving the process aim. If this can be easily accomplished then such improvements may represent low-hanging fruit that can be done at any time during the project.

Process steps whose outcomes are in the Ideal State will tend to be low on your project agenda since they are already consistent and conforming. These process steps are being operated as consistently as they can be, and are not likely to be easily improved.

18.3   Outcomes in the State or Brink of Chaos

Use your Process Map and begin with the first process outcomes that are in the Brink of Chaos or the State of Chaos. Since there is an operational gulf between unpredictable operation and predictable operation, your first priority should be to identify ways to move these chaotic outcomes to the predictable states.

To this end begin with the *Benchmark ECP* values for each of the unpredictable outcomes. Continue as outlined in Chapter Fourteen to compute the *Centered ECP*, the *Predictable ECP*, and the *Minimum ECP* for each of these process outcomes.

If centering will get you into the Economic Zone of Production (where *Centered ECP* ≤ 1.10), and if you can institute a reasonable procedure for maintaining this process outcome on target, then a process centering solution may be sufficient.

If centering is not the solution, then consider predictable operation. Since the *Predictable ECP* is computed using the historical process average, it is always a worst case value. In practice you are almost certain to do better than this value will indicate. So, in conjunction with the *Predictable ECP* you should also consider the *Minimum ECP* which approximates what you can achieve by learning how to operate your current process up to its full potential. If the *Minimum* ECP will get you reasonably close to the Economic Zone of Production (*Minimum ECP* ≤ 1.15) then you will need to take the time and trouble to learn how to operate this process step predictably and on target. Any other course of action will be wasteful.

Finally, if the *Minimum ECP* value is not reasonably close to the Economic Zone of Production, then you may wish to consider reengineering this process step.

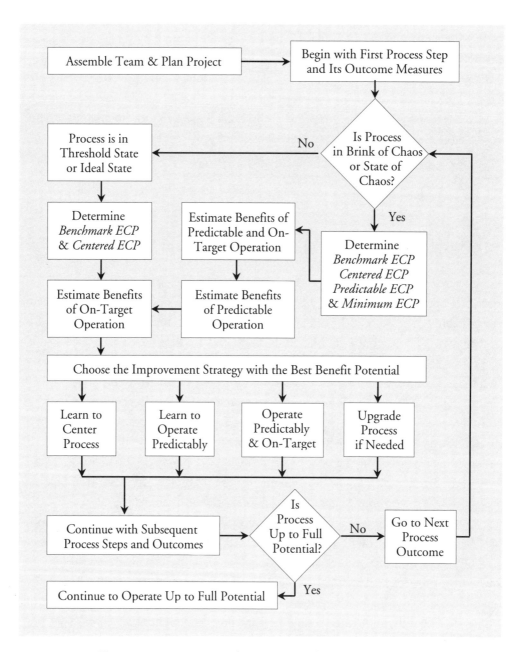

Figure 18.1: How to Get the Most Out of an Existing Process

As you work your way through the various process steps in this manner the reduction of variation and consistency of operation will make subsequent operations better and result in dramatic improvements in the final process outcomes.

In many cases you will find that you will have met your project objectives long before you finish going through the list of unpredictable outcomes. When this happens you will not only have completed your project, but you will have institutionalized an approach to learning from your process that will enable the organization to continue to improve. You will, as an organization, have learned how to take advantage of those opportunities that occur as part of normal operations and thereby to incrementally improve every process with minimum effort and expense. (For an example of this type of continual improvement see Chapter Seven of *Understanding Statistical Process Control, Second Edition*, by this author and David S. Chambers.)

Warning: This approach to process improvement is so powerful, and the results are so dramatic, that you are unlikely to ever need to go on to the following steps. Moreover, since new Assignable Causes will reveal their presence as you peel layers of variation off your process, you may never run out of opportunities for making improvements. This is how process behavior charts can be the locomotive of continual improvement.

18.4 Outcomes in the Threshold State

As you operate the steps of your process more predictably you will find more variables to be in the Threshold State. These outcomes will be predictable but not capable. When you are ready to work on these outcomes you should begin by separating those outcomes that can be moved to the Ideal State by centering from those that will need reengineering. To do this use fresh data to recompute the *Benchmark ECP* and the *Centered ECP*, and identify those for which centering will provide a large payback.

For those process outcomes that cannot be removed from the Threshold State by centering the process, the only way to operate in the Ideal State is to either change the specifications or to change the process. To change the process you will need to investigate the technical possibilities and experiment with the input factors to discover how to achieve the desired objective for the outcome in question.

18.5 Outcomes in the Ideal State

If you get to the point that final process outcomes are in the Ideal State what should you do next? Generally by the time you get to this point you will already be the industry leader. Moreover, you will be in a position to place your competition at a disadvantage. By continuing to use the opportunities that present themselves on the process behavior charts for the outcomes for the various process steps you can usually further improve your product with no capital expenditures. As you have the best product at the lowest cost you can take over the market. In fact you can even go to your customers and ask for tighter specifications, thereby creating a barrier to your competition, while still allowing adequate elbow room for your own process.

This is not theoretical. All of these things have been done using this approach. This model for process improvement has been thoroughly proven time and again in all types of industries.

18.6 Focusing Improvement on Strategic Objectives

The model of Figure 18.2 provides a structure that may be used to organize and guide the activities carried out under the Project Improvement Model of Figure 18.1.

1. The executives should begin by developing a consensus on a set of strategic business objectives. A short list will provide the focus needed to select the best, and most important, projects and areas of emphasis. These strategic objectives can be broken down into three areas: What are the organization's objectives with respect to operational efficiency? What are the organization's objectives with respect to customer satisfaction? And what are the organization's objectives with respect to employee satisfaction?

2. Next you will need to identify the processes in your business. For clarity you should begin by defining your core processes. These are the major things that you do to meet your strategic business objectives. These core processes will extend across the functional boundaries of the organizational chart. Questions to consider when defining these core processes are: What does your organization deliver to your external customers? How does material flow through your organization? And how does work flow from employee to employee?

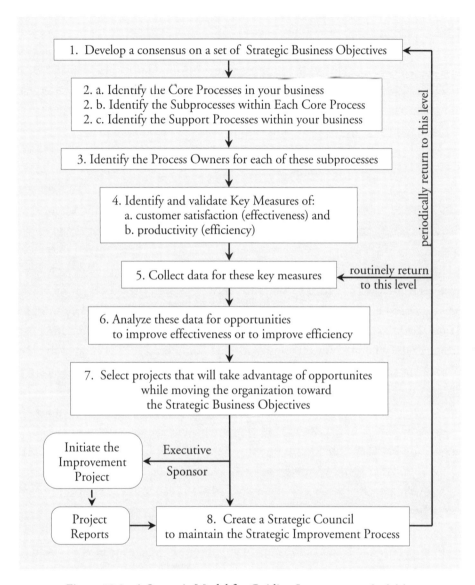

Figure 18.2: A Strategic Model for Guiding Improvement Activities

After you have identified your core processes you can then identify the major components of each of the core processes. Call these your subprocesses. By breaking each core process into its logical steps it will be easier to define workable projects.

Finally you will need to identify the support processes in your business. While support processes are a necessary part of the business, they do not directly serve to meet your strategic business objectives. While you will want these processes to operate efficiently, their efficiency is secondary to the efficiency of the core processes. Since an optimized system will require some components to operate at less than optimal levels, you should always try to concentrate these suboptimal components in the support processes rather than in the core processes.

3. Next you will need to identify the process owners for each of the core processes, each of the subprocesses, and each of the support processes. These process owners will usually include all of the directors of the functional areas, but may also include others. Process owners should be fully knowledgeable regarding their subprocesses. They should be people whose responsibilities include the well-being of their subprocesses, and they should have the leadership skills to work successfully with others.

4. Identify and validate key measures of effectiveness and efficiency. Measures of effectiveness allow the process owner to know how well the process is meeting the customer's needs and requirements. Measures of efficiency are usually things like cycle time, cost, or the net value added. A key measure should be something that is important to the customer and it should also be something that you have the ability to change. The number of key measures should be kept small.

Process owners will usually have some ideas about the key measures for their own process. Some of these measures may even be the right measures. But experience has shown that, when asked, the customers will usually surprise the process owners with what they consider to be important. Therefore, before you spend time collecting data, you should validate the key measures to be used.

5. Collect data for these key measures. Plot these values on an appropriate process behavior chart.

6. Analyze the data for these key measures to discover opportunities for improvement. An opportunity for improvement exists when the effectiveness measures show a gap between performance and the customer needs. A different type of opportunity for improvement exists when the efficiency measures either display unpredictable behavior or when the average efficiency falls short of some benchmark value. Of these different types of opportunities, the opportunity associated with unpredictable operation is by far the easiest to capitalize upon.

7. Select projects to take advantage of the opportunities. In addition to addressing the opportunities identified above, these projects should move the organization toward the strategic business objectives. The projects should be feasible, with a reasonable likelihood of success within a reasonable period of time. At this point the process owner now becomes the project sponsor and initiates the improvement project model.

8. As the process owners and executives review the project reports they will have completed the first cycle of the strategic model. This group should then return to Step 5, reevaluate the key measures, verify the improvements, and initiate the next cycle of projects. From time to time this strategic council should return to Step 1 to maintain the strategic focus for the improvement efforts.

18.7 Summary

The objective of analysis is insight, and the best analysis is the simplest analysis that provides that insight. While many different techniques have been presented in this book, the primary technique of data analysis is the process behavior chart. With this technique you automatically check for the homogeneity that is fundamental to every attempt to extrapolate from the data to the underlying process. Moreover, process behavior charts also minimize the time and effort required for analysis, allowing you to go from collecting data to interpreting those data to communicating what you have found to others in record time.

While there are many different techniques, they all have the same objective of separating the probable noise from the potential signals. Unfortunately, they all do this in differing ways, with different degrees of sensitivity, and under different assumptions and conditions. These differences create complexity for both the analyst and for the managers trying to interpret the analysis. This is why instruction in the techniques rarely provides a unified view of what to do and how to do it.

The key to effective data analysis is a clear understanding of the dual nature of trouble, and a systematic approach to improvement that takes this dual nature of trouble into account. Anything less is simplistic, naive, and ultimately less efficient in terms of time, money, and results than it could be. Learn the concepts of Part Three, and apply the distinctions of Part One, and the techniques of Part Two will come to life. The alternative is continued confusion.

Appendix

Table A.1

Bias Correction Factors for Measures of Dispersion

n	c_4	c_5	c_6	d_2	d_3	d_4
2	0.7979	0.6028	0.675	1.128	0.8525	0.954
3	0.8862	0.4633	0.832	1.693	0.8884	1.588
4	0.9213	0.3889	0.888	2.059	0.8798	1.978
5	0.9400	0.3412	0.916	2.326	0.8641	2.257
6	0.9515	0.3076	0.933	2.534	0.8480	2.472
7	0.9594	0.2820	0.944	2.704	0.8332	2.645
8	0.9650	0.2622	0.952	2.847	0.8198	2.791
9	0.9693	0.2459	0.958	2.970	0.8078	2.915
10	0.9727	0.2321	0.963	3.078	0.7971	3.024
11	0.9754	0.2204	0.966	3.173	0.7873	3.121
12	0.9776	0.2105	0.970	3.258	0.7785	3.207
13	0.9794	0.2019	0.972	3.336	0.7704	3.285
14	0.9810	0.1940	0.974	3.407	0.7630	3.356
15	0.9823	0.1873	0.976	3.472	0.7562	3.422
16	0.9835	0.1809	0.978	3.532	0.7499	3.482
17	0.9845	0.1754	0.979	3.588	0.7441	3.538
18	0.9854	0.1703	0.980	3.640	0.7386	3.591
19	0.9862	0.1656	0.981	3.689	0.7335	3.640
20	0.9869	0.1613	0.982	3.735	0.7287	3.686
21	0.9876	0.1570	0.983	3.778	0.7242	3.730
22	0.9882	0.1532	0.984	3.819	0.7199	3.771
23	0.9887	0.1499	0.985	3.858	0.7159	3.811
24	0.9892	0.1466	0.985	3.895	0.7121	3.847
25	0.9896	0.1438	0.986	3.931	0.7084	3.883
30	0.9915	0.1301	0.988	4.086	0.6927	4.037
35	0.9927	0.1206	0.990	4.213	0.6799	4.166
40	0.9936	0.1130	0.991	4.322	0.6692	4.274
45	0.9943	0.1066	0.992	4.415	0.6601	4.372
50	0.9949	0.1009	0.993	4.498	0.6521	4.450
60	0.9957	0.0926	0.994	4.639	0.6389	4.591
70	0.9964	0.0848	0.995	4.755	0.6283	4.707
80	0.9968	0.0799	0.996	4.854	0.6194	4.806
90	0.9972	0.0748	0.996	4.939	0.6118	4.892
100	0.9975	0.0707	0.997	5.015	0.6052	4.968

$$Sigma(X) = \frac{\overline{s}}{c_4} \text{ or } \frac{\overline{R}}{d_2} \text{ or } \frac{\tilde{R}}{d_4} \text{ or } \frac{\tilde{s}}{c_6}$$

Table A.1

Bias Correction Factors for Measures of Dispersion

For the standard deviation statistic, s, based on n values:

$$MEAN(s) - c_4 \, \sigma \qquad SD(s) = c_5 \, \sigma \qquad MEDIAN(s) = c_6 \, \sigma$$

where:

$$c_4 = \sqrt{\frac{2}{n-1}} \, \frac{\Gamma(\frac{n}{2})}{\Gamma(\frac{n-1}{2})}$$

$$c_5 = \sqrt{1 - c_4^2}$$

and c_6 is defined by:

$$0.5 \, \Gamma\left(\frac{n-1}{2}\right) = \int_0^{c_6^2/2(n-1)} t^{(n-3)/2} \, e^{-t} \, dt$$

For the range statistic, R, based on n values:

$$MEAN(R) = d_2 \, \sigma \qquad SD(R) = d_3 \, \sigma \qquad MEDIAN(R) = d_4 \, \sigma$$

where:

$$d_2 = \int_0^\infty w \, f(w) \, dw$$

$$d_3^2 = \int_0^\infty [w - d_2]^2 f(w) \, dw$$

and d_4 is defined by:

$$0.5000 = \int_0^{d_4} f(w) \, dw$$

where

$$f(w) = \frac{n \, (n-1)}{[\sqrt{2\pi}]^n} \int_{-\infty}^\infty \left[\int_x^{x+w} e^{-(u^2/2)} \, du \right]^{n-2} e^{-((x+w)^2/2)} \, e^{-(x^2/2)} \, dx$$

Table A.2

XmR Charts: Charts for Individual Values

When a *time series consisting of logically comparable values* has a logical subgroup size of $n = 1$ we can plot the individual values and use a two-point moving range to measure the dispersion. The Average Moving Range or the Median Moving Range may then be used to compute the Natural Process Limits for the individual values and the Upper Range Limit for the moving ranges according to the formulas:

$$UNPL = \bar{X} + E_2\, \bar{R} \quad \text{or} \quad \bar{X} + E_5\, \tilde{R}$$

$$Central\ Line = \bar{X}$$

$$LNPL = \bar{X} - E_2\, \bar{R} \quad \text{or} \quad \bar{X} - E_5\, \tilde{R}$$

$$URL = D_4\, \bar{R} \quad \text{or} \quad D_6\, \tilde{R}$$

$$Central\ Line = \bar{R} \quad \text{or} \quad \tilde{R}$$

For two-period moving ranges these constants are:

$$E_2 = \frac{3}{d_2} = 2.660 \qquad\qquad E_5 = \frac{3}{d_4} = 3.145$$

$$D_4 = \left[\, 1 + \frac{3\,d_3}{d_2} \,\right] = 3.268 \qquad\qquad D_6 = \frac{d_2 + 3\,d_3}{d_4} = 3.865$$

where d_2, d_3 and d_4 are the bias correction factors given in Table A.1 for $n = 2$.

> The average of $(k{-}1)$ two-point moving ranges will have approximately $0.62\,(k{-}1)$ degrees of freedom.

> The median of $(k{-}1)$ two-point moving ranges will have approximately $0.32\,(k{-}1)$ degrees of freedom.

Table A.2
XmR Charts: Charts for Individual Values

- Moving ranges which fall above the upper range limit may be taken as indications of a potential break in the time series—some sudden shift which is so large that it is unlikely to have occurred by chance.

- There is no advantage to using any other measure of dispersion besides a two-point moving range. Moving ranges based on any $n > 2$ will be harder to compute and less efficient than the two-point moving ranges. Mean square successive differences will be harder to compute and more prone to being inflated by extreme values while being no more efficient than the two-point moving range. Global measures of dispersion beg the question of homogeneity by making a strong assumption that the data are completely homogeneous, and so they can never be properly used to compute limits for individual values.

- If the data do not come from a time series, i.e., if the individual values do not possess a definite and known time order, then the use of a moving range to measure the dispersion of the data is essentially arbitrary because the order of the data is arbitrary.

- Moreover, if the individual values are *known* to come from different cause systems, as would be the case in a sequence of experimental runs, then the moving ranges may not be used to construct Natural Process Limits even when the data constitute a time series.

Table A.3

Average and Range Charts Based on the Average Range

Given k subgroups each with n observations
with Grand Average, $\bar{\bar{X}}$ and Average Range, $\bar{R}$
use the tabled constants with the formulas to obtain

- limits for Subgroup Averages,
- limits for Subgroup Ranges, or
- Natural Process Limits for X, and
- the approximate Degrees of Freedom for these limits.

n	A_2	D_3	D_4	E_2	*Approximate Degrees of Freedom*
2	1.880	—	3.268	2.660	$.88\,k\,(n{-}1)$
3	1.023	—	2.574	1.772	$.91\,k\,(n{-}1)$
4	0.729	—	2.282	1.457	$.91\,k\,(n{-}1)$
5	0.577	—	2.114	1.290	$.91\,k\,(n{-}1)$
6	0.483	—	2.004	1.184	$.89\,k\,(n{-}1)$
7	0.419	0.076	1.924	1.109	$.88\,k\,(n{-}1)$
8	0.373	0.136	1.864	1.054	$.86\,k\,(n{-}1)$
9	0.337	0.184	1.816	1.010	$.85\,k\,(n{-}1)$
10	0.308	0.223	1.777	0.975	$.83\,k\,(n{-}1)$
11	0.285	0.256	1.744	0.945	$.81\,k\,(n{-}1)$
12	0.266	0.283	1.717	0.921	$.80\,k\,(n{-}1)$
13	0.249	0.307	1.693	0.899	$.78\,k\,(n{-}1)$
14	0.235	0.328	1.672	0.881	$.77\,k\,(n{-}1)$
15	0.223	0.347	1.653	0.864	$.75\,k\,(n{-}1)$

Table A.3

Average and Range Charts Based on the Average Range

*Limits for **Subgroup Averages** will be:*

$$UAL = \bar{\bar{X}} + A_2 \bar{R}$$
$$Central\ Line = \bar{\bar{X}}$$
$$LAL = \bar{\bar{X}} - A_2 \bar{R}$$

*Limits for **Subgroup Ranges** will be:*

$$URL = D_4 \bar{R}$$
$$Central\ Line = \bar{R}$$
$$LRL = D_3 \bar{R}$$

*While **Natural Process Limits for individual values** may be obtained from:*

$$UNPL = \bar{\bar{X}} + E_2 \bar{R}$$
$$Central\ Line = \bar{\bar{X}}$$
$$LNPL = \bar{\bar{X}} - E_2 \bar{R}$$

where

$$A_2 = \frac{3}{d_2 \sqrt{n}}$$

$$D_3 = \left[1 - \frac{3\,d_3}{d_2} \right] \qquad D_4 = \left[1 + \frac{3\,d_3}{d_2} \right]$$

$$E_2 = \frac{3}{d_2}$$

Table A.4
Average and Range Charts Based on the Median Range

Given k subgroups each with n observations

with Grand Average, $\bar{\bar{X}}$ and Median Range, $\tilde{R}$

use the tabled constants with the formulas to obtain

- limits for Subgroup Averages,
- limits for Subgroup Ranges, or
- Natural Process Limits for X, and
- the approximate Degrees of Freedom for these limits.

n	A_4	D_5	D_6	E_5	*Approximate* * *Degrees of Freedom*
2	2.224	—	3.865	3.145	$(1.56 + .023\,k)\,(n{-}1)\,\sqrt{k}$
3	1.091	—	2.745	1.889	$(1.61 + .031\,k)\,(n{-}1)\,\sqrt{k}$
4	0.758	—	2.375	1.517	$(1.61 + .032\,k)\,(n{-}1)\,\sqrt{k}$
5	0.594	—	2.179	1.329	$(1.61 + .028\,k)\,(n{-}1)\,\sqrt{k}$
6	0.495	—	2.055	1.214	$(1.57 + .025\,k)\,(n{-}1)\,\sqrt{k}$
7	0.429	0.078	1.967	1.134	$(1.56 + .023\,k)\,(n{-}1)\,\sqrt{k}$
8	0.380	0.139	1.901	1.075	$(1.52 + .020\,k)\,(n{-}1)\,\sqrt{k}$
9	0.343	0.187	1.850	1.029	$(1.50 + .018\,k)\,(n{-}1)\,\sqrt{k}$
10	0.314	0.227	1.809	0.992	$(1.47 + .016\,k)\,(n{-}1)\,\sqrt{k}$
11	0.290	0.260	1.773	0.961	$(1.43 + .015\,k)\,(n{-}1)\,\sqrt{k}$
12	0.270	0.288	1.744	0.935	$(1.42 + .014\,k)\,(n{-}1)\,\sqrt{k}$
13	0.253	0.312	1.719	0.913	$(1.38 + .013\,k)\,(n{-}1)\,\sqrt{k}$
14	0.239	0.333	1.697	0.894	$(1.36 + .012\,k)\,(n{-}1)\,\sqrt{k}$
15	0.226	0.352	1.678	0.877	$(1.33 + .010\,k)\,(n{-}1)\,\sqrt{k}$

* *formulas for even k— for odd values of k use $(k{-}1)$ in place of k in formula,*

Table A.4

Average and Range Charts Based on the Median Range

Limits for **Subgroup Averages** *will be.*

$$UAL = \bar{\bar{X}} + A_4 \tilde{R}$$
$$Central\ Line = \bar{\bar{X}}$$
$$LAL = \bar{\bar{X}} - A_4 \tilde{R}$$

Limits for **Subgroup Ranges** *will be:*

$$URL = D_6 \tilde{R}$$
$$Central\ Line = \tilde{R}$$
$$LRL = D_5 \tilde{R}$$

While **Natural Process Limits for individual values** *may be obtained from:*

$$UNPL = \bar{\bar{X}} + E_5 \tilde{R}$$
$$Central\ Line = \bar{\bar{X}}$$
$$LNPL = \bar{\bar{X}} - E_5 \tilde{R}$$

where

$$A_4 = \frac{3}{d_4 \sqrt{n}}$$

$$D_5 = \frac{d_2 - 3 d_3}{d_4} \qquad D_6 = \frac{d_2 + 3 d_3}{d_4}$$

$$E_5 = \frac{3}{d_4}$$

Table A.5

Average and Standard Deviation Charts
Based on the Average Standard Deviation Statistic

Given k subgroups each with n observations

with Grand Average, $\overline{\overline{X}}$, and Average Standard Deviation Statistic, $\overline{s}$

use the tabled constants with the formulas to obtain
- limits for Subgroup Averages,
- limits for Subgroup Standard Deviations, or
- Natural Process Limits for individual values, and
- the approximate Degrees of Freedom for these limits.

n	A_3	B_3	B_4	E_3	*Approximate Degrees of Freedom*
2	2.659	--	3.267	3.760	.88 $k\,(n{-}1)$
3	1.954	--	2.568	3.385	.92 $k\,(n{-}1)$
4	1.628	--	2.266	3.256	.93 $k\,(n{-}1)$
5	1.427	--	2.089	3.191	.95 $k\,(n{-}1)$
6	1.287	0.030	1.970	3.153	.96 $k\,(n{-}1)$
7	1.182	0.118	1.882	3.127	.97 $k\,(n{-}1)$
8	1.099	0.185	1.815	3.109	.97 $k\,(n{-}1)$
9	1.032	0.239	1.761	3.095	.98 $k\,(n{-}1)$
10	0.975	0.284	1.716	3.084	.98 $k\,(n{-}1)$
11	0.927	0.322	1.678	3.076	.98 $k\,(n{-}1)$
12	0.886	0.354	1.646	3.069	.98 $k\,(n{-}1)$
13	0.850	0.382	1.619	3.063	.98 $k\,(n{-}1)$
14	0.817	0.407	1.593	3.058	.98 $k\,(n{-}1)$
15	0.789	0.428	1.572	3.054	.98 $k\,(n{-}1)$
20	0.680	0.510	1.490	3.040	.98 $k\,(n{-}1)$
25	0.606	0.564	1.436	3.032	.98 $k\,(n{-}1)$
30	0.552	0.606	1.394	3.026	.98 $k\,(n{-}1)$
35	0.511	0.636	1.364	3.022	.98 $k\,(n{-}1)$
40	0.477	0.659	1.341	3.019	.98 $k\,(n{-}1)$
45	0.450	0.678	1.322	3.017	.98 $k\,(n{-}1)$
50	0.426	0.696	1.304	3.015	.98 $k\,(n{-}1)$

Table A.5
Average and Standard Deviation Charts
Based on the Average Standard Deviation Statistic

Limits for **Subgroup Averages** *will be:*

$$UAL = \bar{\bar{X}} + A_3 \bar{s}$$
$$Central\ Line = \bar{\bar{X}}$$
$$LAL = \bar{\bar{X}} - A_3 \bar{s}$$

Limits for **Subgroup Standard Deviation Statistics** *will be:*

$$USDL = B_4 \bar{s}$$
$$Central\ Line = \bar{s}$$
$$LSDL = B_3 \bar{s}$$

While **Natural Process Limits for individual values** *may be obtained from:*

$$UNPL = \bar{\bar{X}} + E_3 \bar{s}$$
$$Central\ Line = \bar{\bar{X}}$$
$$LNPL = \bar{\bar{X}} - E_3 \bar{s}$$

where

$$A_3 = \frac{3}{c_4 \sqrt{n}}$$

$$B_3 = 1 - \frac{3}{c_4}\sqrt{1-(c_4)^2} \qquad B_4 = 1 + \frac{3}{c_4}\sqrt{1-(c_4)^2}$$

$$E_3 = \frac{3}{c_4}$$

Table A.6

Average and Standard Deviation Charts
Based on the Median Standard Deviation Statistic

Given k subgroups each with n observations
with Grand Average, $\bar{\bar{X}}$, and Median Standard Deviation, $\tilde{s}$
use the tabled constants with the formulas to obtain

- limits for Subgroup Averages,
- limits for Subgroup Standard Deviations, or
- Natural Process Limits for individual values, and
- the approximate Degrees of Freedom for these limits.

n	A_{10}	B_9	B_{10}	E_6	Approximate * Degrees of Freedom
2	3.143	--	3.864	4.444	$(1.55 + .023\,k)\,(n-1)\,\sqrt{k}$
3	2.082	--	2.733	3.606	$(1.74 + .034\,k)\,(n-1)\,\sqrt{k}$
4	1.689	--	2.351	3.378	$(1.64 + .033\,k)\,(n-1)\,\sqrt{k}$
5	1.465	--	2.145	3.275	$(1.67 + .029\,k)\,(n-1)\,\sqrt{k}$
6	1.313	0.031	2.008	3.215	$(1.67 + .027\,k)\,(n-1)\,\sqrt{k}$
7	1.201	0.120	1.913	3.178	$(1.68 + .025\,k)\,(n-1)\,\sqrt{k}$
8	1.114	0.188	1.839	3.151	$(1.68 + .022\,k)\,(n-1)\,\sqrt{k}$
9	1.044	0.242	1.782	3.132	$(1.68 + .020\,k)\,(n-1)\,\sqrt{k}$
10	0.985	0.287	1.735	3.115	$(1.69 + .018\,k)\,(n-1)\,\sqrt{k}$
11	0.936	0.324	1.695	3.106	$(1.69 + .018\,k)\,(n-1)\,\sqrt{k}$
12	0.893	0.357	1.661	3.093	$(1.68 + .016\,k)\,(n-1)\,\sqrt{k}$
13	0.856	0.384	1.631	3.086	$(1.65 + .016\,k)\,(n-1)\,\sqrt{k}$
14	0.823	0.409	1.604	3.080	$(1.64 + .014\,k)\,(n-1)\,\sqrt{k}$
15	0.794	0.431	1.582	3.074	$(1.63 + .014\,k)\,(n-1)\,\sqrt{k}$

* formulas for even k— *for odd values of k use (k–1) in place of k in formula,*

Table A.6
Average and Standard Deviation Charts
Based on the Median Standard Deviation Statistic

Limits for **Subgroup Averages** *will be:*

$$UAL \ = \ \bar{\bar{X}} \ + \ A_{10} \ \tilde{s}$$
$$Central \ Line \ = \ \bar{\bar{X}}$$
$$LAL \ = \ \bar{\bar{X}} \ - \ A_{10} \ \tilde{s}$$

Limits for **Subgroup Standard Deviation Statistics** *will be:*

$$USDL \ = \ B_{10} \ \tilde{s}$$
$$Central \ Line \ = \ \tilde{s}$$
$$LSDL \ = \ B_9 \ \tilde{s}$$

While **Natural Process Limits for individual values** *may be obtained from:*

$$UNPL \ = \ \bar{\bar{X}} \ + \ E_6 \ \tilde{s}$$
$$Central \ Line \ = \ \bar{\bar{X}}$$
$$LNPL \ = \ \bar{\bar{X}} \ - \ E_6 \ \tilde{s}$$

where

$$A_{10} \ = \ \frac{3}{c_6 \ \sqrt{n}}$$

$$B_9 \ = \ \frac{c_4 - 3 \ \sqrt{1 - (c_4)^2}}{c_6} \qquad B_{10} \ = \ \frac{c_4 + 3 \ \sqrt{1 - (c_4)^2}}{c_6}$$

$$E_6 \ = \ \frac{3}{c_6}$$

Table A.7

Critical Values for Student's *t* Distribution

Tabled values are those critical values, t_α,
which have an upper-tail probability of exceedence of α.

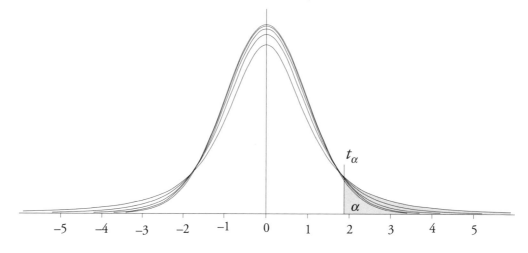

Student's *t* Distribution for 2, 4, 8, 16, & 32 Degrees of Freedom

d.f.	$\alpha = 0.10$	$\alpha = 0.05$	$\alpha = 0.025$	$\alpha = 0.01$	$\alpha = 0.005$
1	3.078	6.314	12.706	31.821	63.657
2	1.886	2.920	4.303	6.965	9.925
3	1.638	2.353	3.182	4.541	5.841
4	1.533	2.132	2.776	3.474	4.604
5	1.476	2.015	2.571	3.365	4.032
6	1.440	1.943	2.447	3.143	3.707
7	1.415	1.895	2.365	2.998	3.499
8	1.397	1.860	2.306	2.896	3.355
9	1.383	1.833	2.262	2.821	3.250
10	1.372	1.812	2.228	2.764	3.169
11	1.363	1.796	2.201	2.718	3.106
12	1.356	1.782	2.179	2.681	3.055
13	1.350	1.771	2.160	2.650	3.012
14	1.345	1.761	2.145	2.624	2.977
15	1.341	1.753	2.131	2.602	2.947

Table A.7

Critical Values for Student's *t* Distribution

Tabled values are those critical values, t_α, which have an upper-tail probability of exceedence of α.

d.f.	$\alpha = 0.10$	$\alpha = 0.05$	$\alpha = 0.025$	$\alpha = 0.01$	$\alpha = 0.005$
16	1.337	1.746	2.120	2.583	2.921
17	1.333	1.740	2.110	2.567	2.898
18	1.330	1.734	2.101	2.552	2.878
19	1.328	1.729	2.093	2.539	2.861
20	1.325	1.725	2.086	2.528	2.845
21	1.323	1.721	2.080	2.518	2.831
22	1.321	1.717	2.074	2.508	2.819
23	1.319	1.714	2.069	2.500	2.807
24	1.318	1.711	2.064	2.492	2.797
25	1.316	1.708	2.060	2.485	2.787
26	1.315	1.706	2.056	2.479	2.779
27	1.314	1.703	2.052	2.473	2.771
28	1.313	1.701	2.048	2.467	2.763
29	1.311	1.699	2.045	2.462	2.756
30	1.310	1.697	2.043	2.459	2.750
35	1.306	1.690	2.030	2.438	2.724
40	1.303	1.684	2.021	2.423	2.704
45	1.301	1.679	2.014	2.412	2.690
50	1.299	1.676	2.009	2.403	2.678
60	1.296	1.671	2.001	2.392	2.660
70	1.294	1.667	1.994	2.381	2.648
80	1.292	1.664	1.990	2.374	2.639
90	1.291	1.662	1.987	2.368	2.632
100	1.290	1.660	1.984	2.364	2.626
200	1.286	1.652	1.972	2.345	2.601
500	1.283	1.648	1.965	2.334	2.586
Z	1.282	1.645	1.960	2.326	2.576

Table A.8
Percentiles of Chi-Square Distributions

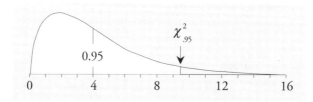

A Chi-Square distribution with 4 degrees of freedom
will have 95 percent of its area to the left of 9.49.

Area to the left of tabled value

d.f.	.005	.01	.025	.05	.10	.90	.95	.975	.99	.995
1	0.00004	0.00016	0.00098	0.0039	0.0158	2.71	3.84	5.02	6.63	7.88
2	0.010	0.020	0.051	0.103	0.211	4.61	5.99	7.38	9.21	10.60
3	0.072	0.115	0.216	0.352	0.584	6.25	7.81	9.35	11.34	12.84
4	0.207	0.297	0.484	0.711	1.064	7.78	9.49	11.14	13.28	14.86
5	0.412	0.554	0.831	1.145	1.610	9.24	11.07	12.83	15.09	16.75
6	0.676	0.872	1.237	1.635	2.204	10.64	12.59	14.45	16.81	18.55
7	0.989	1.239	1.690	2.167	2.833	12.02	14.07	16.01	18.48	20.28
8	1.344	1.646	2.180	2.733	3.490	13.36	15.51	17.53	20.09	21.95
9	1.735	2.088	2.700	3.325	4.168	14.68	16.92	19.02	21.67	23.59
10	2.156	2.558	3.247	3.940	4.865	15.99	18.31	20.48	23.21	25.19
11	2.603	3.053	3.816	4.575	5.578	17.27	19.68	21.92	24.73	26.76
12	3.074	3.571	4.404	5.226	6.304	18.55	21.03	23.34	26.22	28.30
13	3.565	4.107	5.009	5.892	7.042	19.81	22.36	24.74	27.69	29.82
14	4.075	4.660	5.629	6.571	7.790	21.06	23.68	26.12	29.14	31.32
15	4.601	5.229	6.262	7.261	8.547	22.31	25.00	27.49	30.58	32.80
16	5.142	5.812	6.908	7.962	9.312	23.54	26.30	28.85	32.00	34.27
17	5.697	6.408	7.564	8.672	10.09	24.77	27.59	30.19	33.41	35.74
18	6.265	7.015	8.231	9.390	10.86	25.99	28.87	31.53	34.81	37.16
19	6.844	7.633	8.907	10.12	11.65	27.20	30.14	32.85	36.19	38.58
20	7.434	8.260	9.591	10.85	12.44	28.41	31.41	34.17	37.57	40.00
21	8.034	8.897	10.28	11.59	13.24	29.62	32.67	35.48	38.93	41.40
22	8.643	9.542	10.98	12.34	14.04	30.81	33.92	36.78	40.29	42.80
23	9.260	10.20	11.69	13.09	14.85	32.01	35.17	38.08	41.64	44.18
24	9.886	10.86	12.40	13.85	15.66	33.20	36.42	39.36	42.98	45.56
25	10.52	11.52	13.12	14.61	16.47	34.38	37.65	40.65	44.31	46.93
26	11.16	12.20	13.84	15.38	17.29	35.56	38.89	41.92	45.64	48.29
27	11.81	12.88	14.57	16.15	18.11	36.74	40.11	43.19	46.96	49.65
28	12.46	13.56	15.31	16.93	18.94	37.92	41.34	44.46	48.28	50.99
29	13.12	14.26	16.05	17.71	19.77	39.09	42.56	45.76	49.59	52.34
30	13.79	14.95	16.79	18.49	20.60	40.25	43.77	46.98	50.89	53.67
32	15.09	16.33	18.28	20.07	22.28	42.58	46.19	49.48	53.51	56.37
34	16.46	17.76	19.79	21.66	23.96	44.89	48.60	51.97	56.08	59.00
36	17.85	19.21	21.32	23.27	25.65	47.20	50.99	54.44	58.64	61.62
38	19.25	20.67	22.87	24.88	27.35	49.50	53.38	56.90	61.18	64.22
40	20.67	22.14	24.42	26.51	29.06	51.80	55.75	59.35	63.71	66.80

Table A.8

Percentiles of Chi-Square Distributions

d.f.	.005	.01	.025	.05	.10	.90	.95	.975	.99	.995
42	22.10	23.63	25.99	28.14	30.77	54.08	58.12	61.78	66.22	69.37
44	23.55	25.12	27.56	29.79	32.49	56.36	60.48	64.20	68.73	71.93
46	25.01	26.63	29.15	31.44	34.22	58.63	62.83	66.62	71.22	74.47
48	26.48	28.15	30.75	33.10	35.95	60.90	65.17	69.03	73.70	77.00
50	27.96	29.68	32.35	34.76	37.69	63.16	67.50	71.42	76.17	79.52
55	31.70	33.55	36.39	38.96	42.06	68.79	73.31	77.38	82.31	85.78
60	35.50	37.47	40.47	43.19	46.46	74.39	79.08	83.30	88.40	91.98
65	39.35	41.42	44.60	47.45	50.89	79.97	84.82	89.18	94.44	98.13
70	43.25	45.42	48.75	51.74	55.33	85.52	90.53	95.03	100.4	104.2
75	47.18	49.46	52.93	56.05	59.80	91.06	96.21	100.8	106.4	110.3
80	51.15	53.52	57.15	60.39	64.28	96.57	101.9	106.6	112.3	116.3
85	55.14	57.62	61.38	64.75	68.78	102.1	107.5	112.4	118.2	122.3
90	59.17	61.74	65.64	69.13	73.29	107.6	113.1	118.1	124.1	128.3
95	63.22	65.88	69.92	73.52	77.82	113.0	118.7	123.9	130.0	134.3
100	67.30	70.05	74.22	77.93	82.36	118.5	124.3	129.6	135.8	140.2
110	75.53	78.44	82.86	86.79	91.47	129.4	135.5	140.9	147.4	152.0
120	83.83	86.91	91.57	95.7	100.6	140.2	146.6	152.2	159.0	163.7

For large degrees of freedom (*d.f.*)
the Chi-Square Percentiles with area *P* to the left
may be approximated by:

$$\chi_p^2 = d.f. \left\{ 1 - \frac{2}{9\,d.f.} + z_p \sqrt{\frac{2}{9\,d.f.}} \right\}^3$$

P	.005	.01	.025	.05	.10	.90	.95	.975	.99	.995
z_p	−2.576	−2.326	−1.960	−1.645	−1.282	1.282	1.645	1.960	2.326	2.576

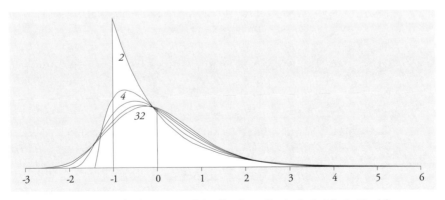

Standardized Chi-Square Distributions for 2, 4, 8, 16, & 32 *d.f.*

Table A.9

Overall Alpha-Levels for AVERAGE Charts

Used with Finite Data Sets Consisting of k Subgroups of Size n

Alpha	$n = 2$	$n = 3$	$n = 4$	$n = 5$	$n = 6$	$n = 7$	$n = 8$	$n = 9$	$n = 10$
$k = 2$	0.042	0.011	0.005	0.003	0.002	0.0010	0.0009	0.0007	0.0005
$k = 3$	0.059	0.022	0.012	0.008	0.006	0.005	0.004	0.003	0.003
$k = 4$	0.063	0.026	0.016	0.011	0.009	0.008	0.007	0.006	0.006
$k = 5$	0.066	0.029	0.018	0.014	0.012	0.011	0.009	0.009	0.008
$k = 6$	0.068	0.032	0.022	0.017	0.014	0.014	0.012	0.011	0.011
$k = 7$	0.070	0.035	0.025	0.020	0.017	0.015	0.014	0.013	0.013
$k = 8$	0.071	0.038	0.027	0.023	0.020	0.018	0.016	0.015	0.015
$k = 9$	0.074	0.040	0.030	0.025	0.022	0.019	0.017	0.017	0.016
$k = 10$	0.076	0.042	0.032	0.028	0.024	0.022	0.021	0.019	0.019
$k = 12$	0.080	0.048	0.039	0.033	0.028	0.026	0.024	0.023	0.023
$k = 14$	0.084	0.052	0.043	0.037	0.031	0.031	0.029	0.026	0.027
$k = 15$	0.086	0.055	0.046	0.039	0.034	0.032	0.030	0.028	0.029
$k = 16$	0.088	0.057	0.047	0.041	0.035	0.035	0.033	0.031	0.031
$k = 18$	0.093	0.064	0.051	0.045	0.040	0.040	0.037	0.035	0.035
$k = 20$	0.097	0.064	0.056	0.049	0.043	0.045	0.042	0.039	0.038
$k = 21$	0.099	0.066	0.056	0.051	0.045	0.048	0.043	0.040	0.041
$k = 24$	0.105	0.072	0.063	0.059	0.053	0.055	0.050	0.048	0.049
$k = 25$	0.108	0.073	0.065	0.059	0.054	0.057	0.052	0.050	0.050
$k = 27$	0.112	0.076	0.069	0.063	0.059	0.062	0.056	0.054	0.053
$k = 28$	0.114	0.078	0.071	0.065	0.061	0.065	0.059	0.057	0.055
$k = 30$	0.119	0.084	0.076	0.069	0.064	0.070	0.064	0.061	0.060
$k = 32$	0.120	0.085	0.079	0.074	0.069	0.076	0.069	0.066	0.064
$k = 35$	0.125	0.093	0.086	0.080	0.076	0.084	0.075	0.072	0.070
$k = 36$	0.127	0.095	0.088	0.081	0.077	0.086	0.077	0.074	0.072
$k = 40$	0.132	0.103	0.096	0.090	0.087	0.094	0.087	0.082	0.081
$k = 42$	0.135	0.108	0.100	0.095	0.091	0.099	0.093	0.086	0.086
$k = 45$	0.140	0.114	0.105	0.101	0.098	0.106	0.098	0.094	0.091
$k = 48$	0.145	0.118	0.109	0.106	0.105	0.113	0.104	0.100	0.098
$k = 49$	0.148	0.121	0.111	0.109	0.109	0.114	0.105	0.102	0.101
$k = 50$	0.149	0.122	0.113	0.110	0.111	0.116	0.107	0.104	0.102
$k = 54$	0.155	0.130	0.122	0.120	0.120	0.126	0.116	0.112	0.111
$k = 56$	0.159	0.134	0.126	0.123	0.124	0.131	0.121	0.117	0.115
$k = 60$	0.167	0.143	0.135	0.131	0.132	0.141	0.131	0.128	0.123

Table A.10

Overall Alpha-Levels for RANGE Charts

Used with Finite Data Sets Consisting of *k* Subgroups of Size *n*

Alpha	n = 2	n = 3	n = 4	n = 5	n = 6	n = 7	n = 8	n = 9	n = 10
k = 2	0.0000	0.0000	0.0000	0.0000	0.0000	0.0000	0.0000	0.0000	0.0000
k = 3	0.0000	0.0007	0.0010	0.0010	0.0008	0.0009	0.0009	0.0009	0.0008
k = 4	0.006	0.006	0.004	0.004	0.003	0.003	0.003	0.003	0.003
k = 5	0.017	0.011	0.009	0.008	0.007	0.006	0.006	0.006	0.006
k = 6	0.027	0.017	0.013	0.012	0.011	0.010	0.010	0.010	0.010
k = 7	0.037	0.023	0.018	0.016	0.015	0.013	0.013	0.013	0.013
k = 8	0.046	0.029	0.022	0.021	0.018	0.017	0.016	0.016	0.016
k = 9	0.057	0.034	0.027	0.024	0.022	0.019	0.019	0.018	0.018
k = 10	0.065	0.040	0.032	0.029	0.026	0.023	0.023	0.022	0.022
k = 12	0.084	0.051	0.041	0.038	0.033	0.030	0.029	0.027	0.026
k = 14	0.102	0.063	0.051	0.045	0.037	0.038	0.035	0.034	0.033
k = 15	0.111	0.068	0.056	0.048	0.042	0.040	0.038	0.035	0.034
k = 16	0.119	0.074	0.058	0.052	0.045	0.044	0.042	0.039	0.037
k = 18	0.136	0.085	0.066	0.057	0.053	0.051	0.048	0.045	0.043
k = 20	0.152	0.093	0.074	0.065	0.058	0.058	0.055	0.051	0.050
k = 21	0.159	0.098	0.076	0.067	0.062	0.061	0.058	0.053	0.051
k = 24	0.184	0.114	0.086	0.078	0.073	0.073	0.068	0.065	0.061
k = 25	0.192	0.117	0.090	0.080	0.075	0.076	0.070	0.068	0.063
k = 27	0.207	0.126	0.096	0.088	0.083	0.084	0.079	0.074	0.069
k = 28	0.215	0.131	0.099	0.092	0.085	0.088	0.082	0.077	0.073
k = 30	0.230	0.141	0.107	0.096	0.092	0.096	0.089	0.083	0.079
k = 32	0.243	0.150	0.112	0.104	0.099	0.102	0.095	0.090	0.086
k = 35	0.262	0.164	0.123	0.111	0.111	0.114	0.105	0.099	0.094
k = 36	0.267	0.169	0.128	0.114	0.114	0.116	0.107	0.102	0.097
k = 40	0.292	0.189	0.140	0.128	0.126	0.132	0.121	0.116	0.109
k = 42	0.304	0.197	0.145	0.134	0.131	0.138	0.127	0.121	0.114
k = 45	0.322	0.208	0.156	0.143	0.142	0.147	0.136	0.130	0.123
k = 48	0.340	0.219	0.167	0.152	0.152	0.158	0.146	0.141	0.133
k = 49	0.346	0.223	0.169	0.155	0.156	0.160	0.149	0.143	0.135
k = 50	0.351	0.228	0.173	0.157	0.157	0.163	0.154	0.147	0.137
k = 54	0.374	0.245	0.186	0.169	0.170	0.178	0.167	0.158	0.147
k = 56	0.384	0.251	0.193	0.175	0.176	0.184	0.172	0.162	0.153
k = 60	0.405	0.267	0.205	0.187	0.188	0.199	0.185	0.176	0.164

Table A.11

Quick Scale Factors for Range-Based ANOM

$\alpha = 0.10$ *factors* $ANOM_{.10}$ *for use with the Average Range Statistic*

$ANOM_{.10}$	$n=2$	$n=3$	$n=4$	$n=5$	$n=6$	$n=7$	$n=8$	$n=9$	$n=10$
$k=2$	1.164	0.487	0.322	0.247	0.203	0.174	0.153	0.137	0.125
$k=3$	1.516	0.678	0.455	0.351	0.289	0.249	0.219	0.197	0.180
$k=4$	1.606	0.747	0.507	0.393	0.324	0.279	0.247	0.222	0.202
$k=5$	1.658	0.791	0.540	0.419	0.348	0.299	0.265	0.238	0.217
$k=6$	1.693	0.821	0.563	0.439	0.364	0.314	0.278	0.250	0.228
$k=7$	1.721	0.845	0.582	0.454	0.377	0.322	0.284	0.255	0.233
$k=8$	1.738	0.863	0.596	0.466	0.387	0.331	0.292	0.263	0.240
$n=9$	1.759	0.881	0.609	0.477	0.396	0.336	0.296	0.267	0.244
$k=10$	1.774	0.892	0.620	0.485	0.399	0.344	0.303	0.272	0.248
$k=12$	1.799	0.915	0.636	0.498	0.411	0.355	0.312	0.281	0.256
$k=14$	1.822	0.932	0.650	0.506	0.419	0.363	0.320	0.287	0.262
$k=15$	1.831	0.941	0.656	0.511	0.424	0.365	0.322	0.290	0.264
$k=16$	1.838	0.947	0.659	0.516	0.426	0.369	0.326	0.293	0.267
$k=18$	1.857	0.960	0.669	0.522	0.433	0.376	0.331	0.298	0.272
$k=20$	1.871	0.964	0.677	0.529	0.438	0.382	0.337	0.302	0.276
$k=21$	1.878	0.970	0.680	0.531	0.441	0.384	0.338	0.304	0.277
$k=24$	1.894	0.982	0.688	0.541	0.448	0.391	0.345	0.311	0.283
$k=25$	1.901	0.986	0.692	0.542	0.450	0.393	0.346	0.311	0.284
$k=27$	1.912	0.990	0.696	0.546	0.455	0.397	0.349	0.314	0.287
$k=28$	1.918	0.995	0.699	0.549	0.457	0.399	0.351	0.316	0.288
$k=30$	1.927	1.002	0.705	0.553	0.461	0.402	0.355	0.319	0.290
$k=32$	1.930	1.005	0.710	0.558	0.464	0.405	0.358	0.321	0.293
$k=35$	1.938	1.014	0.717	0.563	0.469	0.410	0.361	0.325	0.296
$k=36$	1.940	1.017	0.719	0.564	0.470	0.412	0.362	0.326	0.297
$k=40$	1.950	1.026	0.726	0.571	0.475	0.416	0.367	0.330	0.301
$k=42$	1.954	1.032	0.729	0.573	0.478	0.418	0.370	0.332	0.303
$k=45$	1.963	1.038	0.734	0.578	0.482	0.421	0.372	0.334	0.305
$k=48$	1.971	1.043	0.737	0.581	0.486	0.424	0.375	0.337	0.307
$k=49$	1.974	1.045	0.739	0.583	0.487	0.425	0.375	0.338	0.308
$k=50$	1.976	1.046	0.740	0.583	0.488	0.426	0.376	0.338	0.309
$k=54$	1.987	1.054	0.745	0.588	0.492	0.430	0.379	0.341	0.311
$k=56$	1.992	1.057	0.748	0.590	0.494	0.432	0.381	0.343	0.312
$k=60$	2.002	1.065	0.752	0.594	0.497	0.435	0.385	0.346	0.315

ANOM Detection Limits are: *Grand Average* $\pm$ $ANOM_{.10}\ \overline{R}$

Table A.11

Quick Scale Factors for Range-Based ANOM

$\alpha = 0.05$ *factors ANOM$_{.05}$ for use with the Average Range Statistic*

ANOM$_{.05}$	n=2	n=3	n=4	n=5	n-6	n-7	n=8	n=9	n=10
k=2	1.716	0.636	0.406	0.307	0.250	0.213	0.187	0.167	0.152
k=3	2.012	0.831	0.544	0.414	0.338	0.290	0.255	0.229	0.208
k=4	2.027	0.887	0.591	0.453	0.372	0.320	0.282	0.253	0.230
k=5	2.030	0.920	0.619	0.478	0.394	0.339	0.299	0.268	0.245
k=6	2.031	0.947	0.641	0.496	0.409	0.352	0.311	0.280	0.255
k=7	2.033	0.963	0.657	0.509	0.422	0.359	0.317	0.285	0.260
k=8	2.031	0.977	0.669	0.519	0.431	0.368	0.325	0.292	0.266
n=9	2.037	0.990	0.680	0.528	0.439	0.373	0.328	0.295	0.269
k=10	2.041	1.000	0.688	0.537	0.442	0.379	0.335	0.301	0.275
k=12	2.046	1.019	0.704	0.550	0.453	0.389	0.343	0.308	0.281
k=14	2.054	1.030	0.716	0.557	0.459	0.397	0.350	0.314	0.287
k=15	2.057	1.038	0.720	0.560	0.462	0.399	0.353	0.316	0.289
k=16	2.058	1.041	0.723	0.564	0.464	0.402	0.356	0.320	0.292
k=18	2.068	1.056	0.730	0.570	0.471	0.409	0.361	0.324	0.296
k=20	2.072	1.054	0.738	0.577	0.475	0.415	0.366	0.328	0.300
k=21	2.075	1.058	0.739	0.578	0.478	0.417	0.367	0.329	0.301
k=24	2.086	1.067	0.748	0.587	0.485	0.423	0.373	0.336	0.307
k=25	2.092	1.068	0.751	0.588	0.486	0.425	0.374	0.337	0.308
k=27	2.101	1.073	0.755	0.591	0.491	0.428	0.378	0.340	0.310
k=28	2.102	1.076	0.757	0.594	0.493	0.430	0.380	0.341	0.311
k=30	2.106	1.082	0.762	0.597	0.495	0.434	0.383	0.344	0.314
k=32	2.103	1.086	0.766	0.601	0.498	0.438	0.386	0.346	0.316
k=35	2.106	1.095	0.774	0.605	0.502	0.442	0.390	0.350	0.319
k=36	2.108	1.098	0.774	0.607	0.504	0.444	0.391	0.350	0.320
k=40	2.114	1.106	0.781	0.612	0.511	0.447	0.395	0.354	0.323
k=42	2.116	1.110	0.783	0.614	0.513	0.449	0.397	0.356	0.325
k=45	2.121	1.114	0.786	0.617	0.517	0.452	0.400	0.359	0.328
k=48	2.126	1.118	0.791	0.623	0.521	0.455	0.403	0.361	0.330
k=49	2.126	1.121	0.791	0.624	0.523	0.456	0.403	0.362	0.330
k=50	2.131	1.12	0.793	0.625	0.523	0.456	0.404	0.362	0.331
k=54	2.139	1.13	0.798	0.627	0.528	0.460	0.407	0.365	0.334
k=56	2.143	1.13	0.801	0.629	0.529	0.462	0.409	0.367	0.335
k=60	2.151	1.14	0.806	0.632	0.533	0.465	0.411	0.370	0.337

ANOM Detection Limits are: *Grand Average* $\pm$ *ANOM$_{.05}$* $\overline{R}$

Table A.11

Quick Scale Factors for Range-Based ANOM

$\alpha = 0.01$ *factors ANOM*$_{.01}$ *for use with the Average Range Statistic*

ANOM$_{.01}$	n=2	n=3	n=4	n=5	n=6	n=7	n=8	n=9	n=10
k=2	3.97	1.054	0.618	0.448	0.357	0.300	0.260	0.231	0.209
k=3	3.64	1.214	0.751	0.555	0.448	0.380	0.332	0.296	0.268
k=4	3.25	1.228	0.783	0.586	0.478	0.405	0.356	0.318	0.289
k=5	3.04	1.230	0.797	0.605	0.493	0.422	0.370	0.332	0.303
k=6	2.91	1.230	0.812	0.620	0.503	0.434	0.381	0.342	0.311
k=7	2.82	1.235	0.818	0.626	0.512	0.439	0.388	0.346	0.316
k=8	2.75	1.237	0.826	0.634	0.520	0.446	0.393	0.354	0.321
n=9	2.70	1.234	0.833	0.641	0.526	0.448	0.395	0.355	0.324
k=10	2.67	1.234	0.839	0.646	0.530	0.457	0.401	0.360	0.328
k=12	2.61	1.245	0.850	0.655	0.536	0.460	0.407	0.365	0.334
k=14	2.58	1.248	0.854	0.661	0.540	0.468	0.413	0.370	0.338
k=15	2.57	1.248	0.860	0.665	0.545	0.470	0.415	0.372	0.340
k=16	2.55	1.248	0.854	0.667	0.546	0.475	0.418	0.374	0.341
k=18	2.53	1.256	0.857	0.670	0.550	0.478	0.423	0.379	0.346
k=20	2.52	1.252	0.867	0.673	0.556	0.483	0.428	0.383	0.349
k=21	2.52	1.253	0.865	0.672	0.559	0.486	0.429	0.383	0.349
k=24	2.50	1.26	0.868	0.680	0.564	0.491	0.436	0.389	0.354
k=25	2.50	1.26	0.872	0.681	0.564	0.492	0.437	0.389	0.355
k=27	2.50	1.26	0.875	0.684	0.565	0.495	0.438	0.392	0.357
k=28	2.49	1.26	0.874	0.687	0.567	0.498	0.440	0.394	0.360
k=30	2.50	1.26	0.881	0.690	0.572	0.499	0.443	0.397	0.363
k=32	2.49	1.26	0.88	0.69	0.577	0.504	0.445	0.397	0.363
k=35	2.48	1.27	0.89	0.70	0.579	0.506	0.448	0.402	0.364
k=36	2.48	1.27	0.89	0.70	0.581	0.506	0.447	0.402	0.366
k=40	2.48	1.28	0.90	0.70	0.584	0.513	0.453	0.404	0.369
k=42	2.48	1.28	0.90	0.70	0.587	0.513	0.455	0.406	0.369
k=45	2.47	1.28	0.90	0.71	0.59	0.517	0.459	0.411	0.372
k=48	2.47	1.28	0.90	0.71	0.59	0.521	0.461	0.413	0.375
k=49	2.47	1.29	0.90	0.71	0.59	0.522	0.462	0.413	0.376
k=50	2.46	1.29	0.90	0.72	0.60	0.521	0.464	0.414	0.376
k=54	2.47	1.30	0.91	0.72	0.60	0.524	0.467	0.416	0.379
k=56	2.46	1.30	0.91	0.72	0.60	0.527	0.469	0.418	0.380
k=60	2.46	1.31	0.92	0.72	0.60	0.529	0.472	0.421	0.382

ANOM Detection Limits are: *Grand Average* $\pm$ *ANOM*$_{.01}$ $\bar{R}$

Table A.12

Quick Scale Factors for Pooled Variance ANOM

$\alpha = 0.10$ *factors* H_2 *for use with the Pooled Variance Estimate of SD(X)*

H_2	k=2	k=3	k=4	k=5	k=6	k=7	k=8	k=9	k=10
n=2	1.460	1.824	1.892	1.929	1.956	1.977	1.998	2.007	2.026
n=3	0.870	1.188	1.295	1.363	1.407	1.443	1.474	1.497	1.523
n=4	0.686	0.955	1.061	1.123	1.168	1.208	1.235	1.261	1.281
n=5	0.588	0.829	0.922	0.980	1.025	1.060	1.088	1.111	1.129
n=6	0.523	0.740	0.827	0.885	0.924	0.958	0.981	1.006	1.024
n=7	0.476	0.676	0.756	0.811	0.849	0.881	0.904	0.926	0.943
n=8	0.440	0.627	0.703	0.754	0.790	0.820	0.842	0.863	0.880
n=9	0.412	0.585	0.659	0.707	0.742	0.770	0.791	0.811	0.827
n=10	0.387	0.553	0.622	0.668	0.701	0.728	0.750	0.768	0.783
n=12	0.350	0.501	0.564	0.606	0.637	0.662	0.682	0.698	0.711
n=15	0.311	0.444	0.502	0.540	0.568	0.589	0.607	0.623	0.635
n=20	0.266	0.382	0.433	0.466	0.488	0.509	0.525	0.539	0.549
n=30	0.216	0.310	0.351	0.379	0.397	0.414	0.427	0.439	0.447
n=40	0.186	0.267	0.303	0.327	0.343	0.357	0.368	0.378	0.385
n=50	0.166	0.238	0.269	0.291	0.306	0.318	0.328	0.337	0.343
n=60	0.152	0.216	0.245	0.264	0.278	0.289	0.298	0.307	0.312
n=80	0.130	0.187	0.212	0.229	0.241	0.250	0.258	0.266	0.270

H_2	k=11	k=12	k=13	k=14	k=15	k=16	k=17	k=18	k=19	k=20
n=2	2.036	2.045	2.058	2.065	2.070	2.081	2.092	2.103	2.106	2.116
n=3	1.541	1.553	1.573	1.587	1.595	1.610	1.621	1.631	1.641	1.649
n=4	1.301	1.315	1.333	1.342	1.357	1.367	1.379	1.387	1.396	1.404
n=5	1.148	1.164	1.180	1.189	1.201	1.211	1.221	1.231	1.240	1.250
n=6	1.039	1.055	1.069	1.079	1.093	1.102	1.110	1.119	1.127	1.135
n=7	0.957	0.974	0.987	0.996	1.008	1.016	1.024	1.031	1.039	1.046
n=8	0.893	0.909	0.920	0.928	0.939	0.947	0.954	0.964	0.971	0.978
n=9	0.839	0.854	0.865	0.872	0.882	0.892	0.899	0.909	0.916	0.922
n=10	0.794	0.808	0.818	0.827	0.837	0.846	0.853	0.862	0.868	0.874
n=12	0.721	0.737	0.746	0.755	0.763	0.772	0.778	0.786	0.792	0.798
n=15	0.645	0.658	0.667	0.674	0.682	0.690	0.695	0.702	0.708	0.713
n=20	0.558	0.569	0.577	0.583	0.590	0.596	0.601	0.607	0.612	0.616
n=30	0.454	0.463	0.469	0.474	0.480	0.485	0.489	0.494	0.498	0.502
n=40	0.392	0.400	0.405	0.410	0.414	0.419	0.423	0.426	0.429	0.433
n=50	0.350	0.356	0.361	0.365	0.369	0.374	0.377	0.379	0.383	0.386
n=60	0.319	0.324	0.329	0.332	0.336	0.340	0.343	0.345	0.348	0.351
n=80	0.276	0.280	0.285	0.288	0.291	0.294	0.297	0.299	0.301	0.304

ANOM Detection Limits are: *Grand Average* $\pm$ $H_2 s_p$

Table A.12

Quick Scale Factors for Pooled Variance ANOM

$\alpha = 0.05$ *factors* H_2 *for use with the Pooled Variance Estimate of SD(X)*

H_2	k=2	k=3	k=4	k=5	k=6	k=7	k=8	k=9	k=10
n=2	2.150	2.413	2.382	2.353	2.337	2.331	2.322	2.320	2.314
n=3	1.135	1.447	1.535	1.585	1.618	1.646	1.669	1.687	1.703
n=4	0.866	1.139	1.234	1.288	1.328	1.360	1.384	1.407	1.423
n=5	0.730	0.975	1.061	1.116	1.155	1.187	1.213	1.235	1.252
n=6	0.644	0.867	0.948	1.002	1.040	1.070	1.092	1.115	1.133
n=7	0.583	0.787	0.867	0.916	0.954	0.982	1.004	1.025	1.040
n=8	0.535	0.728	0.803	0.851	0.886	0.912	0.933	0.953	0.970
n=9	0.500	0.680	0.751	0.796	0.831	0.855	0.875	0.896	0.912
n=10	0.470	0.642	0.708	0.752	0.784	0.807	0.829	0.847	0.863
n=12	0.424	0.579	0.641	0.682	0.710	0.735	0.754	0.770	0.783
n=15	0.374	0.512	0.569	0.606	0.633	0.654	0.670	0.687	0.699
n=20	0.320	0.439	0.490	0.521	0.544	0.565	0.579	0.594	0.604
n=30	0.258	0.356	0.396	0.424	0.442	0.459	0.471	0.482	0.491
n=40	0.223	0.306	0.341	0.365	0.381	0.396	0.406	0.416	0.424
n=50	0.199	0.272	0.304	0.325	0.340	0.352	0.361	0.370	0.377
n=60	0.181	0.247	0.276	0.296	0.309	0.320	0.328	0.336	0.343
n=80	0.155	0.214	0.239	0.256	0.267	0.277	0.284	0.291	0.297

H_2	k=11	k=12	k=13	k=14	k=15	k=16	k=17	k=18	k=19	k=20
n=2	2.313	2.315	2.323	2.324	2.323	2.328	2.332	2.336	2.340	2.343
n=3	1.718	1.730	1.742	1.752	1.763	1.771	1.779	1.789	1.795	1.801
n=4	1.441	1.452	1.463	1.476	1.490	1.499	1.507	1.515	1.523	1.530
n=5	1.266	1.280	1.293	1.302	1.313	1.323	1.333	1.342	1.351	1.360
n=6	1.145	1.157	1.171	1.181	1.193	1.202	1.210	1.218	1.226	1.234
n=7	1.054	1.068	1.079	1.089	1.099	1.107	1.114	1.121	1.128	1.135
n=8	0.983	0.995	1.005	1.015	1.023	1.030	1.036	1.048	1.055	1.061
n=9	0.924	0.935	0.943	0.953	0.960	0.970	0.977	0.988	0.994	1.000
n=10	0.874	0.884	0.891	0.904	0.910	0.920	0.926	0.937	0.943	0.948
n=12	0.793	0.806	0.813	0.824	0.830	0.840	0.845	0.854	0.860	0.865
n=15	0.708	0.720	0.726	0.736	0.742	0.750	0.755	0.763	0.768	0.772
n=20	0.612	0.623	0.628	0.636	0.641	0.648	0.653	0.659	0.664	0.668
n=30	0.498	0.506	0.511	0.517	0.522	0.527	0.531	0.536	0.540	0.543
n=40	0.430	0.437	0.441	0.446	0.451	0.455	0.459	0.462	0.466	0.468
n=50	0.383	0.389	0.393	0.397	0.402	0.405	0.409	0.411	0.415	0.417
n=60	0.348	0.354	0.357	0.361	0.365	0.369	0.372	0.374	0.377	0.379
n=80	0.302	0.306	0.309	0.312	0.316	0.319	0.322	0.324	0.326	0.328

ANOM Detection Limits are: *Grand Average* $\pm\ H_2\,s_p$

Table A.12

Quick Scale Factors for Pooled Variance ANOM

$\alpha = 0.01$ *factors* H_2 *for use with the Pooled Variance Estimate of SD(X)*

H_2	$k=2$	$k=3$	$k=4$	$k=5$	$k=6$	$k=7$	$k=8$	$k=9$	$k=10$
$n=2$	4.960	4.336	3.797	3.510	3.331	3.208	3.122	3.060	3.012
$n=3$	1.878	2.112	2.105	2.102	2.098	2.095	2.095	2.096	2.098
$n=4$	1.312	1.568	1.624	1.650	1.671	1.688	1.702	1.716	1.722
$n=5$	1.063	1.304	1.371	1.412	1.437	1.460	1.478	1.493	1.502
$n=6$	0.915	1.140	1.209	1.252	1.282	1.308	1.321	1.342	1.354
$n=7$	0.815	1.028	1.097	1.139	1.170	1.194	1.212	1.228	1.237
$n=8$	0.745	0.942	1.011	1.053	1.082	1.108	1.123	1.139	1.153
$n=9$	0.688	0.874	0.943	0.981	1.013	1.036	1.054	1.070	1.083
$n=10$	0.644	0.821	0.887	0.926	0.954	0.977	1.000	1.011	1.023
$n=12$	0.577	0.738	0.799	0.836	0.863	0.887	0.913	0.917	0.927
$n=15$	0.505	0.650	0.705	0.741	0.767	0.786	0.816	0.818	0.827
$n=20$	0.428	0.555	0.605	0.636	0.657	0.679	0.703	0.706	0.714
$n=30$	0.344	0.448	0.488	0.515	0.533	0.550	0.568	0.573	0.580
$n=40$	0.296	0.384	0.419	0.443	0.459	0.473	0.487	0.493	0.499
$n=50$	0.263	0.340	0.372	0.393	0.408	0.421	0.431	0.438	0.444
$n=60$	0.239	0.307	0.337	0.356	0.370	0.381	0.389	0.397	0.403
$n=80$	0.204	0.266	0.291	0.308	0.320	0.330	0.337	0.344	0.349

H_2	$k=11$	$k=12$	$k=13$	$k=14$	$k=15$	$k=16$	$k=17$	$k=18$	$k=19$	$k=20$
$n=2$	2.973	2.945	2.921	2.903	2.883	2.876	2.861	2.852	2.842	2.840
$n=3$	2.103	2.101	2.106	2.110	2.108	2.118	2.121	2.123	2.125	2.127
$n=4$	1.737	1.745	1.749	1.759	1.766	1.774	1.778	1.783	1.788	1.793
$n=5$	1.519	1.529	1.536	1.543	1.547	1.560	1.565	1.573	1.582	1.590
$n=6$	1.367	1.372	1.386	1.395	1.403	1.414	1.419	1.424	1.431	1.438
$n=7$	1.254	1.264	1.276	1.283	1.291	1.299	1.304	1.308	1.313	1.319
$n=8$	1.168	1.176	1.187	1.193	1.200	1.206	1.211	1.222	1.228	1.233
$n=9$	1.096	1.103	1.113	1.118	1.124	1.137	1.141	1.152	1.157	1.162
$n=10$	1.035	1.041	1.050	1.060	1.066	1.078	1.082	1.092	1.097	1.102
$n=12$	0.936	0.949	0.957	0.967	0.972	0.983	0.987	0.996	1.000	1.005
$n=15$	0.836	0.847	0.855	0.863	0.868	0.877	0.882	0.889	0.893	0.897
$n=20$	0.722	0.732	0.738	0.746	0.750	0.758	0.762	0.768	0.772	0.775
$n=30$	0.587	0.594	0.599	0.605	0.609	0.615	0.619	0.623	0.627	0.629
$n=40$	0.506	0.512	0.516	0.521	0.525	0.530	0.533	0.537	0.540	0.542
$n=50$	0.450	0.455	0.459	0.463	0.467	0.471	0.474	0.477	0.480	0.482
$n=60$	0.409	0.413	0.417	0.420	0.424	0.428	0.431	0.433	0.436	0.438
$n=80$	0.354	0.358	0.361	0.364	0.367	0.370	0.373	0.375	0.378	0.379

ANOM Detection Limits are: *Grand Average* $\pm$ $H_2 s_p$

Table A.13

90th Percentiles for the F-Distribution

$\alpha = 0.10$

v_1 = Degrees of Freedom for the Numerator of the F-ratio

v_2	1	2	3	4	5	6	7	8	9	10
1	39.9	49.5	53.6	55.8	57.2	58.2	58.9	59.4	59.9	60.2
2	8.53	9.00	9.16	9.24	9.29	9.33	9.35	9.37	9.38	9.39
3	5.54	5.46	5.39	5.34	5.31	5.28	5.27	5.25	5.24	5.23
4	4.54	4.32	4.19	4.11	4.05	4.01	3.98	3.95	3.94	3.92
5	4.06	3.78	3.62	3.52	3.45	3.40	3.37	3.34	3.32	3.30
6	3.78	3.46	3.29	3.18	3.11	3.05	3.01	2.98	2.96	2.94
7	3.59	3.26	3.07	2.96	2.88	2.83	2.78	2.75	2.72	2.70
8	3.46	3.11	2.92	2.81	2.73	2.67	2.62	2.59	2.56	2.54
9	3.36	3.01	2.81	2.69	2.61	2.55	2.51	2.47	2.44	2.42
10	3.28	2.92	2.73	2.61	2.52	2.46	2.41	2.38	2.35	2.32
11	3.23	2.86	2.66	2.54	2.45	2.39	2.34	2.30	2.27	2.25
12	3.18	2.81	2.61	2.48	2.39	2.33	2.28	2.24	2.21	2.19
13	3.14	2.76	2.56	2.43	2.35	2.28	2.23	2.20	2.16	2.14
14	3.10	2.73	2.52	2.39	2.31	2.24	2.19	2.15	2.12	2.10
15	3.07	2.70	2.49	2.36	2.27	2.21	2.16	2.12	2.09	2.06
16	3.05	2.67	2.46	2.33	2.24	2.18	2.13	2.09	2.06	2.03
18	3.01	2.62	2.42	2.29	2.20	2.13	2.08	2.04	2.00	1.98
20	2.97	2.59	2.38	2.25	2.16	2.09	2.04	2.00	1.96	1.94
22	2.95	2.56	2.35	2.22	2.13	2.06	2.01	1.97	1.93	1.90
24	2.93	2.54	2.33	2.19	2.10	2.04	1.98	1.94	1.91	1.88
26	2.91	2.52	2.31	2.17	2.08	2.01	1.96	1.92	1.88	1.86
28	2.89	2.50	2.29	2.16	2.06	2.00	1.94	1.90	1.87	1.84
30	2.88	2.49	2.28	2.14	2.05	1.98	1.93	1.88	1.85	1.82
40	2.84	2.44	2.23	2.09	2.00	1.93	1.87	1.83	1.79	1.76
60	2.79	2.39	2.18	2.04	1.95	1.87	1.82	1.77	1.74	1.71
120	2.75	2.35	2.13	1.99	1.90	1.82	1.77	1.72	1.68	1.65
inf.	2.71	2.30	2.08	1.94	1.85	1.77	1.72	1.67	1.63	1.60

v_2 = Degrees of Freedom for the Denominator of the F-ratio.

Table A.13

90th Percentiles for the F-Distribution

$\alpha = 0.10$

v_1 = Degrees of Freedom for the Numerator of the F-ratio

v_2	12	15	20	24	30	40	60	120	inf.
1	60.7	61.2	61.7	62.0	62.3	62.5	62.8	63.1	63.3
2	9.41	9.42	9.44	9.45	9.46	9.47	9.47	9.48	9.49
3	5.22	5.20	5.18	5.18	5.17	5.16	5.15	5.14	5.13
4	3.90	3.87	3.84	3.83	3.82	3.80	3.79	3.78	3.76
5	3.27	3.24	3.21	3.19	3.17	3.16	3.14	3.12	3.10
6	2.90	2.87	2.84	2.82	2.80	2.78	2.76	2.74	2.72
7	2.67	2.63	2.59	2.58	2.56	2.54	2.51	2.49	2.47
8	2.50	2.46	2.42	2.40	2.38	2.36	2.34	2.32	2.29
9	2.38	2.34	2.30	2.28	2.25	2.23	2.21	2.18	2.16
10	2.28	2.24	2.20	2.18	2.16	2.13	2.11	2.08	2.06
11	2.21	2.17	2.12	2.10	2.08	2.05	2.03	2.00	1.97
12	2.15	2.10	2.06	2.04	2.01	1.99	1.96	1.93	1.90
13	2.10	2.05	2.01	1.98	1.96	1.93	1.90	1.88	1.85
14	2.05	2.01	1.96	1.94	1.91	1.89	1.86	1.83	1.80
15	2.02	1.97	1.92	1.90	1.87	1.85	1.82	1.79	1.76
16	1.99	1.94	1.89	1.87	1.84	1.81	1.78	1.75	1.72
18	1.93	1.89	1.84	1.81	1.78	1.75	1.72	1.69	1.66
20	1.89	1.84	1.79	1.77	1.74	1.71	1.68	1.64	1.61
22	1.86	1.81	1.76	1.73	1.70	1.67	1.64	1.60	1.57
24	1.83	1.78	1.73	1.70	1.67	1.64	1.61	1.57	1.53
26	1.81	1.76	1.71	1.68	1.65	1.61	1.58	1.54	1.50
28	1.79	1.74	1.69	1.66	1.63	1.59	1.56	1.52	1.48
30	1.77	1.72	1.67	1.64	1.61	1.57	1.54	1.50	1.46
40	1.71	1.66	1.61	1.57	1.54	1.51	1.47	1.42	1.38
60	1.66	1.60	1.54	1.51	1.48	1.44	1.40	1.35	1.29
120	1.60	1.55	1.48	1.45	1.41	1.37	1.32	1.26	1.19
inf.	1.55	1.49	1.42	1.38	1.34	1.30	1.24	1.17	1.00

v_2 = Degrees of Freedom for the Denominator of the F-ratio.

Table A.13

95th Percentiles for the F-Distribution

$$\alpha = 0.05$$

v_1 = Degrees of Freedom for the Numerator of the F-ratio

v_2	1	2	3	4	5	6	7	8	9	10
1	161.4	199.5	215.7	224.6	230.2	234.0	236.8	238.9	240.5	241.9
2	18.51	19.00	19.16	19.25	19.30	19.33	19.35	19.37	19.38	19.40
3	10.13	9.55	9.28	9.12	9.01	8.94	8.89	8.85	8.81	8.79
4	7.71	6.94	6.59	6.39	6.26	6.16	6.09	6.04	6.00	5.96
5	6.61	5.79	5.41	5.19	5.05	4.95	4.88	4.82	4.77	4.74
6	5.99	5.14	4.76	4.53	4.39	4.28	4.21	4.15	4.10	4.06
7	5.59	4.74	4.35	4.12	3.97	3.87	3.79	3.73	3.68	3.64
8	5.32	4.46	4.07	3.84	3.69	3.58	3.50	3.44	3.39	3.35
9	5.12	4.26	3.86	3.63	3.48	3.37	3.29	3.23	3.18	3.14
10	4.96	4.10	3.71	3.48	3.33	3.22	3.14	3.07	3.02	2.98
11	4.84	3.98	3.59	3.36	3.20	3.09	3.01	2.95	2.90	2.85
12	4.75	3.89	3.49	3.26	3.11	3.00	2.91	2.85	2.80	2.75
13	4.67	3.81	3.41	3.18	3.03	2.92	2.83	2.77	2.71	2.67
14	4.60	3.74	3.34	3.11	2.96	2.85	2.76	2.70	2.65	2.60
15	4.54	3.68	3.29	3.06	2.90	2.79	2.71	2.64	2.59	2.54
16	4.49	3.63	3.24	3.01	2.85	2.74	2.66	2.59	2.54	2.49
18	4.41	3.55	3.16	2.93	2.77	2.66	2.58	2.51	2.46	2.41
20	4.35	3.49	3.10	2.87	2.71	2.60	2.51	2.45	2.39	2.35
22	4.30	3.44	3.05	2.82	2.66	2.55	2.46	2.40	2.34	2.30
24	4.26	3.40	3.01	2.78	2.62	2.51	2.42	2.36	2.30	2.25
26	4.23	3.37	2.98	2.74	2.59	2.47	2.39	2.32	2.27	2.22
28	4.20	3.34	2.95	2.71	2.56	2.45	2.36	2.29	2.24	2.19
30	4.17	3.32	2.92	2.69	2.53	2.42	2.33	2.27	2.21	2.16
40	4.08	3.23	2.84	2.61	2.45	2.34	2.25	2.18	2.12	2.08
60	4.00	3.15	2.76	2.53	2.37	2.25	2.17	2.10	2.04	1.99
120	3.92	3.07	2.68	2.45	2.29	2.17	2.09	2.02	1.96	1.91
inf.	3.84	3.00	2.60	2.37	2.21	2.10	2.01	1.94	1.88	1.83

v_2 = Degrees of Freedom for the Denominator of the F-ratio.

Table A.13

95th Percentiles for the F-Distribution

$$\alpha = 0.05$$

	v_1 – Degrees of Freedom for the Numerator of the F-ratio								
	12	15	20	24	30	40	60	120	inf.
v_2									
1	43.9	245.9	248.0	249.1	250.1	251.1	252.2	253.3	254.3
2	9.41	19.43	19.45	19.45	19.46	19.47	19.48	19.49	19.50
3	8.74	8.70	8.66	8.64	8.62	8.59	8.57	8.55	8.53
4	5.91	5.86	5.80	5.77	5.75	5.72	5.69	5.66	5.63
5	4.68	4.62	4.56	4.53	4.50	4.46	4.43	4.40	4.36
6	4.00	3.94	3.87	3.84	3.81	3.77	3.74	3.70	3.67
7	3.57	3.51	3.44	3.41	3.38	3.34	3.30	3.27	3.23
8	3.28	3.22	3.15	3.12	3.08	3.04	3.01	2.97	2.93
9	3.07	3.01	2.94	2.90	2.86	2.83	2.79	2.75	2.71
10	2.91	2.85	2.77	2.74	2.70	2.66	2.62	2.58	2.54
11	2.79	2.72	2.65	2.61	2.57	2.53	2.49	2.45	2.40
12	2.69	2.62	2.54	2.51	2.47	2.43	2.38	2.34	2.30
13	2.60	2.53	2.46	2.42	2.38	2.34	2.30	2.25	2.21
14	2.53	2.46	2.39	2.35	2.31	2.27	2.22	2.18	2.13
15	2.48	2.40	2.33	2.29	2.25	2.20	2.16	2.11	2.07
16	2.42	2.35	2.28	2.24	2.19	2.15	2.11	2.06	2.01
18	2.34	2.27	2.19	2.15	2.11	2.06	2.02	1.97	1.92
20	2.28	2.20	2.12	2.08	2.04	1.99	1.95	1.90	1.84
22	2.23	2.15	2.07	2.03	1.98	1.94	1.89	1.84	1.78
24	2.18	2.11	2.03	1.98	1.94	1.89	1.84	1.79	1.73
26	2.15	2.07	1.99	1.95	1.90	1.85	1.80	1.75	1.69
28	2.12	2.04	1.96	1.91	1.87	1.82	1.77	1.71	1.65
30	2.09	2.01	1.93	1.89	1.84	1.79	1.74	1.68	1.62
40	2.00	1.92	1.84	1.79	1.74	1.69	1.64	1.58	1.51
60	1.92	1.84	1.75	1.70	1.65	1.59	1.53	1.47	1.39
120	1.83	1.75	1.66	1.61	1.55	1.50	1.43	1.35	1.25
inf.	1.75	1.67	1.57	1.52	1.46	1.39	1.32	1.22	1.00

v_2 = Degrees of Freedom for the Denominator of the F-ratio.

Table A.13

99th Percentiles for the F-Distribution

$$\alpha = 0.01$$

v_1 = Degrees of Freedom for the Numerator of the F-ratio

v_2	1	2	3	4	5	6	7	8	9	10
1	4052.	5000.	5403.	5625.	5764.	5859.	5928.	5981.	6022.	6056.
2	98.5	99.0	99.2	99.3	99.3	99.3	99.4	99.4	99.4	99.4
3	34.1	30.8	29.5	28.7	28.2	27.9	27.7	27.5	27.4	27.2
4	21.2	18.0	16.7	16.0	15.5	15.2	15.0	14.8	14.7	14.6
5	16.3	13.3	12.1	11.4	11.0	10.7	10.5	10.3	10.2	10.1
6	13.8	10.9	9.78	9.15	8.75	8.47	8.26	8.10	7.98	7.87
7	12.3	9.55	8.45	7.85	7.46	7.19	6.99	6.84	6.72	6.62
8	11.3	8.65	7.59	7.01	6.63	6.37	6.18	6.03	5.91	5.81
9	10.6	8.02	6.99	6.42	6.06	5.80	5.61	5.47	5.35	5.26
10	10.0	7.56	6.55	5.99	5.64	5.39	5.20	5.06	4.94	4.85
11	9.65	7.21	6.22	5.67	5.32	5.07	4.89	4.74	4.63	4.54
12	9.33	6.93	5.95	5.41	5.06	4.82	4.64	4.50	4.39	4.30
13	9.07	6.70	5.74	5.21	4.86	4.62	4.44	4.30	4.19	4.10
14	8.86	6.51	5.56	5.04	4.69	4.46	4.28	4.14	4.03	3.94
15	8.68	6.36	5.42	4.89	4.56	4.32	4.14	4.00	3.89	3.80
16	8.53	6.23	5.29	4.77	4.44	4.20	4.03	3.89	3.78	3.69
18	8.29	6.01	5.09	4.58	4.25	4.01	3.84	3.71	3.60	3.51
20	8.10	5.85	4.94	4.43	4.10	3.87	3.70	3.56	3.46	3.37
22	7.95	5.72	4.82	4.31	3.99	3.76	3.59	3.45	3.35	3.26
24	7.82	5.61	4.72	4.22	3.90	3.67	3.50	3.36	3.26	3.17
26	7.72	5.53	4.64	4.14	3.82	3.59	3.42	3.29	3.18	3.09
28	7.64	5.45	4.57	4.07	3.75	3.53	3.36	3.23	3.12	3.03
30	7.56	5.39	4.51	4.02	3.70	3.47	3.30	3.17	3.07	2.98
40	7.31	5.18	4.31	3.83	3.51	3.29	3.12	2.99	2.89	2.80
60	7.08	4.98	4.13	3.65	3.34	3.12	2.95	2.82	2.72	2.63
120	6.85	4.79	3.95	3.48	3.17	2.96	2.79	2.66	2.56	2.47
inf.	6.63	4.61	3.78	3.32	3.02	2.80	2.64	2.51	2.41	2.32

v_2 = Degrees of Freedom for the Denominator of the F-ratio.

Table A.13

99th Percentiles for the F-Distribution

$\alpha = 0.01$

v_1 = Degrees of Freedom for the Numerator of the F-ratio

v_2	12	15	20	24	30	40	60	120	inf.
1	6106.	6157.	6209.	6235.	6261.	6287.	6313.	6339.	6366.
2	99.4	99.4	99.4	99.5	99.5	99.5	99.5	99.5	99.5
3	27.1	26.9	26.7	26.6	26.5	26.4	26.3	26.2	26.1
4	14.4	14.2	14.0	13.9	13.8	13.8	13.7	13.6	13.5
5	9.89	9.72	9.55	9.47	9.38	9.29	9.20	9.11	9.02
6	7.72	7.56	7.40	7.31	7.23	7.14	7.06	6.97	6.88
7	6.47	6.31	6.16	6.07	5.99	5.91	5.82	5.74	5.65
8	5.67	5.52	5.36	5.28	5.20	5.12	5.03	4.95	4.86
9	5.11	4.96	4.81	4.73	4.65	4.57	4.48	4.40	4.31
10	4.71	4.56	4.41	4.33	4.25	4.17	4.08	4.00	3.91
11	4.40	4.25	4.10	4.02	3.94	3.86	3.78	3.69	3.60
12	4.16	4.01	3.86	3.78	3.70	3.62	3.54	3.45	3.36
13	3.96	3.82	3.66	3.59	3.51	3.43	3.34	3.25	3.17
14	3.80	3.66	3.51	3.43	3.35	3.27	3.18	3.09	3.00
15	3.67	3.52	3.37	3.29	3.21	3.13	3.05	2.96	2.87
16	3.55	3.41	3.26	3.18	3.10	3.02	2.93	2.84	2.75
18	3.37	3.23	3.08	3.00	2.92	2.84	2.75	2.66	2.57
20	3.23	3.09	2.94	2.86	2.78	2.69	2.61	2.52	2.42
22	3.12	2.98	2.83	2.75	2.67	2.58	2.50	2.40	2.31
24	3.03	2.89	2.74	2.66	2.58	2.49	2.40	2.31	2.21
26	2.96	2.81	2.66	2.58	2.50	2.42	2.33	2.23	2.13
28	2.90	2.75	2.60	2.52	2.44	2.35	2.26	2.17	2.06
30	2.84	2.70	2.55	2.47	2.39	2.30	2.21	2.11	2.01
40	2.66	2.52	2.37	2.29	2.20	2.11	2.02	1.92	1.80
60	2.50	2.35	2.20	2.12	2.03	1.94	1.84	1.73	1.60
120	2.34	2.19	2.03	1.95	1.86	1.76	1.66	1.53	1.38
inf.	2.18	2.04	1.88	1.79	1.70	1.59	1.47	1.32	1.00

v_2 = Degrees of Freedom for the denominator of the F-ratio.

Table A.14

90th Percentiles of the Studentized Range Distribution q

	k = *Number of Subgroup Averages Being Compared*									
	2	3	4	5	6	7	8	9	10	11
v										
1	8.93	13.4	13.4	18.5	20.2	21.5	22.6	23.6	24.5	25.2
2	4.13	5.73	6.77	7.54	8.14	8.63	9.05	9.41	9.72	10.0
3	3.33	4.47	5.20	5.74	6.16	6.51	6.81	7.06	7.29	7.49
4	3.01	3.98	4.59	5.03	5.39	5.68	5.93	6.14	6.33	6.49
5	2.85	3.72	4.26	4.66	4.98	5.24	5.46	5.65	5.82	5.97
6	2.75	3.56	4.07	4.44	4.73	4.97	5.17	5.34	5.50	5.64
7	2.68	3.45	3.93	4.28	4.55	4.78	4.97	5.14	5.28	5.41
8	2.63	3.37	3.83	4.17	4.43	4.65	4.83	4.99	5.13	5.25
9	2.59	3.32	3.76	4.08	4.34	4.54	4.72	4.87	5.01	5.13
10	2.56	3.27	3.70	4.02	4.26	4.47	4.64	4.78	4.91	5.03
11	2.54	3.23	3.66	3.96	4.20	4.40	4.57	4.71	4.84	4.95
12	2.52	3.20	3.62	3.92	4.16	4.35	4.51	4.65	4.78	4.89
13	2.50	3.18	3.59	3.88	4.12	4.30	4.46	4.60	4.72	4.83
14	2.49	3.16	3.56	3.85	4.08	4.27	4.42	4.56	4.68	4.79
15	2.48	3.14	3.54	3.83	4.05	4.23	4.39	4.52	4.64	4.75
16	2.47	3.12	3.52	3.80	4.03	4.21	4.36	4.49	4.61	4.71
17	2.46	3.11	3.50	3.78	4.00	4.18	4.33	4.46	4.58	4.68
18	2.45	3.10	3.49	3.77	3.98	4.16	4.31	4.44	4.55	4.65
19	2.45	3.09	3.47	3.75	3.97	4.14	4.29	4.42	4.53	4.63
20	2.44	3.08	3.46	3.74	3.95	4.12	4.27	4.40	4.51	4.61
24	2.42	3.05	3.42	3.69	3.90	4.07	4.21	4.34	4.44	4.54
30	2.40	3.02	3.39	3.65	3.85	4.02	4.16	4.28	4.38	4.47
40	2.38	2.99	3.35	3.60	3.80	3.96	4.10	4.21	4.32	4.41
60	2.36	2.96	3.31	3.56	3.75	3.91	4.04	4.16	4.25	4.34
120	2.34	2.93	3.28	3.52	3.71	3.86	3.99	4.10	4.19	4.28
inf.	2.33	2.90	3.24	3.48	3.66	3.81	3.93	4.04	4.13	4.21

v = **degrees of freedom for Mean Square Within.**

Table A.14

90th Percentiles of the Studentized Range Distribution *q*

	k = Number of Subgroup Averages Being Compared									
v	12	13	14	15	16	17	18	19	20	24
1	25.9	26.5	27.1	27.6	28.1	28.5	29.0	29.3	29.7	31.0
2	10.3	10.5	10.7	10.9	11.1	11.2	11.4	11.5	11.7	12.2
3	7.67	7.83	7.98	8.12	8.25	8.37	8.48	8.58	8.68	9.03
4	6.65	6.78	6.91	7.02	7.13	7.23	7.33	7.41	7.50	7.79
5	6.10	6.22	6.34	6.44	6.54	6.63	6.71	6.79	6.86	7.14
6	5.76	5.87	5.98	6.07	6.16	6.25	6.32	6.40	6.47	6.71
7	5.53	5.64	5.74	5.83	5.91	5.99	6.06	6.13	6.19	6.42
8	5.36	5.46	5.56	5.64	5.72	5.80	5.87	5.93	6.00	6.21
9	5.23	5.33	5.42	5.51	5.58	5.66	5.72	5.79	5.85	6.05
10	5.13	5.23	5.32	5.40	5.47	5.54	5.61	5.67	5.73	5.93
11	5.05	5.15	5.23	5.31	5.38	5.45	5.51	5.57	5.63	5.83
12	4.99	5.08	5.16	5.24	5.31	5.37	5.44	5.49	5.55	5.74
13	4.93	5.02	5.10	5.18	5.25	5.31	5.37	5.43	5.48	5.67
14	4.88	4.97	5.05	5.12	5.19	5.26	5.32	5.37	5.43	5.61
15	4.84	4.93	5.01	5.08	5.15	5.21	5.27	5.32	5.38	5.56
16	4.81	4.89	4.97	5.04	5.11	5.17	5.23	5.28	5.33	5.52
17	4.77	4.86	4.93	5.01	5.07	5.13	5.19	5.24	5.30	5.48
18	4.75	4.83	4.90	4.98	5.04	5.10	5.16	5.21	5.26	5.44
19	4.72	4.80	4.88	4.95	5.01	5.07	5.13	5.18	5.23	5.41
20	4.70	4.78	4.85	4.92	4.99	5.05	5.10	5.16	5.20	5.38
24	4.63	4.71	4.78	4.85	4.91	4.97	5.02	5.07	5.12	5.29
30	4.56	4.64	4.71	4.77	4.83	4.89	4.94	4.99	5.03	5.20
40	4.49	4.56	4.63	4.69	4.75	4.81	4.86	4.90	4.95	5.11
60	4.42	4.49	4.56	4.62	4.67	4.73	4.78	4.82	4.86	5.02
120	4.35	4.42	4.48	4.54	4.60	4.65	4.69	4.74	4.78	4.92
inf.	4.28	4.35	4.41	4.47	4.52	4.57	4.61	4.65	4.69	4.83

v = degrees of freedom for **Mean Square Within.**

Table A.14

95th Percentiles of the Studentized Range Distribution q

k = *Number of Subgroup Averages Being Compared*

v	2	3	4	5	6	7	8	9	10	11
1	18.0	27.0	32.8	37.1	40.4	43.1	45.4	47.4	49.1	50.6
2	6.08	8.33	9.80	10.9	11.7	12.4	13.0	13.5	14.0	14.4
3	4.50	5.91	6.82	7.50	8.04	8.48	8.85	9.18	9.46	9.72
4	3.93	5.04	5.76	6.29	6.71	7.05	7.35	7.60	7.83	8.03
5	3.64	4.60	5.22	5.67	6.03	6.33	6.58	6.80	6.99	7.17
6	3.46	4.34	4.90	5.30	5.63	5.90	6.12	6.32	6.49	6.65
7	3.34	4.16	4.68	5.06	5.36	5.61	5.82	6.00	6.16	6.30
8	3.26	4.04	4.53	4.89	5.17	5.40	5.60	5.77	5.92	6.05
9	3.20	3.95	4.41	4.76	5.02	5.24	5.43	5.59	5.74	5.87
10	3.15	3.88	4.33	4.65	4.91	5.12	5.30	5.46	5.60	5.72
11	3.11	3.82	4.26	4.57	4.82	5.03	5.20	5.35	5.49	5.61
12	3.08	3.77	4.20	4.51	4.75	4.95	5.12	5.27	5.39	5.51
13	3.06	3.73	4.15	4.45	4.69	4.88	5.05	5.19	5.32	5.43
14	3.03	3.70	4.11	4.41	4.64	4.83	4.99	5.13	5.25	5.36
15	3.01	3.67	4.08	4.37	4.59	4.78	4.94	5.08	5.20	5.31
16	3.00	3.65	4.05	4.33	4.56	4.74	4.90	5.03	5.15	5.26
17	2.98	3.63	4.02	4.30	4.52	4.70	4.86	4.99	5.11	5.21
18	2.97	3.61	4.00	4.28	4.49	4.67	4.82	4.96	5.07	5.17
19	2.96	3.59	3.98	4.25	4.47	4.65	4.79	4.92	5.04	5.14
20	2.95	3.58	3.96	4.23	4.45	4.62	4.77	4.90	5.01	5.11
24	2.92	3.53	3.90	4.17	4.37	4.54	4.68	4.81	4.92	5.01
30	2.89	3.49	3.85	4.10	4.30	4.46	4.60	4.72	4.82	4.92
40	2.86	3.44	3.79	4.04	4.23	4.39	4.52	4.63	4.73	4.82
60	2.83	3.40	3.74	3.98	4.16	4.31	4.44	4.55	4.65	4.73
120	2.80	3.36	3.68	3.92	4.10	4.24	4.36	4.47	4.56	4.64
inf.	2.77	3.31	3.63	3.86	4.03	4.17	4.29	4.39	4.47	4.55

v = **degrees of freedom for Mean Square Within**

Table A.14

95th Percentiles of the Studentized Range Distribution q

k =	*Number of Subgroup Averages Being Compared*									
	12	*13*	*14*	*15*	*16*	*17*	*18*	*19*	*20*	*21*
v										
1	52.0	53.2	54.3	55.4	56.3	57.2	58.0	58.8	59.6	62.1
2	14.7	15.1	15.4	15.7	15.9	16.1	16.4	16.6	16.8	17.5
3	9.95	10.2	10.3	10.5	10.7	10.8	11.0	11.1	11.2	11.7
4	8.21	8.37	8.52	8.66	8.79	8.91	9.03	9.13	9.23	9.58
5	7.32	7.47	7.60	7.72	7.83	7.93	8.03	8.12	8.21	8.55
6	6.79	6.92	7.03	7.14	7.24	7.34	7.43	7.51	7.59	7.86
7	6.43	6.55	6.66	6.76	6.85	6.94	7.02	7.10	7.17	7.43
8	6.18	6.29	6.39	6.48	6.57	6.65	6.73	6.80	6.87	7.11
9	5.98	6.09	6.19	6.28	6.36	6.44	6.51	6.58	6.64	6.88
10	5.83	5.93	6.03	6.11	6.19	6.27	6.34	6.40	6.47	6.69
11	5.71	5.81	5.90	5.98	6.06	6.13	6.20	6.27	6.33	6.54
12	5.61	5.71	5.80	5.88	5.95	6.02	6.09	6.15	6.21	6.41
13	5.53	5.63	5.71	5.79	5.86	5.93	5.99	6.05	6.11	6.31
14	5.46	5.55	5.64	5.71	5.79	5.85	5.91	5.97	6.03	6.22
15	5.40	5.49	5.57	5.65	5.72	5.78	5.85	5.90	5.96	6.15
16	5.35	5.44	5.52	5.59	5.66	5.73	5.79	5.84	5.90	6.08
17	5.31	5.39	5.47	5.54	5.61	5.67	5.73	5.79	5.84	6.02
18	5.27	5.35	5.43	5.50	5.57	5.63	5.69	5.74	5.79	5.97
19	5.23	5.31	5.39	5.46	5.53	5.59	5.65	5.70	5.75	5.93
20	5.20	5.28	5.36	5.43	5.49	5.55	5.61	5.66	5.71	5.89
24	5.10	5.18	5.25	5.32	5.38	5.44	5.49	5.55	5.47	5.76
30	5.00	5.08	5.15	5.21	5.27	5.33	5.38	5.43	5.47	5.64
40	4.90	4.98	5.04	5.11	5.16	5.22	5.27	5.31	5.36	5.51
60	4.81	4.88	4.94	5.00	5.06	5.11	5.15	5.20	5.24	5.39
120	4.71	4.78	4.84	4.90	4.95	5.00	5.04	5.09	5.13	5.27
inf.	4.62	4.68	4.74	4.80	4.85	4.89	4.93	4.97	5.01	5.14

v = **degrees of freedom for Mean Square Within.**

Table A.14

99th Percentiles of the Studentized Range Distribution q

	k =	*Number of Subgroup Averages Being Compared*								
	2	**3**	**4**	**5**	**6**	**7**	**8**	**9**	**10**	**11**
v										
1	90.0	135.	164.	186.	202.	216.	227.	237.	246.	253.
2	14.0	19.0	22.3	24.7	26.6	28.2	29.5	30.7	31.7	32.6
3	8.26	10.6	12.2	13.3	14.2	15.0	15.6	16.2	16.7	17.1
4	6.51	8.12	9.17	9.96	10.6	11.1	11.5	11.9	12.3	12.6
5	5.70	6.97	7.80	8.42	8.91	9.32	9.67	9.97	10.2	10.5
6	5.24	6.33	7.03	7.56	7.97	8.32	8.61	8.87	9.10	9.30
7	4.95	5.92	6.54	7.01	7.37	7.68	7.94	8.17	8.37	8.55
8	4.74	5.63	6.20	6.63	6.96	7.24	7.47	7.68	7.87	8.03
9	4.60	5.43	5.96	6.35	6.66	6.91	7.13	7.32	7.49	7.65
10	4.48	5.27	5.77	6.14	6.43	6.67	6.87	7.05	7.21	7.36
11	4.39	5.14	5.62	5.97	6.25	6.48	6.67	6.84	6.99	7.13
12	4.32	5.04	5.50	5.84	6.10	6.32	6.51	6.67	6.81	6.94
13	4.26	4.96	5.40	5.73	5.98	6.19	6.37	6.53	6.67	6.79
14	4.21	4.89	5.32	5.63	5.88	6.08	6.26	6.41	6.54	6.66
15	4.17	4.83	5.25	5.56	5.80	5.99	6.16	6.31	6.44	6.55
16	4.13	4.78	5.19	5.49	5.72	5.92	6.08	6.22	6.35	6.46
17	4.10	4.74	5.14	5.43	5.66	5.85	6.01	6.15	6.27	6.38
18	4.07	4.70	5.09	5.38	5.60	5.79	5.94	6.08	6.20	6.31
19	4.05	4.67	5.05	5.33	5.55	5.73	5.89	6.02	6.14	6.25
20	4.02	4.64	5.02	5.29	5.51	5.69	5.84	5.97	6.09	6.19
24	3.96	4.54	4.91	5.17	5.37	5.54	5.69	5.81	5.92	6.02
30	3.89	4.45	4.80	5.05	5.24	5.40	5.54	5.65	5.76	5.85
40	3.82	4.37	4.70	4.93	5.11	5.27	5.39	5.50	5.60	5.69
60	3.76	4.28	4.60	4.82	4.99	5.13	5.25	5.36	5.45	5.53
120	3.70	4.20	4.50	4.71	4.87	5.01	5.12	5.21	5.30	5.38
inf.	3.64	4.12	4.40	4.60	4.76	4.88	4.99	5.08	5.16	5.23

v = degrees of freedom for **Mean Square Within.**

Table A.14

99th Percentiles of the Studentized Range Distribution q

v	12	13	14	15	16	17	18	19	20	24
1	260.	266.	272.	277.	282.	286.	290.	294.	298.	311.
2	33.4	34.1	34.8	35.4	36.0	36.5	37.0	37.5	37.9	39.5
3	17.5	17.9	18.2	18.5	18.8	19.1	19.3	19.5	19.8	20.5
4	12.8	13.1	13.3	13.5	13.7	13.9	14.1	14.2	14.4	14.9
5	10.7	10.9	11.1	11.2	11.4	11.6	11.7	11.8	11.9	12.5
6	9.49	9.65	9.81	9.95	10.1	10.2	10.3	10.4	10.5	10.9
7	8.71	8.86	9.00	9.12	9.24	9.35	9.46	9.55	9.65	10.0
8	8.18	8.31	8.44	8.55	8.66	8.76	8.85	8.94	9.03	9.32
9	7.78	7.91	8.03	8.13	8.23	8.32	8.41	8.49	8.57	8.85
10	7.48	7.60	7.71	7.81	7.91	7.99	8.07	8.15	8.22	8.48
11	7.25	7.36	7.46	7.56	7.65	7.73	7.81	7.88	7.95	8.20
12	7.06	7.17	7.26	7.36	7.44	7.52	7.59	7.66	7.73	7.96
13	6.90	7.01	7.10	7.19	7.27	7.34	7.42	7.48	7.55	7.78
14	6.77	6.87	6.96	7.05	7.12	7.20	7.27	7.33	7.39	7.62
15	6.66	6.76	6.84	6.93	7.00	7.07	7.14	7.20	7.26	7.48
16	6.56	6.66	6.74	6.82	6.90	6.97	7.03	7.09	7.15	7.36
17	6.48	6.57	6.66	6.73	6.80	6.87	6.94	7.00	7.05	7.26
18	6.41	6.50	6.58	6.65	6.72	6.79	6.85	6.91	6.96	7.17
19	6.34	6.43	6.51	6.58	6.65	6.72	6.78	6.84	6.89	7.08
20	6.29	6.37	6.45	6.52	6.59	6.65	6.71	6.76	6.82	7.01
24	6.11	6.19	6.26	6.33	6.39	6.45	6.51	6.56	6.61	6.79
30	5.93	6.01	6.08	6.14	6.20	6.26	6.31	6.36	6.41	6.57
40	5.77	5.84	5.90	5.96	6.02	6.07	6.12	6.17	6.21	6.36
60	5.60	5.67	5.73	5.79	5.84	5.89	5.93	5.98	6.02	6.16
120	5.44	5.51	5.56	5.61	5.66	5.71	5.75	5.79	5.83	5.96
inf.	5.29	5.35	5.40	5.45	5.49	5.54	5.57	5.61	5.65	5.77

k = *Number of Subgroup Averages Being Compared*

v = **degrees of freedom for Mean Square Within.**

Table A.15

Factors for Approximate 90% Interval Estimates for C_p and P_p

Having computed a Capability Ratio, C_p, or a Performance Ratio, P_p,
an approximate 90% Interval Estimate
for the underlying quantity estimated by this ratio
may be obtained by multiplying the observed ratio
by each of the two scaling factors given in the following table.
The degrees of freedom listed refer to
the degrees of freedom in the estimate of dispersion
used in the denominator of C_p or P_p.

d.f.	LB	UB	d.f.	LB	UB	d.f.	LB	UB	d.f.	LB	UB
5	.479	1.488	20	.736	1.253	55	.842	1.155	250	.926	1.073
6	.522	1.449	21	.743	1.247	60	.848	1.148	300	.933	1.067
7	.556	1.418	22	.749	1.242	65	.854	1.142	350	.938	1.062
8	.584	1.392	23	.754	1.236	70	.860	1.137	400	.942	1.058
9	.608	1.371	24	.760	1.232	75	.865	1.133	450	.945	1.055
10	.628	1.353	25	.764	1.227	80	.869	1.128	500	.948	1.052
11	.645	1.338	26	.769	1.223	85	.873	1.125	550	.950	1.049
12	.660	1.323	27	.773	1.219	90	.876	1.121	600	.952	1.047
13	.673	1.311	28	.777	1.215	100	.883	1.115	650	.954	1.045
14	.685	1.300	29	.781	1.211	110	.888	1.110	700	.956	1.044
15	.696	1.291	30	.785	1.208	120	.893	1.105	750	.957	1.042
16	.705	1.282	35	.801	1.193	140	.901	1.097	800	.959	1.041
17	.714	1.274	40	.814	1.181	160	.907	1.091	850	.960	1.040
18	.722	1.266	45	.825	1.170	180	.913	1.086	900	.961	1.039
19	.730	1.259	50	.834	1.162	200	.917	1.082	1000	.963	1.037

$$LB \ C_p \ < \ \text{Capability} \ < \ UB \ C_p$$

Table A.16
Factors for Approximate 90% Interval Estimates for C_{pk} and P_{pk}

Having computed a Centered Capability Ratio, C_{pk},
or a Centered Performance Ratio, P_{pk},
an approximate 90% Interval Estimate
for the underlying quantity estimated by this ratio
may be obtained by multiplying the observed ratio
by each of the two scaling factors given in the following table.
The degrees of freedom listed refer to
the degrees of freedom in the estimate of dispersion
used in the denominator of C_{pk} or P_{pk}.

These scaling factors are larger than those in Table A.15 because of the additional uncertainty of estimating the distance to the nearer specification which is part of these centered ratios.

d.f.	LB	UB	d.f.	LB	UB	d.f.	LB	UB	d.f.	LB	UB
5	.340	2.096	20	.665	1.386	55	.803	1.211	250	.910	1.092
6	.384	1.971	21	.673	1.376	60	.812	1.200	300	.920	1.082
7	.423	1.866	22	.680	1.368	65	.821	1.188	350	.927	1.075
8	.458	1.773	23	.686	1.358	70	.828	1.181	400	.933	1.069
9	.492	1.693	24	.693	1.351	75	.835	1.174	450	.936	1.066
10	.525	1.618	25	.698	1.342	80	.839	1.168	500	.939	1.063
11	.544	1.587	26	.704	1.335	85	.844	1.163	550	.941	1.060
12	.561	1.556	27	.710	1.328	90	.848	1.158	600	.942	1.058
13	.577	1.530	28	.715	1.320	100	.857	1.149	650	.944	1.056
14	.592	1.505	29	.720	1.313	110	.862	1.143	700	.946	1.055
15	.606	1.482	30	.725	1.309	120	.868	1.137	750	.947	1.053
16	.619	1.460	35	.746	1.281	140	.878	1.126	800	.949	1.052
17	.632	1.440	40	.764	1.259	160	.885	1.118	850	.950	1.051
18	.644	1.419	45	.780	1.238	180	.893	1.110	900	.951	1.049
19	.656	1.402	50	.793	1.222	200	.899	1.104	1000	.953	1.047

LB C_{pk} < Centered Capability < **UB** C_{pk}

Table A.17
The Effective Cost of Production
when *all* nonconforming units are scrapped

C_p *values*

C_{pk}	0.10	0.20	0.30	0.40	0.50	0.60	0.70	0.80	0.90	1.00
-0.50	20.83	16.19	15.54	15.51	15.56	15.61	15.65	15.68	15.71	15.73
-0.40	13.02	9.74	9.22	9.19	9.24	9.29	9.33	9.37	9.40	9.42
-0.30	8.89	6.38	5.93	5.90	5.94	5.99	6.04	6.07	6.11	6.13
-0.20	6.64	4.54	4.13	4.08	4.11	4.16	4.21	4.25	4.28	4.31
-0.10	5.40	3.51	3.09	3.02	3.04	3.09	3.13	3.17	3.21	3.24
0.00	4.77	2.93	2.48	2.38	2.38	2.42	2.47	2.51	2.55	2.58
0.10	4.58	2.63	2.13	1.98	1.97	1.99	2.03	2.08	2.11	2.15
0.20	-	2.54	1.94	1.74	1.69	1.71	1.74	1.78	1.82	1.85
0.30	-	-	1.88	1.61	1.52	1.51	1.54	1.57	1.61	1.64
0.40	-	-	-	1.57	1.43	1.39	1.39	1.42	1.45	1.48
0.50	-	-	-	-	1.40	1.32	1.29	1.31	1.33	1.36
0.60	-	-	-	-	-	1.29	1.24	1.23	1.25	1.27
0.70	-	-	-	-	-	-	1.22	1.19	1.18	1.20
0.80	-	-	-	-	-	-	-	1.17	1.15	1.15
0.90	-	-	-	-	-	-	-	-	1.14	1.12
1.00	-	-	-	-	-	-	-	-	-	1.11

Blank spaces correspond to impossible combinations of C_p and C_{pk}.

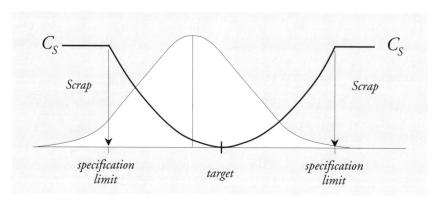

**The Excess Cost Curve for the Effective Cost of Production
When All Nonconforming Items Are Scrapped**

Table A.17

The Effective Cost of Production

when *all* nonconforming units are scrapped

C_{pk}	C_p values									
	1.10	**1.20**	**1.30**	**1.40**	**1.50**	**1.60**	**1.70**	**1.80**	**1.90**	**2.00**
–0.50	15.75	15.77	15.78	15.80	15.81	15.82	15.83	15.83	15.84	15.85
–0.40	9.44	9.46	9.48	9.49	9.51	9.52	9.53	9.53	9.54	9.55
–0.30	6.16	6.18	6.19	6.21	6.22	6.23	6.24	6.25	6.26	6.27
–0.20	4.33	4.36	4.38	4.39	4.41	4.42	4.43	4.44	4.45	4.46
–0.10	3.27	3.29	3.31	3.33	3.35	3.36	3.37	3.39	3.40	3.41
0.00	2.61	2.63	2.66	2.68	2.70	2.71	2.73	2.74	2.75	2.76
0.10	2.18	2.21	2.23	2.25	2.27	2.29	2.31	2.32	2.34	2.35
0.20	1.89	1.92	1.94	1.97	1.99	2.01	2.03	2.04	2.06	2.07
0.30	1.68	1.71	1.74	1.76	1.79	1.81	1.83	1.84	1.86	1.87
0.40	1.52	1.55	1.58	1.61	1.63	1.66	1.68	1.70	1.71	1.73
0.50	1.40	1.43	1.46	1.49	1.51	1.54	1.56	1.58	1.60	1.62
0.60	1.30	1.33	1.36	1.39	1.42	1.44	1.47	1.49	1.51	1.53
0.70	1.22	1.25	1.28	1.31	1.34	1.36	1.39	1.41	1.43	1.46
0.80	1.17	1.19	1.21	1.24	1.27	1.29	1.32	1.34	1.37	1.39
0.90	1.12	1.14	1.16	1.18	1.21	1.24	1.26	1.28	1.31	1.33
1.00	1.10	1.10	1.12	1.14	1.16	1.18	1.21	1.23	1.26	1.28
1.10	1.09	1.08	1.09	1.10	1.12	1.14	1.16	1.19	1.21	1.23
1.20	-	1.08	1.07	1.08	1.09	1.11	1.12	1.15	1.17	1.19
1.30	-	-	1.07	1.06	1.07	1.08	1.09	1.11	1.13	1.15
1.40	-	-	-	1.06	1.05	1.06	1.07	1.08	1.10	1.12
1.50	-	-	-	-	1.05	1.05	1.05	1.06	1.08	1.09
1.60	-	-	-	-	-	1.04	1.04	1.05	1.06	1.07
1.70	-	-	-	-	-	-	1.04	1.04	1.04	1.05
1.80	-	-	-	-	-	-	-	1.03	1.03	1.04
1.90	-	-	-	-	-	-	-	-	1.03	1.03
2.00	-	-	-	-	-	-	-	-	-	1.03

Table A.17
The Effective Cost of Production
when *all* nonconforming units are scrapped

C_{pk}	C_p values							
	2.5	**3.0**	**4.0**	**5.0**	**6.0**	**8.0**	**12.0**	**20.0**
−0.50	15.91	15.93	15.95	15.97	15.98	15.99	16.00	16.01
−0.40	9.59	9.61	9.64	9.65	9.66	9.68	9.69	9.70
−0.30	6.31	6.33	6.36	6.38	6.39	6.40	6.42	6.43
−0.20	4.50	4.52	4.56	4.57	4.59	4.60	4.62	4.63
−0.10	3.45	3.48	3.51	3.53	3.55	3.56	3.58	3.60
0.00	2.80	2.83	2.87	2.90	2.92	2.94	2.96	2.98
0.10	2.40	2.43	2.48	2.50	2.52	2.55	2.57	2.59
0.20	2.12	2.16	2.21	2.24	2.27	2.29	2.32	2.34
0.30	1.94	1.98	2.04	2.07	2.10	2.13	2.16	2.19
0.40	1.80	1.85	1.91	1.95	1.98	2.02	2.05	2.08
0.50	1.70	1.75	1.82	1.87	1.90	1.94	1.98	2.02
0.60	1.61	1.67	1.75	1.81	1.84	1.89	1.94	1.98
0.70	1.54	1.61	1.70	1.76	1.80	1.85	1.90	1.95
0.80	1.48	1.55	1.65	1.72	1.76	1.82	1.88	1.93
0.90	1.43	1.50	1.61	1.68	1.73	1.79	1.86	1.92
1.00	1.38	1.46	1.57	1.65	1.70	1.77	1.84	1.90
1.10	1.33	1.41	1.53	1.61	1.67	1.75	1.83	1.89
1.20	1.29	1.37	1.50	1.58	1.64	1.72	1.81	1.88
1.30	1.25	1.33	1.46	1.55	1.62	1.70	1.80	1.87
1.40	1.21	1.30	1.43	1.52	1.59	1.68	1.78	1.87
1.50	1.18	1.26	1.40	1.49	1.57	1.66	1.77	1.86
1.60	1.15	1.23	1.37	1.47	1.54	1.64	1.75	1.85
1.70	1.12	1.20	1.34	1.44	1.52	1.62	1.74	1.84
1.80	1.10	1.17	1.31	1.41	1.49	1.60	1.72	1.83
1.90	1.08	1.15	1.28	1.39	1.47	1.58	1.71	1.82
2.00	1.06	1.12	1.26	1.36	1.45	1.56	1.70	1.81
2.5	1.02	1.04	1.15	1.25	1.34	1.47	1.63	1.77
3.0	-	1.01	1.07	1.16	1.25	1.39	1.56	1.72
4.0	-	-	1.01	1.04	1.11	1.25	1.45	1.64
5.0	-	-	-	1.00	1.03	1.14	1.34	1.56
6.0	-	-	-	-	1.00	1.06	1.25	1.49
8.0	-	-	-	-	-	1.00	1.11	1.36
12.0	-	-	-	-	-	-	1.00	1.16
20.0	-	-	-	-	-	-	-	1.00

Table A.18
The Effective Cost of Production
when *all* nonconforming units are reworked

	C_p values									
C_{pk}	0.10	0.20	0.30	0.40	0.50	0.60	0.70	0.80	0.90	1.00
1.00	-	-	-	-	-	-	-	-	-	1.11
0.90	-	-	-	-	-	-	-	-	1.14	1.12
0.80	-	-	-	-	-	-	-	1.17	1.15	1.15
0.70	-	-	-	-	-	-	1.21	1.18	1.18	1.20
0.60	-	-	-	-	-	1.27	1.23	1.22	1.24	1.26
0.50	-	-	-	-	1.35	1.29	1.27	1.29	1.31	1.34
0.40	-	-	-	1.44	1.36	1.34	1.35	1.37	1.40	1.43
0.30	-	-	1.56	1.46	1.42	1.42	1.44	1.46	1.49	1.52
0.20	-	1.69	1.57	1.51	1.50	1.51	1.54	1.57	1.59	1.62
0.10	1.84	1.71	1.62	1.59	1.59	1.61	1.64	1.66	1.69	1.71
0.00	1.85	1.74	1.69	1.68	1.69	1.71	1.73	1.75	1.77	1.79
−0.10	1.87	1.79	1.76	1.76	1.78	1.80	1.81	1.83	1.84	1.86
−0.20	1.89	1.84	1.83	1.84	1.85	1.87	1.88	1.89	1.90	1.91
−0.30	1.92	1.89	1.89	1.90	1.91	1.92	1.93	1.93	1.94	1.94
−0.40	1.95	1.93	1.93	1.94	1.95	1.95	1.96	1.96	1.96	1.97
−0.50	1.97	1.96	1.96	1.97	1.97	1.97	1.98	1.98	1.98	1.98

Blank spaces correspond to impossible combinations of C_p and C_{pk}.

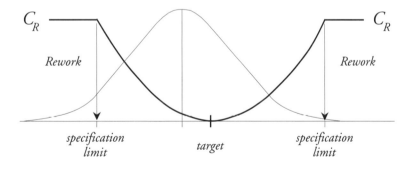

**The Excess Cost Curve for the Effective Cost of Production
When All Nonconforming Items Are Reworked**

Table A.18
The Effective Cost of Production
when *all* nonconforming units are reworked

C_p *values*

C_{pk}	1.10	1.20	1.30	1.40	1.50	1.60	1.70	1.80	1.90	2.00
2.00	-	-	-	-	-	-	-	-	-	1.03
1.90	-	-	-	-	-	-	-	-	1.03	1.03
1.80	-	-	-	-	-	-	-	1.03	1.03	1.04
1.70	-	-	-	-	-	-	1.04	1.04	1.04	1.05
1.60	-	-	-	-	-	1.04	1.04	1.05	1.06	1.07
1.50	-	-	-	-	1.05	1.05	1.05	1.06	1.08	1.09
1.40	-	-	-	1.06	1.05	1.06	1.07	1.08	1.10	1.12
1.30	-	-	1.07	1.06	1.07	1.08	1.09	1.11	1.13	1.15
1.20	-	1.08	1.07	1.08	1.09	1.11	1.12	1.15	1.17	1.19
1.10	1.09	1.08	1.09	1.10	1.12	1.14	1.16	1.19	1.21	1.23
1.00	1.10	1.10	1.12	1.14	1.16	1.18	1.21	1.23	1.26	1.28
0.90	1.12	1.14	1.16	1.18	1.21	1.23	1.26	1.28	1.31	1.33
0.80	1.16	1.19	1.21	1.24	1.27	1.29	1.32	1.34	1.36	1.39
0.70	1.22	1.25	1.28	1.30	1.33	1.36	1.38	1.41	1.43	1.45
0.60	1.29	1.32	1.35	1.38	1.40	1.43	1.45	1.47	1.49	1.51
0.50	1.37	1.40	1.43	1.45	1.48	1.50	1.52	1.55	1.56	1.58
0.40	1.46	1.49	1.51	1.54	1.56	1.58	1.60	1.62	1.63	1.65
0.30	1.55	1.58	1.60	1.62	1.64	1.66	1.67	1.69	1.70	1.71
0.20	1.64	1.66	1.68	1.70	1.72	1.73	1.74	1.76	1.77	1.78
0.10	1.73	1.75	1.76	1.77	1.79	1.80	1.81	1.82	1.82	1.83
0.00	1.80	1.82	1.83	1.84	1.85	1.85	1.86	1.87	1.87	1.88
−0.10	1.87	1.87	1.88	1.89	1.90	1.90	1.91	1.91	1.91	1.92
−0.20	1.91	1.92	1.92	1.93	1.93	1.94	1.94	1.95	1.95	1.95
−0.30	1.95	1.95	1.95	1.96	1.96	1.96	1.97	1.97	1.97	1.97
−0.40	1.97	1.97	1.97	1.98	1.98	1.98	1.98	1.98	1.98	1.98
−0.50	1.98	1.99	1.99	1.99	1.99	1.99	1.99	1.99	1.99	1.99

Table A.18
The Effective Cost of Production
when *all* nonconforming units are reworked

C_{pk}	C_p values							
	2.5	3.0	4.0	5.0	6.0	8.0	12.0	20.0
20.0	-	-	-	-	-	-	-	1.00
12.0	-	-	-	-	-	-	1.00	1.16
8.0	-	-	-	-	-	1.00	1.11	1.36
6.0	-	-	-	-	1.00	1.06	1.25	1.49
5.0	-	-	-	1.00	1.03	1.14	1.34	1.56
4.0	-	-	1.01	1.04	1.11	1.25	1.45	1.64
3.0	-	1.01	1.07	1.16	1.25	1.39	1.56	1.72
2.5	1.02	1.04	1.15	1.25	1.34	1.47	1.63	1.77
2.00	1.06	1.12	1.26	1.36	1.45	1.56	1.70	1.81
1.90	1.08	1.15	1.28	1.39	1.47	1.58	1.71	1.82
1.80	1.10	1.17	1.31	1.41	1.49	1.60	1.72	1.83
1.70	1.12	1.20	1.34	1.44	1.52	1.62	1.74	1.84
1.60	1.15	1.23	1.37	1.47	1.54	1.64	1.75	1.85
1.50	1.18	1.26	1.40	1.49	1.57	1.66	1.77	1.86
1.40	1.21	1.30	1.43	1.52	1.59	1.68	1.78	1.87
1.30	1.25	1.33	1.46	1.55	1.62	1.70	1.80	1.87
1.20	1.29	1.37	1.50	1.58	1.64	1.72	1.81	1.88
1.10	1.33	1.41	1.53	1.61	1.67	1.75	1.83	1.89
1.00	1.38	1.46	1.57	1.64	1.70	1.77	1.84	1.90
0.90	1.43	1.50	1.61	1.68	1.73	1.79	1.86	1.91
0.80	1.48	1.55	1.65	1.71	1.75	1.81	1.87	1.92
0.70	1.53	1.60	1.69	1.74	1.78	1.83	1.89	1.93
0.60	1.59	1.65	1.73	1.78	1.81	1.86	1.90	1.94
0.50	1.65	1.70	1.77	1.81	1.84	1.88	1.92	1.95
0.40	1.71	1.75	1.81	1.84	1.87	1.90	1.93	1.96
0.30	1.76	1.80	1.85	1.87	1.89	1.92	1.95	1.97
0.20	1.82	1.84	1.88	1.90	1.92	1.94	1.96	1.97
0.10	1.86	1.88	1.91	1.93	1.94	1.95	1.97	1.98
0.00	1.90	1.92	1.94	1.95	1.96	1.97	1.98	1.99
−0.10	1.93	1.94	1.96	1.97	1.97	1.98	1.99	1.99
−0.20	1.96	1.96	1.97	1.98	1.98	1.99	1.99	2.00
−0.30	1.98	1.98	1.98	1.99	1.99	1.99	1.99	2.00
−0.40	1.99	1.99	1.99	1.99	1.99	2.00	2.00	2.00
−0.50	1.99	2.00	2.00	2.00	2.00	2.00	2.00	2.00

Table A.19

The Effective Cost of Production

when the cost of rework is 50 percent of the cost of scrap

and the average is on the SCRAP side of the target

C_p *values*

C_{pk}	0.10	0.20	0.30	0.40	0.50	0.60	0.70	0.80	0.90	1.00
−0.50	15.34	15.35	15.42	15.49	15.56	15.61	15.65	15.68	15.71	15.73
−0.40	9.05	9.05	9.10	9.17	9.24	9.29	9.33	9.37	9.40	9.42
−0.30	5.80	5.77	5.81	5.88	5.94	5.99	6.04	6.07	6.11	6.13
−0.20	4.02	3.97	4.00	4.05	4.11	4.16	4.21	4.25	4.28	4.31
−0.10	3.00	2.94	2.94	2.98	3.03	3.09	3.13	3.17	3.21	3.24
0.00	2.39	2.32	2.30	2.33	2.37	2.42	2.47	2.51	2.55	2.58
0.10	2.02	1.94	1.91	1.91	1.94	1.99	2.03	2.08	2.11	2.15
0.20	-	1.72	1.66	1.64	1.66	1.70	1.74	1.78	1.82	1.85
0.30	-	-	1.51	1.47	1.47	1.49	1.53	1.57	1.61	1.64
0.40	-	-	-	1.37	1.35	1.36	1.38	1.41	1.45	1.48
0.50	-	-	-	-	1.28	1.26	1.27	1.30	1.33	1.36
0.60	-	-	-	-	-	1.21	1.20	1.21	1.24	1.27
0.70	-	-	-	-	-	-	1.16	1.16	1.17	1.19
0.80	-	-	-	-	-	-	-	1.13	1.13	1.14
0.90	-	-	-	-	-	-	-	-	1.10	1.10
1.00	-	-	-	-	-	-	-	-	-	1.08

Blank spaces correspond to impossible combinations of C_p and C_{pk}.

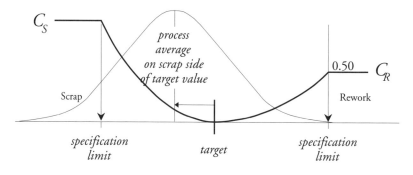

**The Excess Cost Curve for the Effective Cost of Production
When Cost of Rework is 50% the Cost of Scrap
and the Average is on the Scrap Side of the Target Value**

Table A.19

The Effective Cost of Production

when the cost of rework is 50 percent of the cost of scrap

and the average is on the SCRAP side of the target

C_{pk}	C_p values 1.10	1.20	1.30	1.40	1.50	1.60	1.70	1.80	1.90	2.00
−0.50	15.75	15.77	15.78	15.80	15.81	15.82	15.83	15.83	15.84	15.85
−0.40	9.44	9.46	9.48	9.49	9.51	9.52	9.53	9.53	9.54	9.55
−0.30	6.16	6.18	6.19	6.21	6.22	6.23	6.24	6.25	6.26	6.27
−0.20	4.33	4.36	4.38	4.39	4.41	4.42	4.43	4.44	4.45	4.46
−0.10	3.27	3.29	3.31	3.33	3.35	3.36	3.37	3.39	3.40	3.41
0.00	2.61	2.63	2.66	2.68	2.70	2.71	2.73	2.74	2.75	2.76
0.10	2.18	2.21	2.23	2.25	2.27	2.29	2.31	2.32	2.34	2.35
0.20	1.89	1.92	1.94	1.97	1.99	2.01	2.03	2.04	2.06	2.07
0.30	1.68	1.71	1.74	1.76	1.78	1.81	1.83	1.84	1.86	1.87
0.40	1.52	1.55	1.58	1.61	1.63	1.66	1.68	1.70	1.71	1.73
0.50	1.40	1.43	1.46	1.49	1.51	1.54	1.56	1.58	1.60	1.62
0.60	1.30	1.33	1.36	1.39	1.42	1.44	1.47	1.49	1.51	1.53
0.70	1.22	1.25	1.28	1.31	1.34	1.36	1.39	1.41	1.43	1.46
0.80	1.16	1.19	1.21	1.24	1.27	1.29	1.32	1.34	1.37	1.39
0.90	1.12	1.14	1.16	1.18	1.21	1.24	1.26	1.28	1.31	1.33
1.00	1.09	1.10	1.12	1.14	1.16	1.18	1.21	1.23	1.26	1.28
1.10	1.07	1.07	1.08	1.10	1.12	1.14	1.16	1.19	1.21	1.23
1.20	-	1.06	1.06	1.07	1.09	1.10	1.12	1.15	1.17	1.19
1.30	-	-	1.05	1.05	1.06	1.08	1.09	1.11	1.13	1.15
1.40	-	-	-	1.04	1.05	1.06	1.07	1.08	1.10	1.12
1.50	-	-	-	-	1.04	1.04	1.05	1.06	1.07	1.09
1.60	-	-	-	-	-	1.03	1.04	1.04	1.05	1.07
1.70	-	-	-	-	-	-	1.03	1.03	1.04	1.05
1.80	-	-	-	-	-	-	-	1.03	1.03	1.04
1.90	-	-	-	-	-	-	-	-	1.02	1.03
2.00	-	-	-	-	-	-	-	-	-	1.02

When $C_{pk} = C_p$ the average is at the target.

Table A.19

The Effective Cost of Production

when the cost of rework is 50 percent of the cost of scrap

and the average is on the SCRAP side of the target

C_{pk}	C_p values							
	2.5	3.0	4.0	5.0	6.0	8.0	12.0	20.0
−0.50	15.91	15.93	15.95	15.97	15.98	15.99	16.00	16.01
−0.40	9.59	9.61	9.64	9.65	9.66	9.68	9.69	9.70
−0.30	6.31	6.33	6.36	6.38	6.39	6.40	6.42	6.43
−0.20	4.50	4.52	4.56	4.57	4.59	4.60	4.62	4.63
−0.10	3.45	3.48	3.51	3.53	3.55	3.56	3.58	3.60
0.00	2.81	2.84	2.88	2.90	2.92	2.94	2.96	2.98
0.10	2.40	2.43	2.48	2.50	2.52	2.55	2.57	2.59
0.20	2.12	2.16	2.21	2.24	2.27	2.29	2.32	2.34
0.30	1.94	1.98	2.04	2.07	2.10	2.13	2.16	2.19
0.40	1.80	1.85	1.91	1.95	1.98	2.02	2.05	2.08
0.50	1.70	1.75	1.82	1.87	1.90	1.94	1.98	2.02
0.60	1.61	1.67	1.75	1.81	1.84	1.89	1.94	1.98
0.70	1.54	1.61	1.70	1.76	1.80	1.85	1.90	1.95
0.80	1.48	1.55	1.65	1.72	1.76	1.82	1.88	1.93
0.90	1.43	1.50	1.61	1.68	1.73	1.79	1.86	1.92
1.00	1.38	1.46	1.57	1.65	1.70	1.77	1.84	1.90
1.10	1.33	1.41	1.53	1.61	1.67	1.75	1.83	1.89
1.20	1.29	1.37	1.50	1.58	1.64	1.72	1.81	1.88
1.30	1.25	1.33	1.46	1.55	1.62	1.70	1.80	1.87
1.40	1.21	1.30	1.43	1.52	1.59	1.68	1.78	1.87
1.50	1.18	1.26	1.40	1.49	1.57	1.66	1.77	1.86
1.60	1.15	1.23	1.37	1.47	1.54	1.64	1.75	1.85
1.70	1.12	1.20	1.34	1.44	1.52	1.62	1.74	1.84
1.80	1.10	1.17	1.31	1.41	1.49	1.60	1.72	1.83
1.90	1.08	1.15	1.28	1.39	1.47	1.58	1.71	1.82
2.00	1.06	1.12	1.26	1.36	1.45	1.56	1.70	1.81
2.5	1.01	1.04	1.15	1.25	1.34	1.47	1.63	1.77
3.0	-	1.01	1.07	1.16	1.25	1.39	1.56	1.72
4.0	-	-	1.01	1.04	1.11	1.25	1.45	1.64
5.0	-	-	-	1.00	1.03	1.14	1.34	1.56
6.0	-	-	-	-	1.00	1.06	1.25	1.49
8.0	-	-	-	-	-	1.00	1.11	1.36
12.0	-	-	-	-	-	-	1.00	1.16
20.0	-	-	-	-	-	-	-	1.00

Table A.20

The Effective Cost of Production

when the cost of rework is 50 percent of the cost of scrap

and the average is on the REWORK side of the target

C_{pk}	C_p values 0.10	0.20	0.30	0.40	0.50	0.60	0.70	0.80	0.90	1.00
1.00	-	-	-	-	-	-	-	-	-	1.08
0.90	-	-	-	-	-	-	-	-	1.10	1.08
0.80	-	-	-	-	-	-	-	1.13	1.09	1.08
0.70	-	-	-	-	-	-	1.16	1.12	1.10	1.10
0.60	-	-	-	-	-	1.21	1.15	1.13	1.12	1.13
0.50	-	-	-	-	1.28	1.19	1.16	1.15	1.16	1.17
0.40	-	-	-	1.37	1.25	1.20	1.18	1.19	1.20	1.21
0.30	-	-	1.51	1.32	1.25	1.22	1.22	1.23	1.25	1.26
0.20	-	1.72	1.43	1.31	1.27	1.26	1.27	1.28	1.30	1.31
0.10	2.02	1.58	1.40	1.33	1.31	1.31	1.32	1.33	1.34	1.35
0.00	1.80	1.51	1.39	1.36	1.35	1.36	1.37	1.38	1.39	1.39
−0.10	1.66	1.48	1.41	1.39	1.39	1.40	1.41	1.42	1.42	1.43
−0.20	1.58	1.47	1.43	1.42	1.43	1.43	1.44	1.44	1.45	1.45
−0.30	1.54	1.47	1.45	1.45	1.45	1.46	1.46	1.47	1.47	1.47
−0.40	1.51	1.48	1.47	1.47	1.47	1.48	1.48	1.48	1.48	1.48
−0.50	1.50	1.49	1.48	1.48	1.49	1.49	1.49	1.49	1.49	1.49

Blank spaces correspond to impossible combinations of C_p and C_{pk}.

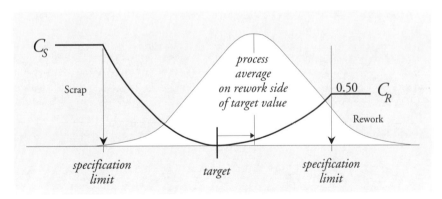

The Excess Cost Curve for the Effective Cost of Production
When Cost of Rework is 50% the Cost of Scrap
and the Average is on the Rework Side of the Target Value

Table A.20

The Effective Cost of Production

when the cost of rework is 50 percent of the cost of scrap

and the average is on the REWORK side of the target

C_{pk}	C_p values									
	1.10	**1.20**	**1.30**	**1.40**	**1.50**	**1.60**	**1.70**	**1.80**	**1.90**	**2.00**
2.00	-	-	-	-	-	-	-	-	-	1.02
1.90	-	-	-	-	-	-	-	-	1.02	1.02
1.80	-	-	-	-	-	-	-	1.03	1.02	1.02
1.70	-	-	-	-	-	-	1.03	1.02	1.02	1.03
1.60	-	-	-	-	-	1.03	1.03	1.03	1.03	1.03
1.50	-	-	-	-	1.04	1.04	1.03	1.03	1.04	1.05
1.40	-	-	-	1.04	1.03	1.03	1.04	1.04	1.05	1.06
1.30	-	-	1.05	1.04	1.04	1.04	1.05	1.06	1.07	1.08
1.20	-	1.06	1.05	1.04	1.05	1.05	1.06	1.07	1.08	1.09
1.10	1.07	1.05	1.05	1.05	1.06	1.07	1.08	1.09	1.10	1.12
1.00	1.06	1.06	1.06	1.07	1.08	1.09	1.10	1.12	1.13	1.14
0.90	1.07	1.07	1.08	1.09	1.10	1.12	1.13	1.14	1.15	1.16
0.80	1.09	1.10	1.11	1.12	1.13	1.15	1.16	1.17	1.18	1.19
0.70	1.11	1.12	1.14	1.15	1.17	1.18	1.19	1.20	1.21	1.22
0.60	1.15	1.16	1.17	1.19	1.20	1.21	1.23	1.24	1.25	1.26
0.50	1.19	1.20	1.21	1.23	1.24	1.25	1.26	1.27	1.28	1.29
0.40	1.23	1.24	1.26	1.27	1.28	1.29	1.30	1.31	1.32	1.32
0.30	1.28	1.29	1.30	1.31	1.32	1.33	1.34	1.34	1.35	1.36
0.20	1.32	1.33	1.34	1.35	1.36	1.37	1.37	1.38	1.38	1.39
0.10	1.36	1.37	1.38	1.39	1.39	1.40	1.40	1.41	1.41	1.42
0.00	1.40	1.41	1.41	1.42	1.42	1.43	1.43	1.43	1.44	1.44
−0.10	1.43	1.44	1.44	1.44	1.45	1.45	1.45	1.46	1.46	1.46
−0.20	1.46	1.46	1.46	1.46	1.47	1.47	1.47	1.47	1.47	1.47
−0.30	1.47	1.48	1.48	1.48	1.48	1.48	1.48	1.48	1.48	1.48
−0.40	1.49	1.49	1.49	1.49	1.49	1.49	1.49	1.49	1.49	1.49
−0.50	1.49	1.49	1.49	1.49	1.49	1.49	1.49	1.49	1.50	1.50

When $C_{pk} = C_p$ the average is at the target.

Table A.20
The Effective Cost of Production
when the cost of rework is 50 percent of the cost of scrap and the average is on the REWORK side of the target

C_{pk}	C_p values							
	2.5	3.0	4.0	5.0	6.0	8.0	12.0	20.0
20.0	-	-	-	-	-	-	-	1.00
12.0	-	-	-	-	-	-	1.00	1.08
8.0	-	-	-	-	-	1.00	1.06	1.18
6.0	-	-	-	-	1.00	1.03	1.13	1.25
5.0	-	-	-	1.00	1.02	1.07	1.17	1.28
4.0	-	-	1.01	1.02	1.06	1.13	1.22	1.32
3.0	-	1.01	1.03	1.28	1.13	1.20	1.28	1.36
2.5	1.01	1.02	1.07	1.13	1.17	1.24	1.31	1.38
2.00	1.03	1.06	1.13	1.18	1.22	1.28	1.35	1.41
1.90	1.04	1.07	1.14	1.19	1.24	1.29	1.35	1.41
1.80	1.05	1.09	1.15	1.21	1.25	1.30	1.36	1.41
1.70	1.06	1.10	1.17	1.22	1.26	1.31	1.37	1.42
1.60	1.07	1.12	1.18	1.23	1.27	1.32	1.38	1.42
1.50	1.09	1.13	1.20	1.25	1.28	1.33	1.38	1.43
1.40	1.11	1.15	1.21	1.26	1.30	1.34	1.39	1.43
1.30	1.12	1.17	1.23	1.28	1.31	1.35	1.40	1.44
1.20	1.14	1.19	1.25	1.29	1.32	1.36	1.41	1.44
1.10	1.17	1.21	1.27	1.31	1.34	1.37	1.41	1.45
1.00	1.19	1.23	1.28	1.32	1.35	1.38	1.42	1.45
0.90	1.21	1.25	1.30	1.34	1.36	1.39	1.43	1.46
0.80	1.24	1.27	1.32	1.35	1.38	1.41	1.44	1.46
0.70	1.27	1.30	1.34	1.37	1.39	1.42	1.44	1.47
0.60	1.30	1.32	1.36	1.39	1.41	1.43	1.45	1.47
0.50	1.32	1.35	1.38	1.41	1.42	1.44	1.46	1.48
0.40	1.35	1.38	1.40	1.42	1.43	1.45	1.47	1.48
0.30	1.38	1.40	1.42	1.44	1.45	1.46	1.47	1.48
0.20	1.41	1.42	1.44	1.45	1.46	1.47	1.48	1.49
0.10	1.43	1.44	1.46	1.46	1.47	1.48	1.49	1.49
0.00	1.45	1.46	1.47	1.48	1.48	1.48	1.49	1.49
−0.10	1.47	1.47	1.48	1.48	1.49	1.49	1.49	1.50
−0.20	1.48	1.48	1.49	1.49	1.49	1.49	1.50	1.50
−0.30	1.49	1.49	1.49	1.49	1.49	1.50	1.50	1.50
−0.40	1.49	1.49	1.50	1.50	1.50	1.50	1.50	1.50
−0.50	1.50	1.50	1.50	1.50	1.50	1.50	1.50	1.50

Table A.21

The Effective Cost of Production from Counts of Items
When Rework Salvages No Raw Material

Proportion Reworked	Proportion of Items Scrapped									
	0.00	*0.02*	*0.04*	*0.06*	*0.08*	*0.10*	*0.12*	*0.14*	*0.16*	*0.18*
0.00	1.000	1.020	1.042	1.064	1.087	1.111	1.136	1.163	1.190	1.220
0.02	1.020	1.041	1.063	1.085	1.109	1.133	1.159	1.186	1.214	1.244
0.04	1.040	1.061	1.083	1.106	1.130	1.156	1.182	1.209	1.238	1.268
0.06	1.060	1.082	1.104	1.128	1.152	1.178	1.205	1.233	1.262	1.293
0.08	1.080	1.102	1.125	1.149	1.174	1.200	1.227	1.256	1.286	1.317
0.10	1.100	1.122	1.146	1.170	1.196	1.222	1.250	1.279	1.310	1.341
0.12	1.120	1.143	1.167	1.191	1.217	1.244	1.273	1.302	1.333	1.366
0.14	1.140	1.163	1.188	1.213	1.239	1.267	1.295	1.326	1.357	1.390
0.16	1.160	1.184	1.208	1.234	1.261	1.289	1.318	1.349	1.381	1.415
0.18	1.180	1.204	1.229	1.255	1.283	1.311	1.341	1.372	1.405	1.439
0.20	1.200	1.224	1.250	1.277	1.304	1.333	1.364	1.395	1.429	1.463
0.22	1.220	1.245	1.271	1.298	1.326	1.356	1.386	1.419	1.452	1.488
0.24	1.240	1.265	1.292	1.319	1.348	1.378	1.409	1.442	1.476	1.512
0.26	1.260	1.286	1.313	1.340	1.370	1.400	1.432	1.465	1.500	1.537
0.28	1.280	1.306	1.333	1.362	1.391	1.422	1.455	1.488	1.524	1.561
0.30	1.300	1.327	1.354	1.383	1.413	1.444	1.477	1.512	1.548	1.585
0.32	1.320	1.347	1.375	1.404	1.435	1.467	1.500	1.535	1.571	1.610
0.34	1.340	1.367	1.396	1.426	1.457	1.489	1.523	1.558	1.595	1.634
0.36	1.360	1.388	1.417	1.447	1.478	1.511	1.545	1.581	1.619	1.659
0.38	1.380	1.408	1.438	1.468	1.500	1.533	1.568	1.605	1.643	1.683
0.40	1.400	1.429	1.458	1.489	1.522	1.556	1.591	1.628	1.667	1.707
0.42	1.420	1.449	1.479	1.511	1.543	1.578	1.614	1.651	1.690	1.732
0.44	1.440	1.469	1.500	1.532	1.565	1.600	1.636	1.674	1.714	1.756
0.46	1.460	1.490	1.521	1.553	1.587	1.622	1.659	1.698	1.738	1.780
0.48	1.480	1.510	1.542	1.574	1.609	1.644	1.682	1.721	1.762	1.805
0.50	1.500	1.531	1.563	1.596	1.630	1.667	1.705	1.744	1.786	1.829
0.52	1.520	1.551	1.583	1.617	1.652	1.689	1.727	1.767	1.810	1.854
0.54	1.540	1.571	1.604	1.638	1.674	1.711	1.750	1.791	1.833	1.878
0.56	1.560	1.592	1.625	1.660	1.696	1.733	1.773	1.814	1.857	1.902
0.58	1.580	1.612	1.646	1.681	1.717	1.756	1.795	1.837	1.881	1.927
0.60	1.600	1.633	1.667	1.702	1.739	1.778	1.818	1.860	1.905	1.951

Table A.21

The Effective Cost of Production from Counts of Items
When Rework Salvages No Raw Material

Proportion Reworked	Proportion of Items Scrapped									
	0.20	*0.22*	*0.24*	*0.26*	*0.28*	*0.30*	*0.32*	*0.34*	*0.36*	*0.38*
0.00	1.250	1.282	1.316	1.351	1.389	1.429	1.471	1.515	1.563	1.613
0.02	1.275	1.308	1.342	1.378	1.417	1.457	1.500	1.545	1.594	1.645
0.04	1.300	1.333	1.368	1.405	1.444	1.486	1.529	1.576	1.625	1.677
0.06	1.325	1.359	1.395	1.432	1.472	1.514	1.559	1.606	1.656	1.710
0.08	1.350	1.385	1.421	1.459	1.500	1.543	1.588	1.636	1.688	1.742
0.10	1.375	1.410	1.447	1.486	1.528	1.571	1.618	1.667	1.719	1.774
0.12	1.400	1.436	1.474	1.514	1.556	1.600	1.647	1.697	1.750	1.806
0.14	1.425	1.462	1.500	1.541	1.583	1.629	1.676	1.727	1.781	1.839
0.16	1.450	1.487	1.526	1.568	1.611	1.657	1.706	1.758	1.813	1.871
0.18	1.475	1.513	1.553	1.595	1.639	1.686	1.735	1.788	1.844	1.903
0.20	1.500	1.538	1.579	1.622	1.667	1.714	1.765	1.818	1.875	1.935
0.22	1.525	1.564	1.605	1.649	1.694	1.743	1.794	1.848	1.906	1.968
0.24	1.550	1.590	1.632	1.676	1.722	1.771	1.824	1.879	1.938	2.000
0.26	1.575	1.615	1.658	1.703	1.750	1.800	1.853	1.909	1.969	2.032
0.28	1.600	1.641	1.684	1.730	1.778	1.829	1.882	1.939	2.000	2.065
0.30	1.625	1.667	1.711	1.757	1.806	1.857	1.912	1.970	2.031	2.097
0.32	1.650	1.692	1.737	1.784	1.833	1.886	1.941	2.000	2.063	2.129
0.34	1.675	1.718	1.763	1.811	1.861	1.914	1.971	2.030	2.094	2.161
0.36	1.700	1.744	1.789	1.838	1.889	1.943	2.000	2.061	2.125	2.194
0.38	1.725	1.769	1.816	1.865	1.917	1.971	2.029	2.091	2.156	2.226
0.40	1.750	1.795	1.842	1.892	1.944	2.000	2.059	2.121	2.188	2.258
0.42	1.775	1.821	1.868	1.919	1.972	2.029	2.088	2.152	2.219	2.290
0.44	1.800	1.846	1.895	1.946	2.000	2.057	2.118	2.182	2.250	2.323
0.46	1.825	1.872	1.921	1.973	2.028	2.086	2.147	2.212	2.281	2.355
0.48	1.850	1.897	1.947	2.000	2.056	2.114	2.176	2.242	2.313	2.387
0.50	1.875	1.923	1.974	2.027	2.083	2.143	2.206	2.273	2.344	2.419
0.52	1.900	1.949	2.000	2.054	2.111	2.171	2.235	2.303	2.375	2.452
0.54	1.925	1.974	2.026	2.081	2.139	2.200	2.265	2.333	2.406	2.484
0.56	1.950	2.000	2.053	2.108	2.167	2.229	2.294	2.364	2.438	2.516
0.58	1.975	2.026	2.079	2.135	2.194	2.257	2.324	2.394	2.469	2.548
0.60	2.000	2.051	2.105	2.162	2.222	2.286	2.353	2.424	2.500	2.581

Table A.22

The Effective Cost of Production from Counts of Items
When Rework Salvages Material Worth 25% of Nominal Cost

Proportion Reworked	Proportion of Items Scrapped									
	0.00	0.02	0.04	0.06	0.08	0.10	0.12	0.14	0.16	0.18
0.00	1.000	1.020	1.042	1.064	1.087	1.111	1.136	1.163	1.190	1.220
0.02	1.015	1.036	1.057	1.080	1.103	1.128	1.153	1.180	1.208	1.238
0.04	1.030	1.051	1.073	1.096	1.120	1.144	1.170	1.198	1.226	1.256
0.06	1.045	1.066	1.089	1.112	1.136	1.161	1.188	1.215	1.244	1.274
0.08	1.060	1.082	1.104	1.128	1.152	1.178	1.205	1.233	1.262	1.293
0.10	1.075	1.097	1.120	1.144	1.168	1.194	1.222	1.250	1.280	1.311
0.12	1.090	1.112	1.135	1.160	1.185	1.211	1.239	1.267	1.298	1.329
0.14	1.105	1.128	1.151	1.176	1.201	1.228	1.256	1.285	1.315	1.348
0.16	1.120	1.143	1.167	1.191	1.217	1.244	1.273	1.302	1.333	1.366
0.18	1.135	1.158	1.182	1.207	1.234	1.261	1.290	1.320	1.351	1.384
0.20	1.150	1.173	1.198	1.223	1.250	1.278	1.307	1.337	1.369	1.402
0.22	1.165	1.189	1.214	1.239	1.266	1.294	1.324	1.355	1.387	1.421
0.24	1.180	1.204	1.229	1.255	1.283	1.311	1.341	1.372	1.405	1.439
0.26	1.195	1.219	1.245	1.271	1.299	1.328	1.358	1.390	1.423	1.457
0.28	1.210	1.235	1.260	1.287	1.315	1.344	1.375	1.407	1.440	1.476
0.30	1.225	1.250	1.276	1.303	1.332	1.361	1.392	1.424	1.458	1.494
0.32	1.240	1.265	1.292	1.319	1.348	1.378	1.409	1.442	1.476	1.512
0.34	1.255	1.281	1.307	1.335	1.364	1.394	1.426	1.459	1.494	1.530
0.36	1.270	1.296	1.323	1.351	1.380	1.411	1.443	1.477	1.512	1.549
0.38	1.285	1.311	1.339	1.367	1.397	1.428	1.460	1.494	1.530	1.567
0.40	1.300	1.327	1.354	1.383	1.413	1.444	1.477	1.512	1.548	1.585
0.42	1.315	1.342	1.370	1.399	1.429	1.461	1.494	1.529	1.565	1.604
0.44	1.330	1.357	1.385	1.415	1.446	1.478	1.511	1.547	1.583	1.622
0.46	1.345	1.372	1.401	1.431	1.462	1.494	1.528	1.564	1.601	1.640
0.48	1.360	1.388	1.417	1.447	1.478	1.511	1.545	1.581	1.619	1.659
0.50	1.375	1.403	1.432	1.463	1.495	1.528	1.563	1.599	1.637	1.677
0.52	1.390	1.418	1.448	1.479	1.511	1.544	1.580	1.616	1.655	1.695
0.54	1.405	1.434	1.464	1.495	1.527	1.561	1.597	1.634	1.673	1.713
0.56	1.420	1.449	1.479	1.511	1.543	1.578	1.614	1.651	1.690	1.732
0.58	1.435	1.464	1.495	1.527	1.560	1.594	1.631	1.669	1.708	1.750
0.60	1.450	1.480	1.510	1.543	1.576	1.611	1.648	1.686	1.726	1.768

Table A.22

The Effective Cost of Production from Counts of Items
When Rework Salvages Material Worth 25% of Nominal Cost

Proportion Reworked	Proportion of Items Scrapped									
	0.20	*0.22*	*0.24*	*0.26*	*0.28*	*0.30*	*0.32*	*0.34*	*0.36*	*0.38*
0.00	1.250	1.282	1.316	1.351	1.389	1.429	1.471	1.515	1.563	1.613
0.02	1.269	1.301	1.336	1.372	1.410	1.450	1.493	1.538	1.586	1.637
0.04	1.288	1.321	1.355	1.392	1.431	1.471	1.515	1.561	1.609	1.661
0.06	1.306	1.340	1.375	1.412	1.451	1.493	1.537	1.583	1.633	1.685
0.08	1.325	1.359	1.395	1.432	1.472	1.514	1.559	1.606	1.656	1.710
0.10	1.344	1.378	1.414	1.453	1.493	1.536	1.581	1.629	1.680	1.734
0.12	1.363	1.397	1.434	1.473	1.514	1.557	1.603	1.652	1.703	1.758
0.14	1.381	1.417	1.454	1.493	1.535	1.579	1.625	1.674	1.727	1.782
0.16	1.400	1.436	1.474	1.514	1.556	1.600	1.647	1.697	1.750	1.806
0.18	1.419	1.455	1.493	1.534	1.576	1.621	1.669	1.720	1.773	1.831
0.20	1.438	1.474	1.513	1.554	1.597	1.643	1.691	1.742	1.797	1.855
0.22	1.456	1.494	1.533	1.574	1.618	1.664	1.713	1.765	1.820	1.879
0.24	1.475	1.513	1.553	1.595	1.639	1.686	1.735	1.788	1.844	1.903
0.26	1.494	1.532	1.572	1.615	1.660	1.707	1.757	1.811	1.867	1.927
0.28	1.513	1.551	1.592	1.635	1.681	1.729	1.779	1.833	1.891	1.952
0.30	1.531	1.571	1.612	1.655	1.701	1.750	1.801	1.856	1.914	1.976
0.32	1.550	1.590	1.632	1.676	1.722	1.771	1.824	1.879	1.938	2.000
0.34	1.569	1.609	1.651	1.696	1.743	1.793	1.846	1.902	1.961	2.024
0.36	1.588	1.628	1.671	1.716	1.764	1.814	1.868	1.924	1.984	2.048
0.38	1.606	1.647	1.691	1.736	1.785	1.836	1.890	1.947	2.008	2.073
0.40	1.625	1.667	1.711	1.757	1.806	1.857	1.912	1.970	2.031	2.097
0.42	1.644	1.686	1.730	1.777	1.826	1.879	1.934	1.992	2.055	2.121
0.44	1.663	1.705	1.750	1.797	1.847	1.900	1.956	2.015	2.078	2.145
0.46	1.681	1.724	1.770	1.818	1.868	1.921	1.978	2.038	2.102	2.169
0.48	1.700	1.744	1.789	1.838	1.889	1.943	2.000	2.061	2.125	2.194
0.50	1.719	1.763	1.809	1.858	1.910	1.964	2.022	2.083	2.148	2.218
0.52	1.738	1.782	1.829	1.878	1.931	1.986	2.044	2.106	2.172	2.242
0.54	1.756	1.801	1.849	1.899	1.951	2.007	2.066	2.129	2.195	2.266
0.56	1.775	1.821	1.868	1.919	1.972	2.029	2.088	2.152	2.219	2.290
0.58	1.794	1.840	1.888	1.939	1.993	2.050	2.110	2.174	2.242	2.315
0.60	1.813	1.859	1.908	1.959	2.014	2.071	2.132	2.197	2.266	2.339

Table A.23

The Effective Cost of Production from Counts of Items

When Rework Salvages Material Worth 50% of Nominal Cost

Proportion Reworked	Proportion of Items Scrapped									
	0.00	*0.02*	*0.04*	*0.06*	*0.08*	*0.10*	*0.12*	*0.14*	*0.16*	*0.18*
0.00	1.000	1.020	1.042	1.064	1.087	1.111	1.136	1.163	1.190	1.220
0.02	1.010	1.031	1.052	1.074	1.098	1.122	1.148	1.174	1.202	1.232
0.04	1.020	1.041	1.063	1.085	1.109	1.133	1.159	1.186	1.214	1.244
0.06	1.030	1.051	1.073	1.096	1.120	1.144	1.170	1.198	1.226	1.256
0.08	1.040	1.061	1.083	1.106	1.130	1.156	1.182	1.209	1.238	1.268
0.10	1.050	1.071	1.094	1.117	1.141	1.167	1.193	1.221	1.250	1.280
0.12	1.060	1.082	1.104	1.128	1.152	1.178	1.205	1.233	1.262	1.293
0.14	1.070	1.092	1.115	1.138	1.163	1.189	1.216	1.244	1.274	1.305
0.16	1.080	1.102	1.125	1.149	1.174	1.200	1.227	1.256	1.286	1.317
0.18	1.090	1.112	1.135	1.160	1.185	1.211	1.239	1.267	1.298	1.329
0.20	1.100	1.122	1.146	1.170	1.196	1.222	1.250	1.279	1.310	1.341
0.22	1.110	1.133	1.156	1.181	1.207	1.233	1.261	1.291	1.321	1.354
0.24	1.120	1.143	1.167	1.191	1.217	1.244	1.273	1.302	1.333	1.366
0.26	1.130	1.153	1.177	1.202	1.228	1.256	1.284	1.314	1.345	1.378
0.28	1.140	1.163	1.188	1.213	1.239	1.267	1.295	1.326	1.357	1.390
0.30	1.150	1.173	1.198	1.223	1.250	1.278	1.307	1.337	1.369	1.402
0.32	1.160	1.184	1.208	1.234	1.261	1.289	1.318	1.349	1.381	1.415
0.34	1.170	1.194	1.219	1.245	1.272	1.300	1.330	1.360	1.393	1.427
0.36	1.180	1.204	1.229	1.255	1.283	1.311	1.341	1.372	1.405	1.439
0.38	1.190	1.214	1.240	1.266	1.293	1.322	1.352	1.384	1.417	1.451
0.40	1.200	1.224	1.250	1.277	1.304	1.333	1.364	1.395	1.429	1.463
0.42	1.210	1.235	1.260	1.287	1.315	1.344	1.375	1.407	1.440	1.476
0.44	1.220	1.245	1.271	1.298	1.326	1.356	1.386	1.419	1.452	1.488
0.46	1.230	1.255	1.281	1.309	1.337	1.367	1.398	1.430	1.464	1.500
0.48	1.240	1.265	1.292	1.319	1.348	1.378	1.409	1.442	1.476	1.512
0.50	1.250	1.276	1.302	1.330	1.359	1.389	1.420	1.453	1.488	1.524
0.52	1.260	1.286	1.313	1.340	1.370	1.400	1.432	1.465	1.500	1.537
0.54	1.270	1.296	1.323	1.351	1.380	1.411	1.443	1.477	1.512	1.549
0.56	1.280	1.306	1.333	1.362	1.391	1.422	1.455	1.488	1.524	1.561
0.58	1.290	1.316	1.344	1.372	1.402	1.433	1.466	1.500	1.536	1.573
0.60	1.300	1.327	1.354	1.383	1.413	1.444	1.477	1.512	1.548	1.585

Table A.23
The Effective Cost of Production from Counts of Items
When Rework Salvages Material Worth 50% of Nominal Cost

Proportion Reworked	Proportion of Items Scrapped									
	0.20	0.22	0.24	0.26	0.28	0.30	0.32	0.34	0.36	0.38
0.00	1.250	1.282	1.316	1.351	1.389	1.429	1.471	1.515	1.563	1.613
0.02	1.263	1.295	1.329	1.365	1.403	1.443	1.485	1.530	1.578	1.629
0.04	1.275	1.308	1.342	1.378	1.417	1.457	1.500	1.545	1.594	1.645
0.06	1.288	1.321	1.355	1.392	1.431	1.471	1.515	1.561	1.609	1.661
0.08	1.300	1.333	1.368	1.405	1.444	1.486	1.529	1.576	1.625	1.677
0.10	1.313	1.346	1.382	1.419	1.458	1.500	1.544	1.591	1.641	1.694
0.12	1.325	1.359	1.395	1.432	1.472	1.514	1.559	1.606	1.656	1.710
0.14	1.338	1.372	1.408	1.446	1.486	1.529	1.574	1.621	1.672	1.726
0.16	1.350	1.385	1.421	1.459	1.500	1.543	1.588	1.636	1.688	1.742
0.18	1.363	1.397	1.434	1.473	1.514	1.557	1.603	1.652	1.703	1.758
0.20	1.375	1.410	1.447	1.486	1.528	1.571	1.618	1.667	1.719	1.774
0.22	1.388	1.423	1.461	1.500	1.542	1.586	1.632	1.682	1.734	1.790
0.24	1.400	1.436	1.474	1.514	1.556	1.600	1.647	1.697	1.750	1.806
0.26	1.413	1.449	1.487	1.527	1.569	1.614	1.662	1.712	1.766	1.823
0.28	1.425	1.462	1.500	1.541	1.583	1.629	1.676	1.727	1.781	1.839
0.30	1.438	1.474	1.513	1.554	1.597	1.643	1.691	1.742	1.797	1.855
0.32	1.450	1.487	1.526	1.568	1.611	1.657	1.706	1.758	1.813	1.871
0.34	1.463	1.500	1.539	1.581	1.625	1.671	1.721	1.773	1.828	1.887
0.36	1.475	1.513	1.553	1.595	1.639	1.686	1.735	1.788	1.844	1.903
0.38	1.488	1.526	1.566	1.608	1.653	1.700	1.750	1.803	1.859	1.919
0.40	1.500	1.538	1.579	1.622	1.667	1.714	1.765	1.818	1.875	1.935
0.42	1.513	1.551	1.592	1.635	1.681	1.729	1.779	1.833	1.891	1.952
0.44	1.525	1.564	1.605	1.649	1.694	1.743	1.794	1.848	1.906	1.968
0.46	1.538	1.577	1.618	1.662	1.708	1.757	1.809	1.864	1.922	1.984
0.48	1.550	1.590	1.632	1.676	1.722	1.771	1.824	1.879	1.938	2.000
0.50	1.563	1.603	1.645	1.689	1.736	1.786	1.838	1.894	1.953	2.016
0.52	1.575	1.615	1.658	1.703	1.750	1.800	1.853	1.909	1.969	2.032
0.54	1.588	1.628	1.671	1.716	1.764	1.814	1.868	1.924	1.984	2.048
0.56	1.600	1.641	1.684	1.730	1.778	1.829	1.882	1.939	2.000	2.065
0.58	1.613	1.654	1.697	1.743	1.792	1.843	1.897	1.955	2.016	2.081
0.60	1.625	1.667	1.711	1.757	1.806	1.857	1.912	1.970	2.031	2.097

Table A.24

The Effective Cost of Production from Counts of Items
When Rework Salvages Material Worth 75% of Nominal Cost

Proportion Reworked	*Proportion of Items Scrapped*									
	0.00	*0.02*	*0.04*	*0.06*	*0.08*	*0.10*	*0.12*	*0.14*	*0.16*	*0.18*
0.00	1.000	1.020	1.042	1.064	1.087	1.111	1.136	1.163	1.190	1.220
0.02	1.005	1.026	1.047	1.069	1.092	1.117	1.142	1.169	1.196	1.226
0.04	1.010	1.031	1.052	1.074	1.098	1.122	1.148	1.174	1.202	1.232
0.06	1.015	1.036	1.057	1.080	1.103	1.128	1.153	1.180	1.208	1.238
0.08	1.020	1.041	1.063	1.085	1.109	1.133	1.159	1.186	1.214	1.244
0.10	1.025	1.046	1.068	1.090	1.114	1.139	1.165	1.192	1.220	1.250
0.12	1.030	1.051	1.073	1.096	1.120	1.144	1.170	1.198	1.226	1.256
0.14	1.035	1.056	1.078	1.101	1.125	1.150	1.176	1.203	1.232	1.262
0.16	1.040	1.061	1.083	1.106	1.130	1.156	1.182	1.209	1.238	1.268
0.18	1.045	1.066	1.089	1.112	1.136	1.161	1.188	1.215	1.244	1.274
0.20	1.050	1.071	1.094	1.117	1.141	1.167	1.193	1.221	1.250	1.280
0.22	1.055	1.077	1.099	1.122	1.147	1.172	1.199	1.227	1.256	1.287
0.24	1.060	1.082	1.104	1.128	1.152	1.178	1.205	1.233	1.262	1.293
0.26	1.065	1.087	1.109	1.133	1.158	1.183	1.210	1.238	1.268	1.299
0.28	1.070	1.092	1.115	1.138	1.163	1.189	1.216	1.244	1.274	1.305
0.30	1.075	1.097	1.120	1.144	1.168	1.194	1.222	1.250	1.280	1.311
0.32	1.080	1.102	1.125	1.149	1.174	1.200	1.227	1.256	1.286	1.317
0.34	1.085	1.107	1.130	1.154	1.179	1.206	1.233	1.262	1.292	1.323
0.36	1.090	1.112	1.135	1.160	1.185	1.211	1.239	1.267	1.298	1.329
0.38	1.095	1.117	1.141	1.165	1.190	1.217	1.244	1.273	1.304	1.335
0.40	1.100	1.122	1.146	1.170	1.196	1.222	1.250	1.279	1.310	1.341
0.42	1.105	1.128	1.151	1.176	1.201	1.228	1.256	1.285	1.315	1.348
0.44	1.110	1.133	1.156	1.181	1.207	1.233	1.261	1.291	1.321	1.354
0.46	1.115	1.138	1.161	1.186	1.212	1.239	1.267	1.297	1.327	1.360
0.48	1.120	1.143	1.167	1.191	1.217	1.244	1.273	1.302	1.333	1.366
0.50	1.125	1.148	1.172	1.197	1.223	1.250	1.278	1.308	1.339	1.372
0.52	1.130	1.153	1.177	1.202	1.228	1.256	1.284	1.314	1.345	1.378
0.54	1.135	1.158	1.182	1.207	1.234	1.261	1.290	1.320	1.351	1.384
0.56	1.140	1.163	1.188	1.213	1.239	1.267	1.295	1.326	1.357	1.390
0.58	1.145	1.168	1.193	1.218	1.245	1.272	1.301	1.331	1.363	1.396
0.60	1.150	1.173	1.198	1.223	1.250	1.278	1.307	1.337	1.369	1.402

Table A.24

The Effective Cost of Production from Counts of Items
When Rework Salvages Material Worth 75% of Nominal Cost

Proportion Reworked	Proportion of Items Scrapped									
	0.20	0.22	0.24	0.26	0.28	0.30	0.32	0.34	0.36	0.38
0.00	1.250	1.282	1.316	1.351	1.389	1.429	1.471	1.515	1.563	1.613
0.02	1.256	1.288	1.322	1.358	1.396	1.436	1.478	1.523	1.570	1.621
0.04	1.263	1.295	1.329	1.365	1.403	1.443	1.485	1.530	1.578	1.629
0.06	1.269	1.301	1.336	1.372	1.410	1.450	1.493	1.538	1.586	1.637
0.08	1.275	1.308	1.342	1.378	1.417	1.457	1.500	1.545	1.594	1.645
0.10	1.281	1.314	1.349	1.385	1.424	1.464	1.507	1.553	1.602	1.653
0.12	1.288	1.321	1.355	1.392	1.431	1.471	1.515	1.561	1.609	1.661
0.14	1.294	1.327	1.362	1.399	1.438	1.479	1.522	1.568	1.617	1.669
0.16	1.300	1.333	1.368	1.405	1.444	1.486	1.529	1.576	1.625	1.677
0.18	1.306	1.340	1.375	1.412	1.451	1.493	1.537	1.583	1.633	1.685
0.20	1.313	1.346	1.382	1.419	1.458	1.500	1.544	1.591	1.641	1.694
0.22	1.319	1.353	1.388	1.426	1.465	1.507	1.551	1.598	1.648	1.702
0.24	1.325	1.359	1.395	1.432	1.472	1.514	1.559	1.606	1.656	1.710
0.26	1.331	1.365	1.401	1.439	1.479	1.521	1.566	1.614	1.664	1.718
0.28	1.338	1.372	1.408	1.446	1.486	1.529	1.574	1.621	1.672	1.726
0.30	1.344	1.378	1.414	1.453	1.493	1.536	1.581	1.629	1.680	1.734
0.32	1.350	1.385	1.421	1.459	1.500	1.543	1.588	1.636	1.688	1.742
0.34	1.356	1.391	1.428	1.466	1.507	1.550	1.596	1.644	1.695	1.750
0.36	1.363	1.397	1.434	1.473	1.514	1.557	1.603	1.652	1.703	1.758
0.38	1.369	1.404	1.441	1.480	1.521	1.564	1.610	1.659	1.711	1.766
0.40	1.375	1.410	1.447	1.486	1.528	1.571	1.618	1.667	1.719	1.774
0.42	1.381	1.417	1.454	1.493	1.535	1.579	1.625	1.674	1.727	1.782
0.44	1.388	1.423	1.461	1.500	1.542	1.586	1.632	1.682	1.734	1.790
0.46	1.394	1.429	1.467	1.507	1.549	1.593	1.640	1.689	1.742	1.798
0.48	1.400	1.436	1.474	1.514	1.556	1.600	1.647	1.697	1.750	1.806
0.50	1.406	1.442	1.480	1.520	1.563	1.607	1.654	1.705	1.758	1.815
0.52	1.413	1.449	1.487	1.527	1.569	1.614	1.662	1.712	1.766	1.823
0.54	1.419	1.455	1.493	1.534	1.576	1.621	1.669	1.720	1.773	1.831
0.56	1.425	1.462	1.500	1.541	1.583	1.629	1.676	1.727	1.781	1.839
0.58	1.431	1.468	1.507	1.547	1.590	1.636	1.684	1.735	1.789	1.847
0.60	1.438	1.474	1.513	1.554	1.597	1.643	1.691	1.742	1.797	1.855

Index

After the index was prepared
this book was reformatted.
As a result, some of the page
number entries in this index
may be off by one in either direction..